ECOLOGY AND ECONOMIC DEVELOPMENT
IN TROPICAL AFRICA

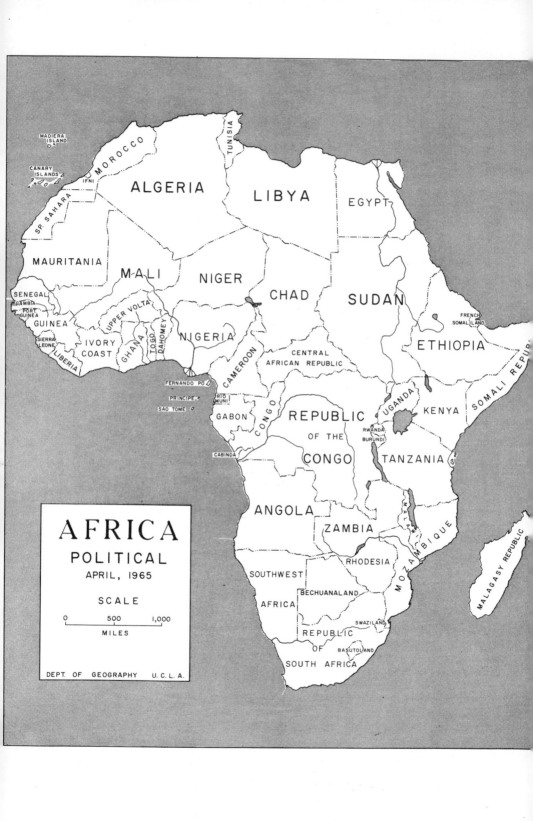

Ecology and Economic Development In Tropical Africa

DAVID BROKENSHA, Editor

CONTRIBUTORS:

Herbert G. Baker

Wilbert McLeod Chapman

J. Desmond Clark

Luther P. Gerlach

Harold F. Heady

William O. Jones

Mildred E. Mathias

Akin L. Mabogunje

Priscilla Copeland Reining

Bernard W. Riley

Benjamin E. Thomas

Harold E. Thomas

John D. Thomas

Price—$2.95

Institute of International Studies

University of California, Berkeley

1965

The photograph which appears on page 114 is used by permission of Hunting Services, Ltd., Hertfordshire, England.

The map which appears on page 189 is used by permission of the Goode Base Map Series, Department of Geography, The University of Chicago. Copyright by the University of Chicago.

CONTRIBUTORS

HERBERT G. BAKER is Professor of Botany and Director of
the Botanical Garden, University of California, Berkeley. He
was head of the Department of Botany at the University of Ghana
from 1954 to 1957. He is Vice-President, International Association of Botanical Gardens, and a past president of the California
Botanical Society. Professor Baker has published numerous articles in leading botanical journals.

DAVID BROKENSHA is Assistant Research Anthropologist and
Chairman of the Committee for African Studies at the University
of California, Berkeley. He lived in tropical Africa from 1951
to 1963. He is co-editor of the African Studies Bulletin, and
author of a forthcoming book Social Change at Larteh, Ghana.

WILBERT MCLEOD CHAPMAN is director of the Van Camp Foundation, and has worked extensively in fisheries research. In
the course of his work he has made several trips to Africa, and
has represented the U.S. government on several commissions.

J. DESMOND CLARK is Professor of Anthropology and Curator
of African Archeology at the University of California, Berkeley.
He was Director of the Rhodes-Livingstone Museum in Zambia from
1938 to 1961. His publications include The Prehistory of Southern
Africa, Prehistoric Cultures of Northeast Angola, Prehistoric
Cultures of the Horn of Africa, and The Stone Age Cultures of
Northern Rhodesia.

LUTHER P. GERLACH is Associate Professor of Anthropology
at the University of Minnesota. He spent the period from 1958
to 1960 engaged in research in Tanzania and Kenya; his main
interests include economic anthropology and human ecology.

HAROLD F. HEADY is Professor of Forestry and Plant Ecolo-
gist at the Experimental Station, University of California,
Berkeley. He spent several months in Kenya as a Fulbright
Research Scholar in 1958-59. His publications include five articles on East Africa.

WILLIAM O. JONES is Director of the Food Research Institute at Stanford University. He is a past president of the
African Studies Association and of the Western Economic Association, and is a member of the Advisory Committee for Africa of the
National Academy of Sciences/National Research Council. He has
wide research experience in tropical Africa, and his publications
include Manioc in Africa.

AKIN L. MABOGUNJE is a Senior Lecturer in Geography at
the University of Ibadan. He has studied in Britain and the

United States. His major interests are urbanization and economic development. He is editor of the <u>Nigerian Geographical Journal</u> and author of <u>Yoruba Towns</u>.

MILDRED E. MATHIAS is Professor of Botany and Director of the Botanical Gardens at the University of California, Los Angeles. She visited Tanzania on a medicinal plant collecting expedition in 1963, having made similar expeditions previously in Latin America.

PRISCILLA COPELAND REINING is Research Associate at the American University. She conducted field work in Tanzania (1951-1953 and 1954-1955) and subsequently in the Sudan, Congo, and neighboring countries. She is particularly interested in ecology and in economic anthropology.

BERNARD W. RILEY is Instructor in Geography at Ohio University. He taught in Tanzania (1952-1955), Rhodesia (1955-1959), and Ghana (1961-1962), and has travelled extensively in adjoining areas. His principal interests are human ecology and urban geography.

BENJAMIN E. THOMAS is Professor of Geography and Acting Director of African Studies at the University of California, Los Angeles. He has made numerous visits to Africa, including periods of teaching at Makerere University College and Khartoum University. His publications include <u>Trade Routes of Algeria and the Sahara</u> and <u>Transportation and Physical Geography in West Africa</u>.

HAROLD E. THOMAS is a Research Hydrologist in the Water Resources Division of the U.S. Geological Survey. He has visited Africa several times, his main area interest being Tunisia. He is the author of many papers on water resources in the United States and Africa, and is a member of the Advisory Committee for Africa of the National Academy of Sciences/National Research Council.

JOHN D. THOMAS is Lecturer in Ecology at the School of Biological Sciences, University of Sussex. He spent from 1954 to 1965 at the University of Ghana, where he taught and engaged in research. His main research interests center around the ecology of parasites, fresh-water ecology, and conservation.

TABLE OF CONTENTS

INTRODUCTION

by

David Brokensha

    Scholars who are interested in African Studies are fre-
quently so involved in their own disciplines that they lose sight
of the contributions of other disciplines, an acquaintance with
which would enlarge their understanding of their own subject.

    This is especially true of political scientists, and
understandably so, for the most spectacular events of recent years
in Africa have been the manifestations of nationalism, the drives
for political independence and for political and economic modernization. These political processes have in some cases been analyzed with great skill and insight, adding an invaluable dimension
to our knowledge of Africa--and, indeed, to our knowledge of political processes elsewhere. While there is no doubt that the
ablest commentators have shown an enviable awareness of all the
relevant factors, they have unfortunately frequently been followed by a number of lesser men who have lacked the ability to
appraise a situation properly because they lacked the necessary
wider knowledge. Political scientists form the largest group of
the many researchers in Africa (for example, 23 per cent of the
362 fellows of the African Studies Association in 1963 were political scientists, followed by anthropologists, who accounted for
20 per cent). Thus it is pertinent to comment on their training
and outlook, and to suggest that most would benefit from exposure
to a wider range of facts and theories, and from an awareness of
work in other fields. There are, of course, dangers of producing
merely generalists who have a wide but superficial acquaintance
with a dozen fields, and who are incapable of perceiving, with
any profundity, the deeper aspects of relationships between phenomena. These dangers may be avoided by an emphasis on the case-
study, as is favored by anthropologists, in conjunction with the
more theoretical approach.

    Although, in theory, cultural anthropologists have wider
interests than political scientists, frequently this appearance
is misleading. That is, almost all anthropological writing makes
a nod towards discussing the ecological factors involved in the
study of man, but these are often dismissed summarily in a few
paragraphs, the rest of the text treating man in effect as though
he is not part of nature. There is nothing new in the ecological
or natural science approach--anthropologists of previous generations were frequently trained in natural science. One example

1

of a highly successful use of a knowledge of ecology is Professor E. E. Evans-Pritchard's classic monograph The Nuer,[1] which opens with a section on ecology, and which states explicitly that "political institutions cannot be understood without taking into account the environment and modes of livelihood." (June Helm's article "The Ecological Approach in Anthropology" provides a useful discussion of this subject.)[2]

THE INTER-DISCIPLINARY APPROACH TO AFRICA

The necessity for the inter-disciplinary approach could be argued for any area, but nowhere more easily than for Africa, the study of which poses special problems. All the essays in this volume concentrate on "Middle Africa"--that vast area of tropical Africa south of the Sahara and north of the Republic of South Africa. There are obvious reasons for excluding the extreme northern and southern areas, because physical, cultural, and political factors in these areas make comparisons between them much more difficult than is the case for countries within Middle Africa. As defined here, Middle Africa contains some 165 million people in 29 independent nations. Four of the essays in this volume deal with West Middle Africa, four with East Middle Africa, and the balance with the whole area. Although most of them deal with conditions in English-speaking territories, the conditions are much the same in the Francophone countries of Middle Africa, as is attested in the voluminous literature on the subject.

Within Middle Africa, about 85 per cent of the working population is engaged in agriculture or livestock raising. This means that any increase in the standard of living, as well as any substantial progress towards industrialization, depends on an increase in agricultural output. Despite the preponderance of the rural population, agriculture is often overlooked in studies on Africa, in favor of more dramatic processes such as urbanization, beginnings of industrialization, and modernization of institutions. Although in the past agricultural development has been neglected by both colonial and independent governments, there are now encouraging signs of a change of emphasis--witness the 1964 Seven-Year Development Plan of the government of Ghana, which explicitly states that "Ghana is an agricultural country. . . . The general level of prosperity cannot increase significantly unless agriculture, which employs nearly two-thirds of the labor force, also undergoes a revolutionary change. During the next two decades the rate of growth in agriculture will condition the rate of growth of the whole economy." The plan lays great emphasis on the modernization of agriculture, stressing the interrelationship of the agricultural and industrial revolutions which it is hoped can be produced. Not all African states have been as realistic as Ghana, but nearly all face the same basic problem of modernizing agriculture. Africa is on the threshold of a techno-

logical and industrial revolution, which can only be made more
rapid, and more painless, if the natural resources are adequately
developed. Because of different cultural values, each African
nation will find its own way of directing this revolution.[*]

Given this dependence on agriculture (or in a few cases
on a specific natural resource, usually a mineral), it is reasonable to expect a general acquaintance with problems associated
with agriculture on the part of African "specialists." It is, of
course, also essential for them to have a thorough knowledge of
national policies and governmental structures, as well as of international relations both within and outside of Africa. Here is
the difficulty--the specialist needs at the same time both a broad
background, to enable him to see problems within the wide physical
and political framework of "Africa," and also a detailed knowledge
of the specific situation with which he is immediately concerned.
There are dangers, in seeking the latter, of becoming so parochial
that one is concerned with only one unit (one community, one town,
one nation, or one river, tree species, game animal, or parasite),
but it is possible to direct one's studies so that the specific
situation constantly illuminates the wider enquiry, and vice versa.
The following essays present examples, on various levels, of this
interaction.

THE ROLE OF NATURAL RESOURCES

"By expressly not setting the study of man and his behavior apart from other fields of knowledge, by recognizing that man
is a part, and an active part, of nature, and has been so from
earliest times . . . [we can have] more meaningful formulations
of research designs to learn more about what and how environmental
factors influence man's development and behavior."[3] In line with
this view, there is no attempt in these essays to see man as opposed to nature, nor as being a helpless creature of his environment. All participants stress the unity of man and nature, and
take into account man's influence on his environment as well as
the converse, which is usually readily apparent in rural Africa.
They are primarily concerned with the efforts by man to establish
dominion over the earth, to understand the processes involved,
and to suggest improved ways of dealing with the many problems
which arise.

----

[*]There is currently in progress an interesting study, under the
auspices of the World Bank, "to define factors which have influenced the success or failure of past and present attempts to
raise agricultural productivity." It involves a series of case
studies of agricultural schemes in several parts of Middle Africa.

INTRODUCTION

The essays are clearly not intended to be definitive, nor to give comprehensive coverage to the subject of ecology in Middle Africa. (This would in any case be impossible in one volume.) They do not cover all natural resources, important exceptions being soils and game, in detail. (The failure to give specific detailed attention to domestic and wild animals is no reflection on their importance: the present and potential value of game animals is very great for East Africa.) Not all disciplines are represented, and while area coverage is also limited, the essays do indicate what sort of work is being done in different fields, which problems are receiving attention, and which kinds of knowledge and relationships are regarded as meaningful. By stressing the sorts of questions which are being asked in the various disciplines, they suggest new outlooks and approaches, whatever one's field. The main theme uniting the papers is the use of natural resources: what are they, how are they being used, what changes could be made to use them more effectively? These are the questions which arise again and again.

Most of the papers are concerned with contemporary problems, but Desmond Clark, in his paper, discusses the importance of ecological factors in the Pleistocene Age, showing the past significance of climatic change for the human population. His paper serves to remind us of the importance of history, and perhaps to counteract, to some extent, one common misconception--that pre-1945 events in Africa are not worth studying, because the political revolutions did not really start until that year.

Resources specifically covered include water (Harold Thomas, Akin Mabogunje), other minerals (Bernard Riley), fish (Wilbert Chapman), and flora (Harold Heady). Each writer considers such matters as technical advances in the use of resources, costs and benefits of such use, infra-structure necessary in terms of social overhead, and political factors; throughout, cultural factors are given prominence, indicating an acute awareness that technological advances depend ultimately on human factors. Thus Riley, in writing of mineral developments, stresses the economic, political, and cultural conditions conducive to rapid development, emphasizing the essential presence of certain skills, which can be obtained either by importing foreigners or by long-term educational plans. In writing of rangeland development, Heady insists that no advance can be made without local cooperation. And Chapman, when discussing possibilities of making up some of the protein deficiency common in Africa by increasing the sale of fish, also considers the complex cultural factors which determine diet. Luther Gerlach and Priscilla Reining, both cultural anthropologists, present case studies showing the viewpoints of particular peoples--the Digo and Haya respectively--going on to consider how resources are used by these people, how these resources are regarded, and how to study the "complex of relationships among living organisms in their habitat."

4

In treating of the use of natural resources, several of
the writers put forward a case for conservation, while recognizing
that attitudes in Africa are necessarily different from those in
North America or Europe. Harold Thomas uses the analogy of generational difference, comparing African attitudes to those of
younger men--vigorous, impatient, intent on reaching certain specific goals quickly--while Americans and North Europeans are like
older men--cautious, patient, desirous not to endanger what is
best from the past. Although the aesthetic aspects of conservation are important in the West, there is no sentimentality in
these papers regarding fauna or flora or other resources, but only
an assessment of the social and economic consequences of conservation. William Jones mentions the prevalent notion in the West--
one not necessarily applicable in Africa--that conservation suggests a prior exploitation, and Heady demonstrates that depletion
of resources in the field of game animals has been exaggerated.
There is an honest attempt to consider the place of conservation
in national development plans from the standpoint of particular
African countries. The concern with conservation expressed by
these writers is also reflected in statements made by political
leaders, though the emphasis often differs. For example, President Nyerere of Tanzania is reported to have said: "Personally
I have no wish ever to see a wild animal, but if they bring in
money which can be used for development, then they must be looked
after." This pragmatic approach is typical of many African leaders, in regarding natural resources, most of whom believe in President Nkrumah's dictum: "Seek Ye First the Political Kingdom."
But they also appreciate that once political independence is
achieved, continuing viability as a political unit depends to a
great degree on the use made of natural resources, and on their
extent.

SOME RECURRING THEMES

Recurring themes emerge in different papers, indicating
a number of common basic problems confronting workers in each
field. These themes fall into four groups, each one related to
economic development: (1) climate and water, (2) health, nutrition, and population growth, (3) nationalism, and (4) the application of science.

In the one paper dealing specifically with climatic factors, Benjamin Thomas is able to relate all aspects of ecology to
climate, showing that it is one of the most important variables.
If climate is neglected, comparisons between areas may be difficult or invalid, and even when it is considered, one needs to know
how representative the climatic conditions are. John Thomas' es-
say, for example, deals with a quite atypical climatic area, a
fact which does not lessen the paper's importance, but which is
essential to bear in mind when considering his conclusions. Clark

notes the significance of climate in prehistoric times, in accounting for changes which enabled man to improve his mastery over his
environment. Gerlach and Reining write of the influence of climate
on agricultural practices in Tanzania communities, recognizing that
climate is merely a limiting and not a determining factor.

Water is studied both as the single most important mineral
resource, and as a part of the study of climate. Harold Thomas
provides a general discussion of costs and benefits of water development, and Mabogunje considers the specialized case of ground and
surface water in Nigeria from the viewpoint of urbanization and
industrial use, showing how closely these latter depend on adequate
water supplies, and discussing the prospects for development.
Heady is concerned with water development for more effective land
use in East Africa; John Thomas discusses water in terms of a
small reservoir in Ghana, showing the close association which man
and the parasitic hosts retain with water and the influence on
health of man's wide use of one aquatic source. It is clearly impossible to be familiar with all the minute details behind each of
these studies. What is important is to be aware of the different
uses of water, and to understand some of the problems associated
with its development, so that one will at least remember that such
a simple question as "Are water supplies adequate?" may be extremely relevant in any study of political or economic development.

The second group of recurring themes relates to health,
diet, nutrition, and population growth. Although seldom explicitly noted in these papers, population growth was evidently much
in the minds of the participants, and concern with it does provide one of the obvious links between natural and social scientists. It is clearly associated with such factors as health,
housing, and education, the adequate provision of which occupies
much of the time and finances of Middle Africa. Satisfactory
demographic statistics are not available, but it is likely that
the overall natural increase of population for Africa is 1 - 1 1/2
per cent per annum, a figure considerably below that for Asia or
Latin America. This is not to deny the importance of population
growth in Africa, because it is a crucial factor for any person
concerned with the use of natural resources. "How many people
are there to look after?" is a basic question in considering resource use.

In the associated field of diet, Gerlach's case study
shows the relevance of socio-cultural factors to diet, and Clark
traces the increased specialization in diet which resulted from
improved tools. Chapman mentions the process of urbanization and
the consequent fairly rapid changes in diet. Several papers treat
of nutrition and nutritional deficiencies. In circumstances of
peace, with developed communications and a good distribution system, the caloric intake per person in most parts of Africa should
be adequate, but this cannot be said of protein intake. Two to

four per cent of all the children in rural tropical Africa suffer from an easily recognizable form of protein malnutrition known as kwashiorkor, which is a post-weaning disease affecting about one million children in the one- to four-year age group. In some areas many children suffer from marasmas, a calorific malnutrition caused by children's simply not having enough to eat. Calorific malnutrition generally leads to protein malnutrition.

Among ways of remedying the protein deficiency is through the development of the fishing industry, particularly on the West African coast, where there has been promising progress. Chapman discusses the problems involved in introducing more fish into the diet, both from the technological and human viewpoints. Heady considers the possibilities of another source of protein--wild ungulates which can be cropped--and gives examples of successful projects. Experimentation with ungulates is continuing in East and Central Africa.

Other aspects of health are covered by Benjamin Thomas, who describes the increasing importance of medical geography and the close relationship of disease--for example, malaria--and climate. He notes that malaria is a major obstacle to economic development in a country such as Somalia. John Thomas is concerned with the parasitical vectors which so debilitate the health of millions of Africans: his paper indicates the detailed research necessary to produce results in controlling such vectors. From another viewpoint, Mildred Mathias describes a comparatively little-known investigation into the pharmaceutical and botanical properties of medicinal plants, and indicates an area where science can join with traditional customs in promoting health.

The third recurring theme in these papers is nationalism, particularly as it relates to government planning and foreign investment. Like other governments, those in Africa are committed to a fuller exploitation of natural resources in order to improve standards of living. The kind and degree of commitment obviously varies greatly. Government plans and policies in education, types of leadership, and legal sanctions are significant variables, as have been the forms of transition from colonial status to independence. Although in many cases independence has proved a powerful stimulant to development, it has also posed grave problems. In some instances, political instability has deterred outside investors, whose capital is necessary to promote development. In the case of some parts of the Congo Republic, civil strife and chaos have so disrupted the infrastructure of government that development has practically ceased. Riley mentions the influence of political stability on mineral development, and Heady discusses the influence of political factors on decisions regarding ecological projects. Chapman is much concerned with political factors in his study of the fishing industry, pointing out how independence has led to a dispersal of experts in some instances, thus

handicapping research; he also observes that new political boundaries in West Africa hamper the movement of fishermen, thus dis-
rupting the harvesting of fish, since the latter "are not aware of
boundaries."

Several authors describe examples of cooperation between
governments. Chapman gives an account of international cooperation organized by the Commission de Coopération Technique pour
l'Afrique (CCTA), and Harold Thomas describes cooperation arranged
by the International Union for the Conservation of Nature and
Natural Resources. In addition to these non-governmental agencies,
the United Nations is an effective force in Africa in helping man
to improve his relations with his environment. Gerlach writes of
the work of the United Nations' Children's Fund; and other activities of the United Nations, working through such agencies as the
Food and Agricultural Organization, the World Health Organization,
and the Economic Commission for Africa, are described in other
papers. There is still much scope for increased action in the
development of hydro-electric projects, the establishment of commissions to control rivers which are international boundaries, and
in scientific research and the exchange of information. In all
these areas, it is the African states which, properly, are taking
the lead, yet there is ample opportunity for other countries to
provide technical assistance. More effective forms of assistance
in training may in some cases better promote agricultural productivity than would large scale capital investment.

In Middle Africa there are countless examples of private
foreign investment being responsible for all or part of some form
of exploitation of the natural resources. These include the
enormous mining corporations of the U.S.A., Britain, and Belgium;
the commercial fishing interests of Japan, the U.S.A., and the
U.S.S.R., which, as described by Chapman, operate successfully on
the West African coast; and the tentative interests of drug companies in African medicinal plants, as noted by Mathias. [*] Most
of the African forest exploitation is still directed by European
interests. Despite the continuing preference for private investment in the Republic of South Africa, rather than in the newly
independent nations of Middle Africa, there are good possibilities
for private foreign interests to help develop resources in independent African states, as evidenced by Kaiser Engineers' leading
part in the Volta River Project of Ghana. Even Ghana, which is
one of the most militant of the new states on all aspects of neo-
colonialism, and which stresses its aim to create a socialist economy, expressly welcomes--and makes provision in her plans for--
participation by private foreign investors.

---

[*]It might be mentioned that a Dutch firm has for many years
been extracting cortisone from sisal waste in Tanzania.

The fourth recurring theme in these papers is the application of science. It is appropriate that several of our writers address themselves specifically to the role of science and scientists. Here there is no sharp division--as sometimes occurs between the conservationists, who bemoan "our plundered planet," and the technologists, who offer airy assurances that nothing is beyond the power of modern knowledge to set right. Rather it is clear that while all are concerned about conservation, they also take into account both what science can offer and also the realities of the social and political scene in Africa. Clark, going back many ages, demonstrates how primitive science, in developing more effective tools, allowed an increased mastery by man over his environment. The remaining essays are all concerned, in one way or another, with the application of more complex scientific procedures and concepts to present-day situations, and with the gulf between knowledge and practice in Africa. This gulf at times, as Jones says, appears "infinite," and Chapman describes the path between knowledge and its application as "long, tedious, and exasperating."

Two of the essays admirably illustrate scientific methodology through detailed case studies--Herbert Baker's account of the kapok tree and John Thomas' pond saga. Baker's researches have little practical significance, but should be of interest to the historian, or indeed to any behavioral scientist, by showing how useful an aid ethno-botany is in African studies. Thomas' paper, on the other hand, has clear and immediate relevance to medical research.

In connection with scientific research, two points emerge in several of the essays: the difficulties of long term research, and the acute shortage of African scientists. As Chapman notes, the aims of African states are generally short term, not surprising in view of their urgently felt need to modernize economic and political institutions. Although there may be a degree of scientific advance under pressure, eventually the government aims will be inimical to science, which relies mainly on long term research projects. Says Chapman, "Anyone asking a scientist to produce useful results in less than five years is simply making his request of the wrong type of man." This pressure is not confined to Africa, but certainly appears in an acute form there. It leads on to the problem of the limited number of African scientists and technologists.

The Commission for Higher Education in Africa recommended that all African countries should emphasize science and technology, aiming at having 60 per cent of their university students in these fields. Some states are assiduously trying to achieve this aim. In Ghana, for example, not only are American Peace Corps volunteers teaching science subjects in the high schools, but they are doing it alongside Russian teachers brought in for the same purpose. There are also many African students at universities, both in Africa and abroad, studying science, and there are already several African scientists of distinction. Generally, however, there is a paucity of African personnel trained as scientists and as technologists, particularly in the sub-professional fields (such as laboratory technicians) which are vital to successful scientific endeavor. In such areas as fish-culture, forestry, game management, there are virtually no trained Africans; there are a few geologists, and increasing numbers in biological sciences who are working in agriculture. The following figures, relating to African students from five selected countries studying in the U.S.A. in 1963-4, are apposite.

Country	Total Students	Studying Biological and Geo-sciences	Studying Agriculture
Kenya	775	86	31
Uganda	159	23	10
Tanzania	251	37	33
Ghana	279	23	23
Nigeria	1140	100	19
Totals	2604	269 (10.4%)	176 (6.8%)

Figures given in the 1963 UNESCO Report on Higher Education in Africa indicate that, of a total of 12,940 African students studying abroad, 2.7 per cent were studying natural sciences, 3.5 per cent agriculture. Of those studying natural sciences and agriculture, fewer than 18 per cent were graduate students, so that it will be several years before there is any appreciable number of specialists. Until there are more Africans who are both fully trained and prepared to devote themselves to the laborious task of scientific research, enquiries will necessarily be delayed.* However congenial, understanding, and wise the foreign expert is, he remains a foreigner, and is likely to be much more effective when advising, and working under, African scientists.

---

*An additional obstacle to research is the lack of reliable statistics concerning Africa (mentioned by Chapman, Benjamin Thomas, and Mabogunje), which might be partly remedied by the encouragement of more African demographers, meteorologists, etc.

CONCLUSION

The essays in this book are intended to provide an introduction to the scope and substance of enquiries being made on man
and nature in Africa. They suggest some of the important ecological factors which need to be taken into account in African studies, whatever specialized form a particular enquiry may take.
For example, a straightforward study of political institutions,
or elites, or education, or modernization, is likely to be misleading, or at best inadequate, unless the writing is informed by
some knowledge of the physical environment. This applies with
greater force to comparative studies, for to neglect the relation
of man to his environment is to neglect one of the most important
variable factors which influence human behavior, and to risk
ascribing false properties to other variables.

In many quarters there has been a deep concern with the
basic problems of man's relationship to nature, of how he can more
effectively use the natural resources of his environment. It
would be unfortunate if interest in the spectacular political
events in Africa were to cause students--and indeed governments--
to ignore these basic ecological problems. To say this is in no
way to minimize the importance of political institutions, alli-
ances, processes--nor of their study--but merely to insist that
they constitute, as it were, the immediately visible one-ninth
of the iceberg. An awareness of the complexity and interrelationship of the many other factors involved will illuminate all
enquiries.

Says William Thomas, "Man, the ecological dominant on the
planet, needs the insights of scholars in nearly all branches of
learning to understand what has happened and what is happening to
the earth under man's impress--what the soil scientist, climatol-
ogist, geomorphologist, and others are doing are direct contributions to man's understanding of himself."[4]

NOTES

[1]Oxford: Clarendon Press, 1940.

[2]The American Journal of Sociology, LXVII, 6, May, 1962.

[3]Wm. L. Thomas, Jr., in Wm. L. Thomas, Jr., ed., Man's Role in
Changing the Face of the Earth (Chicago: University of Chicago
Press, 1956), p. xxxvii.

[4]Ibid.

INTRODUCTION

REFERENCES

There are several excellent regional studies and other works which deal with the general problems of this volume, and which contain bibliographies for more detailed reading. The following are a few of the more accessible works:

BOARD, C. The Border Region: Natural Environment and Land Use in the Eastern Cape. Cape Town, 1962.

de SCHLIPPE, PIERRE. Shifting Cultivation in Africa: The Zande System of Agriculture. London, 1956.

DUMONT, RENE. L'Afrique noire est mal partie. Paris, 1962. (An English translation will soon be published by Praeger, New York.)

HAILEY, LORD. An African Survey. Revised edition. London, 1956.

PHILLIPS, JOHN. The Development of Agriculture and Forestry in the Tropics: Patterns, Problems and Promise. New York, 1962.

RUSSEL, E. W. (ed.). The Natural Resources of East Africa. Nairobi, 1962.

UNESCO. A Review of the Natural Resources of the African Continent. New York: Columbia University Press, 1963.

UNESCO. Conference on Development of Higher Education in Africa. Paris, 1963.

UNESCO - ECA. International Conference on the Organization of Research and Training in Africa in Relation to the Study, Conservation and Utilization of Natural Resources. Lagos, July-August, 1964. Final Report.

YUDELMAN, MONTAGUE. Africans on the Land. Cambridge, Mass., 1964.

ACKNOWLEDGMENTS

I wish to record my thanks to Dr. David Apter, Acting Director of the Institute of International Studies at the University of California, Berkeley, who facilitated the holding of the conference at which these papers were originally presented, to Dr. Ethel Albert, who was then Chairman of the Committee for African Studies, which initiated the conference, and to Mrs. Ruth Brandwynne and Mr. Peter Steager, who helped arrange the conference.

I also wish to express my appreciation for the friendly cooperation which we received from our colleagues at the African Studies Center at the University of California, Los Angeles.

Finally, I am much indebted to Mr. Paul Gilchrist, Editor for the Institute of International Studies, for his invaluable help in preparing these papers for publication, and to Mrs. Ila Jungnickel, who was responsible for the final typing of the papers.

CULTURE AND ECOLOGY IN PREHISTORIC AFRICA

by

J. Desmond Clark

Early man was a hunter and a food gatherer. As such he was entirely dependent upon the immediate resources of his environment--water, game, and vegetable foods--to support life. His manner of behavior, the social and economic structure of his group organization, probably did not show much variation between groups, taking the broad view. He must have resembled a member of recent hunter-gathering groups, though ways of life differed much in detail according to the richness of the environment and the efficacy of the technology being used to exploit it.

Prehistory provides the record of man's steadily increasing ability to make greater and more effective use of the resources of his habitat. At first this ability was little greater than that with which the chimpanzee exploits its environment. Also like the chimpanzee, man was at this time, it would seem, considerably restricted as to the type of surroundings in which he could live successfully.

Although biology knows of several tool-using species-- Darwin finches, parrots, sea otters, digging wasps, for example-- only the chimpanzee among the higher primates, as we now know from the work of Jane Goodall in Tanzania,[1] actually manufactures tools, albeit in the lowest category of tool-making. Benjamin Franklin's definition of man as "the tool-making animal," a definition that has remained unassailable for so long, now requires modification. For it is now apparent that it is not so much tool-making as such but the ability to envisage the use of one tool for improving the efficiency or contributing to the manufacture of another to achieve a desired end, more often than not connected with food getting, that is the essential characteristic of man. In this respect the working of stone was of the greatest importance. In fact, it may not be going too far to say that it was stone-working that started our hominid ancestors on their long road to civilization.

Up to now, Africa has produced most of the fossil evidence for a knowledge of the earliest stage of hominid evolution. Moreover, it also provides a wealth of material for later periods and great potential for studying the interrelationship of biological and cultural evolution, biome, and habitat. It was the interrelationship between these factors, in the ecologically very different regions of the continent, that contributed to produce the characteristics of the indigenous populations of present-day Africa.

Prehistory, at least Pleistocene prehistory, has all too often been reduced to detailed classificatory systems for stone tools, largely because it is generally only stone that has survived. But prehistorians are now becoming increasingly conscious of the need to study early man in relation to ethology and the environment in which he lived. Consequently, in recent years, interdisciplinary investigations have been initiated with most promising results that have demonstrated the great importance of such studies, not only for the prehistorian, but for all who are concerned with the palaeo-ecology of Africa. Much of what was previously obscure to prehistorians regarding certain cultural distributions, to botanists or zoologists regarding discontinuous habitats, or to pathologists concerning certain tropical diseases becomes appreciably clearer in the light of the team studies that have been carried out. We hope to see many more of them in the future.

In this paper I want to examine the evidence for the biological and cultural evolution of man and the changing relationship between him and his environment, in particular where it concerns sub-Saharan Africa, from the earliest evidence of toolmaking up to the coming of husbandry and metal-working into the sub-continent.

THE IMPORTANCE OF THE PHYSICAL ENVIRONMENT

Prehistoric culture cannot be interpreted effectively without first knowing the nature of the environment in which it was practised. Very varied environments exist in Africa today--desert and semi-desert, low and high altitude grasslands, savanna, woodland and montane forest, and the Mediterranean and Cape macchia. All these environments were equally present in the Pleistocene and, indeed, must have been in existence since at least the Miocene. Their zones of distribution have varied, however, in accordance with the climatic changes--increases or decreases in rainfall, temperature, winds, etc.--which were contemporary with the advances and retreats of the continental glaciations in the temperate and higher latitudes, as in Europe and North America.

Attempts have been made to assess the degree of change that took place in Africa during the Pleistocene. Without considerable additional evidence such studies cannot, of course, be considered precise or of general application, yet they do suggest that rainfall may have fluctuated by as much as 40-45 per cent from the present, and that temperature varied between the present and a climate of 5-6°C. lower. It is probable that temperature

change was the more important. Such conclusions have been obtained from studies of the mineral composition of sands, of mech-
anical and chemical weathering of soils, and of the pollens present in certain horizons in relation to the chronological framework
based upon stratigraphy and an absolute time scale.

Since the food supply is always the chief concern of
hunter-gatherers, the area of greatest population density may be
considered to be that providing the best continual, all the year
round, supply of meat, vegetable foods, and water. In the case
of Africa, it was the savanna and the grasslands that were best
suited to man's physiological needs. This is, in fact, the area
in which the earliest human remains and the earliest cultural evidence occur, dating to approximately 1.75 million years ago. Until somewhere between 100,000 and 50,000 years ago this would seem
to have been the only type of environment that was permanently
occupied, but as climatic change brought about modifications of
the ecological zones, the human and animal populations would have
made related adjustments, moving into country that would previously have been unfavorable, or vice versa.

Attempts have been made by H. B. S. Cooke and others to
construct vegetation distribution maps to show the vegetation
changes brought about by Pleistocene climatic fluctuation.[2] R. B.
Lee has shown how the regions which were ecologically favorable,
marginal, or unfavorable for early hominid occupation might have
changed in response to the changes in the vegetation pattern.[3]

Today the hunter-gatherers live in some of the most unfavorable and inaccessible areas of the globe. This is certainly
true of the Bushmen, Bergdama, Pygmies and certain Batwa groups
in Africa. This pattern, however, represents a survival distribution. The physical and cultural evidence is considerable, certainly in respect of the Bush type, that peoples who were physically of that stock occupied much of the permanently favorable
region of southern Africa during final and post-Pleistocene times.
They continued to do so until subsequent events and peoples removed and replaced them. So long as the population remained small
enough, there can have been no need for man to occupy the unfavorable or even the marginal areas. As I shall show, there is good
evidence from cultural distributions and chronological data that
such regions were avoided until the end of the Later Pleistocene,
except at times when climatic change made places like the Sahara
attractive to settlement.

The present-day population density of the northern Kala-
hari /Kung Bushmen is estimated at 17-25 persons per 100 square
miles,[4] that of the Hadza in the savanna of northern Tanzania at
perhaps 40 persons per 100 square miles,[5] and that of the Bushmen
in the southwest corner of the Northern Rhodesian savanna at
around 16 persons per 100 square miles.[6] In North America the

population densities of hunting-collecting groups varied between 6 per 100 square miles in the arid Great Basin to 250 per 100 in parts of California.[7] Lee estimates for the human population of southern Africa during the early Upper Pleistocene a density of 25-100 persons per 100 square miles for favorable areas and 1-25 per 100 square miles for marginal zones.[8] Lee's estimates, however, are based on the population densities of recent hunter-gatherers, who have advanced a great deal further physiologically, intellectually, and technically than had the hominids of 100,000 to 50,000 years ago. Indeed the Mesolithic population of England and Wales in the period 7000 to 5000 B.C. is estimated at about 12 persons per 100 square miles.[9] The population density of tropical Africa during the earlier Pleistocene is much more likely to have been close to that of the hunter-gatherer populations living in the unfavorable zones today, since the prehistoric people would have been incapable of such a successful exploitation of the resources of their environment as would the specialized Homo sapiens hunters of later times. Even with the higher estimates, however, it is apparent that the favorable zones were easily capable of supporting all the human population of Africa until the closing stages of the Pleistocene, when technological efficiency enabled man to transcend environmental restrictions.

The effects induced by Pleistocene climatic change in the marginal zones are, I believe, of the greatest importance for explaining intellectual and cultural evolution. Especially important were the effects of the changes that altered the habitat from favorable to unfavorable in the regions of lower rainfall. It is true that, during periods of ecological stability, natural selection would favor the populations living under optimum conditions. However, at times of ecological instability, the stimuli to survival and the resulting response in populations trapped in these marginal zones would have produced the greatest improvement in technical skill among those groups that did not succumb.

The oldest fossil remains of tool-making hominids and the associated artifacts come from East and South Africa.[10] The earliest are of creatures who lived 1.75 million years ago at the Olduvai Gorge in northern Tanzania during the later part of the Lower Pleistocene. The occurrence of these hominid fossils in the same tectonically unstable region as that of the much older Miocene apes, the Proconsulidae, suggests that this region must have been an extremely favorable one for primate evolution and tool using. It was a habitat of limited stands of forest--on the slopes of the volcanoes and in galleries along the stream courses-- but where wide use could also be made of intervening savanna. The deterioration of climate during the later Tertiary would have destroyed some of these forest microclimates, and thus may have been responsible for producing fully savanna-dwelling forms and for the evolution of the Tertiary primates to the fully bipedal, erect walking Australopithecines during the Lower Pleistocene. There

can be no doubt that for a very long time these latter creatures
had been adapted to using tools and, on the evidence of the chimpanzees, to making simple tools also, before they took to working
stone.

The Lower Pleistocene hominids may or may not all fall
within the range of the Australopithecines, but they all occupied a semi-arid environment that would today be considered mar-
ginal-to-favorable park savanna and grassland with plenty of permanent water and large quantities of game for meat. This was the
environment of Olduvai, of the Transvaal/Sterkfontein group of
caves, and of Taungs in the northern Cape. It was much the same
then as it is today.[11]

THE DEVELOPMENT OF TOOLS

There were at least three hominid forms living at this
time in Africa that were capable of making stone tools. These
were Australopithecus africanus, Australopithecus robustus, and
the recently discovered Homo habilis. It is possible that all
three of them actually did make tools, although only one can have
given rise to Homo sapiens through the Homo habilis stage. At
Olduvai the tool maker lived close to the margin of the lake. His
occupation sites (for such one may truthfully call them) were,
judging from the one that has been completely excavated and in
part described, small--15 feet in diameter--the limits being determined by the distribution of bone and stone. He ate a variety
of small and juvenile animals--frogs, snakes, lizards, tortoises,
young antelopes, gazelles, and pigs--and the bones lay broken and
scattered among his stone artifacts. There are no large animal
remains. The stone tools belong to what is known as the Oldowan
Culture, and consist of natural stones, numbers of hammer and
bashing stones, some choppers, and numerous flakes. There is not
much evidence of intentional retouch, though some good examples
of small tools have been found, and the tools represent mostly
stones that were utilized, rather than purposefully shaped implements. The commonest form of utilization was bashing and hammer-
ing, and it is apparent that the flakes are the result of (on the
one hand) unintentional and (on the other) unskilled but intentional stone working.

From the earliest Australopithecine sites in South Africa
the stone tools are missing, but some utilized bone certainly occurs. The remains of small creatures, including crabs, occur at
Taungs, and the remains of small to medium-sized antelopes are
commonly associated with the Transvaal ape-men. It is, of course,
not yet proven that these animal remains represent the food debris
of the hominids. No doubt there were several factors contributing
to these bone collections in the caves, but it seems more and more
probable that the main one of these was, in fact, the hominids.

CULTURE AND ECOLOGY IN PREHISTORIC AFRICA

It is significant that the animal remains in these and the Olduvai deposits are selected, and that only portions of the animals are represented. The limbs and the skulls are most commonly preserved, and much less often the body parts. This strongly suggests that scavenging was one of the main sources of the meat supply, and it may be supposed that the earliest hominids were but another of the scavengers that hung around the kills of the larger carnivores, as is still the practice of some peoples even today. It might be asked why they did not also scavenge large animals naturally dead. They probably did on rare occasions--witness the chalicothere and hippopotamus at Makapan--but it is possible that they had not any equipment that would penetrate the thickness of hide of an elephant or a hippopotamus, and so had to rely on the help of the carnivore with his teeth. Physiologically these early hominids were hardly equipped to be successful hunters of larger game, and the smaller creatures in the faunal lists probably represent the limit of their hunting efficiency.

Most of their food may with certainty be considered to have been vegetable, which was also the traditional diet. On the basis of evidence concerning present-day hunter-gatherers, it can be estimated that vegetable foods comprised 70-80 per cent of the total diet. That Australopithecus robustus was primarily a vegetarian can be seen by the wear on his teeth. Australopithecus africanus and Homo habilis were omnivorous. It is likely that the sudden appearance of stone tools in the geological record was connected as much with an improved vegetable diet as with meat eating. A stone chopper for pointing a digging stick would have meant that man could increase greatly the variety as well as the quantity of his vegetable foods by using the tool to obtain more deeply buried articles of food, which could then often be rendered more palatable by being softened or pulped by bashing between two stones. In the same way this simple stone equipment would have been effective for breaking long bones to get at the marrow, and the flakes would have greatly facilitated skinning, or scraping the meat from bones.

The hominid makers of the Oldowan Culture evolved physiologically very slowly in their favorable dry savanna environment. However, because of their cultural ability, even though it was so rudimentary, they were able to exploit more of their potential food resources than had been possible without any tools at all, and their physiological development was thus correspondingly more rapid than would have been possible without culture. By 500,000 years ago, even perhaps as early as one million years ago, Homo habilis had evolved genetically into a form clearly within the Homo erectus pattern, and from sites not much later in age in northwest Africa come jaws and jaw fragments belonging to an African version of Pithecanthropus. The most characteristic large tool was then the handaxe, though at first it was very rare, and the majority of the large tools consisted of bashing stones, choppers, and polyhedral stones. With these there are numbers of small tools, often showing careful retouch, made on irregular flakes and nodules. Some of these were very small and must have been used for fairly delicate work.

The occupation sites were still close to water, along the edges of lakes and rivers, and are notable for the quantities of artifacts and remains of large animals that are found associated with them. These animals include elephants, rhinoceroses, hippopotamuses, giraffids, and large antelopes, as well as smaller animals, including horses and pigs. One such site at Olduvai is associated with a stream course, and it appears that the animals had been driven in, bogged down, and butchered. Such an activity implies group organization for hunting purposes as well, no doubt, as for protection, just as does the increased size of the occupation area. In the base of Bed II at Olduvai there are Oldowan Culture choppers associated with the articulated bones of an almost complete deinothere. Even so, these tools at best must have been inefficient for dismembering an animal of that size, and it is not unlikely that the handaxe and, later, the cleaver were developed for skinning and cutting out the meat from the larger mammals that occupied the African savanna during the Middle Pleistocene, which was a period that saw much proliferation of mammal species and the appearance of giant forms.

More is known about the Acheulian cultural stage in the later part of the Middle Pleistocene and the early Upper Pleistocene between approximately 200,000 and 50,000 years ago. The tool kit then was comprised of handaxes, cleavers, knives, choppers, picks, spheroids, core and flake scrapers, and grooving tools. To this one should add wooden spears (known from Europe) and probably a number of other wooden tools. The skill of the stone worker is now clearly seen in the large cutting tools--the handaxes, cleavers, and knives--which are often very fine, and go, perhaps for aesthetic reasons, far beyond the bounds dictated by utility alone. Acheulian occupation sites have a wide distribution throughout the savanna but avoid the lowveld of southeast Africa, the semi-desert country of the Horn, and the lowland rainforest of Equatoria and West Africa. A few sites do occur in these marginal or unfavorable zones, but they are extremely rare in comparison with the profusion of sites in the savanna and grasslands. Country now desert in southwest Africa and in the Sahara was also occupied when climatic amelioration permitted these now arid regions to support a thicker vegetation and a richer fauna.

It might be expected that the pattern of hominid behavior would be different in the north and the south, but one of the most outstanding features of Middle Pleistocene culture is its homogeneity. It is true that some four or five variants can be observed in the stone culture of these times, but these are all connected with special activities rather than with regional differences. The evidence is now quite clear that stone tools were being made and used for individual specific purposes by Acheulian man,[12] but it is equally clear that these same forms occur throughout all the vast area of the Old World where the Handaxe Culture was practised. Handaxe man used a greater variety of raw materials than had been used at any other period of the Stone Age, and from the faunal lists it would seem that in his dietary habits, at least as far as meat was concerned, he was equally diversified.

The pattern of hominid behavior of this time is now beginning to become clear. Settlements seem to have consisted of several family groups, probably totalling about 25 individuals. One living floor which has been discovered is 30 feet in diameter. (For comparison, one /Kung Bushman band of 32 persons--8 family fires--occupied an area 40 feet by 20 feet for maximum warmth, light, and protection.) The settlements were still tied to sites immediately adjacent to water, and the groups might have come together for seasonal foraging and hunting. The people ate a very wide variety of foods, and their technology, though it showed a mastery of the principles of stone flaking, was yet restricted to a low level of efficiency by their inability to exploit to more than a very limited degree any of the natural resources. If the ability to do even crude stone working enabled the Australopithecines to obtain the advantages of a meat and buried vegetable diet, then the skill that produced the Acheulian handaxe and cleaver would seem to be connected with the better exploiting of the meat supply offered by the large animals.

The tool kit of Middle Pleistocene man was restricted and, within broad limits, still unspecialized. There were large cutting tools, heavy duty implements for chopping, bashing, gouging, adzing or shaving, and light duty--scraping, grooving, and small cutting--tools. All these are present in a normal Acheulian assemblage in Africa and southwestern Europe. The so-called "flake, chopper, and handaxe traditions" present at that time in the Old World can better be explained as the most favorable adaptations permitted by the ecological extremes in which his behavioral limitations enabled man to live.

The first evidence for the use of fire in Africa dates to the closing stages of the Acheulian Culture, during a period of climate like that of the present day, but later changing to cooler and wetter conditions. At the Kalambo Falls site there are charred logs, charcoals, and wooden tools--digging sticks, clubs, and machetes--worked by fire which have been dated to approximately 58,300 years ago.

A considerable change in the distribution of culture then took place, and there is evidence for broad regional adaptation within the favorable savanna and grassland zones and also in the forest. This behavioral change was accompanied or induced by climatic variation--lowered temperatures and increased rainfall, that corresponded to the period of the early Würm in Europe--which brought about considerable modification of the favorable zones. The regular use of fire also contributed to the change, since it vastly increased the efficiency of the cultural equipment, permitted the use of materials other than stone for the manufacture of tools, and led to very greatly improved methods of wood working.

About this time also there was a revolution in social behavior. Man began to make permanent use of caves and rock shelters as regular places for habitation. Occupation sites were no longer invariably by the water side, and from this time onward tools became increasingly specialized. Whereas it had taken some 1,700,000 years to reach the stage of technical efficiency of Later Acheulian man, it required only 60,000 to 50,000 years to go the rest of the way and to achieve full urbanization. The reason for this must surely lie in man's ability to organize his social structure and economy with improved efficiency, once his technical skill has assured the basic dietary requirements of the group.

THREE MAIN CULTURAL TRADITIONS

Between 60,000 and 40,000 years ago prehistoric culture in the African continent could be divided into three broad traditions:

(1) A continuation of the Acheulian handaxe tradition in the grasslands and dry savanna of the south and southwest (known as the Fauresmith or Acheulio-Levalloisian Culture);

(2) A tradition with many heavy duty tools--core-axes, picks, choppers, etc.--and a number of light duty tools with denticulated edges in the savanna grassland/forest margin region of Equatoria, following the retreat of the lowland humid forest and the advance of the montane elements (called the Sangoan Culture); and

(3) A tradition of light flake tools present in Africa north of the Sahara, which may or may not be intrusive from Europe or southwest Asia (known as the Mousterian or Levallois-Mousterian Culture).

Each of these three traditions must be expected to have developed the technology best suited to the pattern of life and food resources of its makers. The difficulty comes in trying to assess the relative importance of the stone equipment in a material culture from which usually the remains of all the more perishable elements are missing. However, if the site at Hajj Creiem in Cyrenaica is any indication, the North African Mouste-

rian population were skillful hunters, since a small temporary
camp site, which can have provided living space for a small group
for a few days only, yielded the remains of five to ten Barbary
sheep, three or four zebra, two or three buffalo, and a gazelle.[13]
The delicate flint scrapers and points found there support the belief that hunting was of prime importance to this North African
Mousterian population.

In the higher rainfall, thicker vegetation region of the
Sangoan Culture, enhanced importance must have been given to vegetable foods, since game is not so plentiful in such areas, and
the vegetable potential is much greater. More emphasis was here
placed on wood working, and the Kalambo Falls site shows that man
had already learned how to work wood by charring and scraping. In
the savanna, however, game must always have been very plentiful
and man's taste unselective, as the long faunal lists from the
Broken Hill cave show.

The remains of the Fauresmith or Acheulio-Levalloisian
Culture are found in what today is grassland, often high altitude or semi-arid steppe country, sometimes even desert, seemingly the result of the continuation of the traditional ecological
conditions of Middle Pleistocene times.

The makers of these prehistoric cultures were of early
Homo sapiens stock--Neanderthaloids in North Africa, Rhodesioids
and others in sub-Saharan Africa. These cultures of the early
Upper Pleistocene became differentiated because they were adapted
to different ecological conditions. The technological level from
locality to locality in each of the cultural zones seems to show
little individual variation, however, and one is forced to the
conclusion that, although regional specialization in Africa had
already begun at this time, it was based on only a comparatively
shallow level of unselective efficiency in exploitation of the
natural resources.

By the later stages of the Upper Pleistocene the pattern
of prehistoric culture is very different, and there was then a
variety of specialized regional forms. Their makers belonged to
the modern Homo sapiens stock which, from 35,000 years ago, began
to replace everywhere the older Neanderthaloid and Rhodesioid
populations. These regional culture forms seem to have had their
origin in the three earlier complexes--the Levallois-Mousterian,
the Sangoan, and the Fauresmith--producing in turn the Aterian,
the Lupemban, and the Stillbay/Pietersburg traditions, which date
from between about 35,000 to about 12,000 years ago.

Within these broad cultural divisions quite a variety of
secondary differentiation existed, and a host of regional cultural
stages can be distinguished, the characteristics of which are
likely to be related to the resources of the local environment.

There was a much larger range of specialized stone tools present in the equipment of the Later Pleistocene hunter-gatherers than in the equipment of their Early Pleistocene predecessors. In addition, the relative importance of one form of tool over another, seen in the percentage variations of Middle Stone Age times, could be due only to the interaction of cultural tradition and ecology selecting for greatest efficiency. That cultural tradition was of importance by this time is shown not only by the clear evolutionary development of the local Middle Stone Age cultures from their earlier Upper Pleistocene antecedents, but also by the way the intrusive Upper Palaeolithic Blade and Burin cultures maintained their individuality unaffected by the autochthonous African cultures of the northwest and south.

The Later Pleistocene saw movement into the Sahara from both north and south activated by the spread southwards of the Mediterranean flora, probably as far as Chad, and the northward transgression of the Sudanic vegetation belt to make the Sahara a favorable region for hunter-gatherers. By 20,000 years ago the makers of the Aterian Culture had penetrated into the southeastern Sahara to Wanyanga and probably to the Nile. Contemporaneously, the bearers of the Lupemban Culture moved north from the Guinea and dry savanna, so that in such areas as far removed as Adrar in the west and Kharga in the east there took place a blending of these two traditions.

REGIONAL ADAPTATION AND CULTURAL DEVELOPMENT

The greater degree of specialization in the material culture at this time is probably to be connected with the greater specialization in the diet. The source of meat was most often medium-sized animals, and, while the range of species at any site is still fairly wide, it is usual that one or two species predominate--wildebeests, hartebeests, zebra, or pigs, for example-- depending on the local ecology. Bones of large animals are rarely found in the cave and rock shelter sites. This is not because these animals were no longer eaten, but because from the time that semi-permanent occupation of sites was possible, only the meat was carried back to the camp, and the band no longer had to camp around the meat.

The enormous number of Middle Stone Age sites in Africa, even in such unfavorable areas as the Namib desert or the Lybian Sand Sea, show that, during the cooler, optimum climate of the Later Pleistocene, man in Africa was capable of occupying, though probably only seasonally, regions that today are among some of the most inhospitable on the continent. That man found it attractive to do this must surely imply a considerable population in the optimum zones during this period.

CULTURE AND ECOLOGY IN PREHISTORIC AFRICA

From the evidence of many new cultural traits it is also apparent that the appearance of Homo sapiens produced a quickening and intensification of regional adaptability. Groups or bands now used camping places which could be seasonally, or perhaps semi-permanently, occupied and regularly revisited. From the occupation of caves and rock shelters, it would also seem that they were able to live continually in these sites for much longer than had been possible to Middle Pleistocene man. To such places the proceeds of the hunt were regularly carried back, and the maintenance of a semi-permanent home must have encouraged specialization of activities as between man and woman. Aesthetic and magico-religious beliefs are attested to by the presence of personal adornment, pigment, art, and ritual burial. Technical improvements, especially in hunting weapons such as the spear and knife, resulted from the regular hafting of tools, and it is probable that the bow and arrow made its appearance in the northwest at this time. All this goes to show that, by the close of the Pleistocene 10,000 years ago, the organization of prehistoric society in the continent is unlikely to have differed in many essential respects from that of recent hunter-gatherers. There is also good reason to believe that by this time the indigenous racial groupings--the Khoisan, Negroid, and Afro-Mediterranean--had already made their appearance.

At the close of the Pleistocene there is evidence for climatic deterioration and a swing to aridity which had a concentrating effect upon the human and animal population, emptying the unfavorable areas and scattering the population of the marginal zones. That man was able to maintain himself in these marginal zones throughout Later Stone Age/Mesolithic times after 8000 B.C. shows that his technical ability had reached a higher level of efficiency than at any time previously.

The period from about 6,000 to 2,500 B.C.--known in Europe as the Climatic Optimum--was one of increased rainfall in Africa and resulted in another expansion of the favorable zones and a repopulation of the Sahara from both directions. Either population explosion, the climatic deterioration terminating the Pleistocene, or cultural diffusion--probably a combination of the three--was responsible for the establishment of large, near permanent or permanent settlements adjacent to lakes, rivers, and the sea shore. These were made possible by the exploitation for the first time on a significant scale of fresh water and sea foods. Such sites are found near waterways in the Congo Basin, up the Nile, around the lakes of East Africa, and in the Sahel and Sudanic belts of the Sahara. In addition, around the Mediterranean and southern African coasts, middens, composed largely of the fossil refuse from sea foods, accumulated up to thirty feet in thickness. Around the fringes of the forest also, the wild Dioscorea, oil palm, and other near permanent sources of vegetable food probably led to the development of a vegecultural way of life.

In the savanna at this time were a large number of region-
ally adapted groups who were capable of making what is probably
the maximum use of the material resources for a hunting-gathering
way of life. Their food included large and small animals in near
equal amounts, and there can be no doubt that improved hunting
techniques, particularly in the use of the bow and poisoned arrow,
permitted a reduction in the territorial range of the hunting area.
The Saharan, or Makalian Wet Phase, as this period is called, must
have been an extremely advantageous time for the hunting populations of the favorable zones, so much so that, when cultivated
wheat and barley were introduced into the Nile valley during the
early fifth or sixth millennium B.C., farming was unable, until
two millennia later, to compete successfully with the hunting-
gathering way of life south of the Sahara. Something of this
living pattern can be gathered from the rock art of the period.

By 3,500 B.C. the new cereal plants and domestic cattle,
sheep, and goats had spread rapidly throughout the Mediterranean
littoral and north Atlantic coast as well as in the marginally
favorable but winter rainfall region of the Sahara. In the oases
and river valleys cereal cultivation must have been of major importance, but the emphasis in the Sahara was on pastoralism, particularly cattle raising. When the climate again deteriorated,
after 2,500 B.C., there was a general movement out of the Sahara,
and the evidence suggests that it was at this time that the populations in the Sudanic belt began, or intensified, experimentation
with local food plants, since in the tropical summer rainfall regions the north African winter rainfall crops only grow well under
irrigation.

It was not, however, until a further 2,000 years had
elapsed that the benefits of the agricultural way of life began
to penetrate to the sub-continent, though some of the regions of
West and northeast Africa--Senegal, Guinea, Ghana, Nigeria, and
Ethiopia--saw the establishment of local Neolithic communities.
These groups lived on the margins of the West African rainforest
and in the savanna and grasslands of the East African high plateau, showing that by this time culture was able to cut across
several very different ecological zones by reason of the success
achieved with the local domesticates. Perhaps 2,000 years were
necessary to develop these domesticates; certainly the equipment
of the Neolithic slash-and-burn cultivators was fairly inefficient
for any large scale agricultural activity, and this method cannot
have had the appeal to the populations of the game-stocked, well-
watered tropical savanna that it had for the occupants of the
semi-arid North African region where it was the sole means of
maintaining population growth and stability. The detailed history
of domestication in Africa can, however, only be learned from
properly controlled, stratigraphic archaeology and, as yet, there
is little of this available.

CULTURE AND ECOLOGY IN PREHISTORIC AFRICA

Whatever the reason or reasons, it was not until a knowledge of metallurgy, with its resultant immeasurably more effective metal tools, spread south of the Sahara during the last half of the first millennium B.C. that agriculture and domestic stock spread into southern Africa with immigrations from the southern Sudan. These seem to have started about the beginnings of the Christian Era, and the crops that were introduced were the Sudanic ones--sorghum, bullrush millet, and finger millet--along with cattle, sheep, and goats. From this time on (and the stages now begin to be better documented by radiocarbon dating) the superiority of the mixed farming way of life shows itself in the disappearance of the hunting-gathering economy, though both these activities have remained of considerable importance in the life of the Bantu populations of central and southern Africa. For example, in the savanna country of the Luapula District of Northern Rhodesia, 46 adults spent 4.6 per cent of their time collecting, 4.3 per cent fishing, and 1.6 per cent hunting--the last a small percentage because there is little left to hunt.[14] Among the Valley Tonga on the Middle Zambezi, the source of relish for midday and evening meals for three households on 169 days indicates that gathering accounted for 547 meals, and hunting and fishing for 12 each, totalling 571 out of a grand total of 712 meals.[15]

With the coming of domestication, the most favorable ecological zones were, on the one hand, the marginal, drier habitats, where disease of cattle and other stock was reduced to a minimum, and, on the other hand, the marginal rainforest country where, though disease might eliminate most livestock, this was compensated for by the agricultural richness of the environment, especially after the Asian food plants of the humid tropics had reached Equatoria in the early centuries A.D.

From this time onwards man's activities began to have a more permanent effect on his environment in the tropics, as they must surely have done in the Sahara during Neolithic times. It is probable that intensified and regular burning by man at this time began the replacement of forest by tall grass savanna in the higher rainfall zones. At this period, also, the thorn thicket probably began to encroach on grassland in the semi-arid zones where over-stocking and regular burning preceded soil erosion and, indeed, must have hastened the desertification of the Sahara.

Because of its sparseness, the hunter-gatherer population is unlikely to have affected significantly the distribution and density of the game. For example, an !Kung Bushman band kills an average of 15-18 large animals (i.e. large antelopes and giraffes) in a normal year. No doubt, under optimum conditions, the number of animals killed by earlier hunter-gatherers would have been greater, but, even if doubled, it can have had no appreciable effect on game distribution. Significant reduction of the game can only have begun with the coming of food production and the establishment of large permanent settlements by Bantu and Negroes. In regions where disease excluded domestic stock, the growing scarcity of game and thus of a balanced protein diet, must have been one of the causes of population pressure leading to migration.

SUMMARY

Ecology has played a major role in the distribution and evolution of man and his culture in Africa. It provided the basic stimulus for tool-making. Knowledge of palaeo-environments shows that the striking differences that exist today between North, West, and East Africa began at least 50,000 years ago. It shows, moreover, if we are interpreting the data correctly, that climatic change was capable of producing a variety of responses in the human population--movement of peoples and thus cultural and genetic diffusion, stimulus to more intensified technical efficiency, population increase (especially after colonization of empty environments), and isolation, which gave increased opportunity for genetic drift.

Environmental factors alone, however, could at best have had only a stabilizing effect on human groups, but the steady growth of new technical skills keeping pace with intellectual evolution permitted populations to increase and develop ever more efficient livelihood patterns, and so to reach the realization that the most efficient are those who make the best use of the resources of their habitat.

NOTES

[1] "Tool-using and Aimed Throwing in a Community of Free-Living Chimpanzees," Nature, CCI (1964), p. 1264.

[2] F. C. Howell and F. Bourliere, eds., African Ecology and Human Evolution [Viking Fund Publications in Anthropology, 36 (1963)], pp. 606-10.

[3] "The Population Ecology of Man in the Early Upper Pleistocene of Southern Africa," Proceedings of the Prehistoric Society, XXVI (1960), pp. 235-57.

[4] L. Marshall, "!Kung Bushman Bands," Africa, XXX (1960), pp. 326-27.

[5] H. A. Fosbrooke, "A Stone Age Tribe in Tanganyika," South African Archaeological Bulletin, XI (1956), pp. 3-8.

[6] P. V. Tobias, "On the Survival of the Bushmen," Africa, XXVI

(1956), pp. 174-86.

[7]A. L. Kroeber, Cultural and Natural Areas of Native North America (Berkeley: University of California Press, 1939), pp. 137-43. [U.C. Publications in American Archaeology and Ethnology, XXXVIII.]

[8]Op. cit., pp. 253-55 (see note 3).

[9]R. J. Braidwood and C. A. Reed, "The Achievement and Early Consequences of Food Production: A Consideration of the Archaeological and Natural-Historical Evidence," Cold Spring Harbor Symposia on Quantitative Biology, XXII (1957), pp. 19-31.

[10]L. S. B. Leakey, "Very Earliest East African Hominidae and Their Ecological Setting," in Howell and Bourliere, op. cit., pp. 448-57 (see note 2).

[11]C. K. Brain, The Transvaal Ape-Man-Bearing Cave Deposits, Transvaal Museum Memoir XI (1958); R. L. Hay, "Stratigraphy of Beds I through IV, Olduvai Gorge, Tanganyika," Science, CXXXIX (1963), 3557, pp. 829-33.

[12]M. R. Kleindienst, "Variability within the Late Acheulian Assemblage in East Africa," South African Archaeological Bulletin, XVI (1961), pp. 35-52.

[13]C. B. M. McBurney, The Stone Age of Northern Africa (Baltimore: Penguin Books, Inc., 1960), pp. 167-68.

[14]G. Kay, Chief Kalaba's Village (Manchester: 1964), pp. 51-60. [Rhodes-Livingstone Paper No. 35.]

[15]T. Scudder, The Ecology of the Gwembe Tonga (Manchester: Manchester University Press, 1962), p. 202.

ENVIRONMENT, TECHNICAL KNOWLEDGE, AND ECONOMIC DEVELOPMENT

by

William O. Jones

"For out of olde feldes, as men seyth,
Cometh al this newe corn fro yer to yere;
And out of olde bokes, in good feyth,
Cometh al this newe science that men lere."

Geoffrey Chaucer,
The Parlement of Foules

We can say that an economy is growing, or developing, when its total output of useful (wanted) goods and services, measured in some aggregative fashion, is increasing--total output taken to include not only goods and services purchased by consumers, but also their own produce, services (including structures) provided by government, and commodities and services sold or traded to persons outside the economy. Some services, such as medical care, public health, and education, are not easily measured by the economist's numeraire of market value. These can be gauged in other ways, however, and if weights can be assigned in an agreed fashion, may be combined in a more general index of economic product: medical care and health can be evaluated directly through statistics of mortality and morbidity, indirectly through the ratio of doctors and hospital beds to population, or amount and character of sanitary facilities; and education can be measured directly through the degree of literacy, or indirectly as the per cent of children in school or the average years of schooling.

A simple measure of economic achievement, widely used when estimating the success of non-human populations in adapting to their environment, is the rate of change in total population. (In recent decades we have come to regard rapid human population growth as somehow undesirable, as a thing to be feared and discouraged, especially when it occurs outside the Western world. There are, of course, good reasons for our concern, although they may stem in part from an urge for racial survival that is aroused when we see other competing populations growing more rapidly than our own.)

To have more babies live to adulthood and to have more adults live out their full life span in vigor and in health must be accepted by all men as desirable in themselves. If the conse-

quence is that the world contains more of our kind, this should
be cause for rejoicing, not for despair. To be fruitful, and multiply, and replenish the earth, and subdue it, was the first charge
given to man. (The rest of that charge is also pertinent to our
discussions here.) Taken by itself, increase in population is a
sign of increasing efficiency in the utilization of resources;
only when it is accompanied by a decline in level of living, or
when it prevents an urgently desired rise in level of living and
alleviation of human misery, can it properly be feared. To decide
on purely objective grounds whether in any given situation the
values attendant upon declining mortality, better health, and increasing numbers outweigh the costs of other benefits foregone may
not be possible; the comparison is essentially subjective and to
be made by the populations in which these changes are occurring.
It would be bold even to judge whether a long life with impaired
health is better or worse than a short life in good health. On
the other hand, when a population has made a choice that it is unable to implement, or when, as is too often the case, the full
consequences of its choice are not seen, the social scientist can
be of assistance. It is important to recognize at the outset that
population growth is not only a likely consequence, but an objective of economic progress, and that population growth inevitably
brings with it a heightened impact of man on his natural surroundings, animate and inanimate.

The interaction between man and his environment is an integral part of the study of economic growth. No place is this more
true than in tropical Africa, where plentiful resources of land
would permit a considerable expansion of output without any changes
in agricultural techniques if only a larger labor force were available. But if man is to multiply, and if he is to subdue the earth,
the earth must be changed by his dominion to minister to his welfare.

Welfare, of course, is not a thing to be measured directly,
nor is it to be summed up in estimates of gross national product
which provide an index of goods and services to which weights can
be assigned on the basis of some system of market valuation. For
welfare, or level of living, includes many other things in addition to health and knowledge that are not measured in the market
place. Furthermore, welfare is, in some sense, a net concept affected by costs as well as benefits. More than this, it is not
enough to choose between present benefits and present costs: account must also be taken of future benefits and of benefits foregone. This choice is difficult enough when man's perception of
his environment remains unchanged, when technical knowledge is
constant; it is many times confounded when technical knowledge is
growing at a rapid but unpredictable rate.

It must also be remembered that rapid economic growth is
rarely, if ever, achieved without significant, sometimes radical,

alteration of existing social arrangements and relationships.
These modifications of the cultural environment are paralleled in
the natural environment; just as many highly prized cultural attributes are likely to be lost in the social revolution accompanying
economic change, so will many of the natural amenities also be
destroyed. These are among the costs of what its proponents like
to call "economic progress"; whether they are too great to be borne,
whether they outweigh the benefits that are expected in their train,
is a decision, and not an easy one, that the human community must
make.

ECONOMIC DEVELOPMENT AND THE NATURAL ENVIRONMENT

The economic process is the transformation of elements of
the natural environment into things necessary, useful, and plea-
surable to man. In this process we identify three major components: the natural resources themselves, the knowledge and skill
that change their forms, and the allocation of limited resources
and skills among various uses to achieve the greatest possible
total of human satisfactions.

Not all of the natural environment can be classified as
natural resource; only some elements can be transformed into in-
come-yielding assets. Other elements are burdensome or painful to
man, and neutralizing their effects is part of the economic process.
And many elements of the environment are economically neutral. The
economic value, or usefulness, of the various components of the
environment depends primarily on our knowledge and skill in identifying, combining, and transforming them. As technical knowledge
changes, therefore, the character and amount of natural resources
also change. Things that were once highly prized, like flint rock,
for example, may no longer be prized as raw material for tools, but
pass to a lower use as building aggregate or even take on a negative value as something to be cleared from the soil before it can
be put to economic use. Other things that had no value before,
such as heavy soils of river valleys, covered with rank vegetation,
become highly productive when sophisticated techniques are brought
to bear on them.

As technical knowledge grows and becomes more complex, the
range of uses to which elements of the environment can be put ex-
pands, and the choices to be made in utilizing those elements more
complex. In general, the number of elements that can be usefully
employed also increases, despite the loss of knowledge of inferior
uses that seems to be a regular concomitant of change. In brief,
the resource base changes as technical knowledge changes.

What then can we say about the influence of environment on
economic development? That it must depend on the level of technology is obvious; that it must weaken as technical knowledge be-

comes more complex seems reasonable, but only if the economic links among various parts of human society are strong, so that the allocation process is well performed. If this is so, correspondence between environment and economic product is more likely to be high among societies employing relatively simple industrial techniques than in those with more complex techniques. In a very broad way, this seems to be confirmed by students of the evolution of man. Can this sort of correspondence be found in tropical Africa?

Both technical and allocative knowledge, of course, vary greatly across the subcontinent, but regional differences are less in agriculture than in manufacturing. Furthermore, the impact of modern medicine and hygiene on health and mortality is probably less in the country than in the urban centers. If population density is taken as a measure of the level of economic achievement, a map of rural populations might be expected to correlate with some aspects of the natural environment.

Examination of the Trewartha and Zelinsky map of the distribution of rural population in about 1950 does in fact show that density tends to be correlated with some of the grosser features of the environment: the rainforest of the Congo Basin, the droughty regions of Tanzania, the semi-desert of northern Kenya, and the borders of the Sahara are populated relatively lightly, although the density in some of these areas is higher than might have been expected on the basis of other accounts; and population concentrations are associated with certain obvious natural features, such as the Senegal and Gambia Rivers, the upper courses of the Nile and Niger Rivers (but not the lower course of the Niger, nor the Benue), the shores of Lake Victoria, the highlands of Ethiopia, Kenya, Rwanda and Burundi, Malawi, and Cameroun. Other variations in population are not as easily explained by natural features: the relatively high densities in the rainforests of Eastern Nigeria and the low rainfall lands of Northern Nigeria contrast strangely with those of the riverain provinces; and explanation of the sizable populations of parts of Kwango and Kasai requires more than knowledge of the natural environment.[1]

M. K. Bennett, in 1962, attempted an agro-climatic mapping of all of Africa that may be set against the population map of Trewartha and Zelinsky in a search for overall correlation.[2] Bennett identifies zones where rainfall is sufficient for different types of agriculture: (B) single-crop winter growth (Mediterranean littoral and Cape of Good Hope only); (C) single-crop summer growth; (D) moister single-crop summer growth; and (E) potential successive crops. When the distribution of major foodcrops is mapped against these zones, their agricultural significance is confirmed. Banana-plantains, rice, manioc, and yams are rather narrowly confined to Zone E; the millets, sorghum, and maize to Zones C and D. Comparison of Bennett's zones with population density, however, does not show clear-cut correspondence

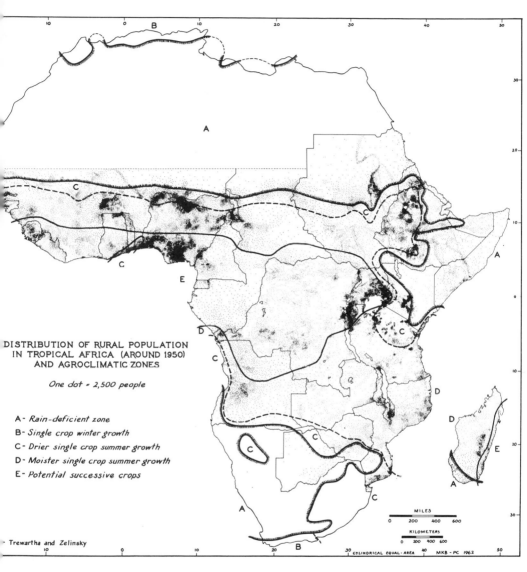

DISTRIBUTION OF RURAL POPULATION
IN TROPICAL AFRICA (AROUND 1950)
AND AGROCLIMATIC ZONES

One dot = 2,500 people

A- *Rain-deficient zone*
B- *Single crop winter growth*
C- *Drier single crop summer growth*
D- *Moister single crop summer growth*
E- *Potential successive crops*

Trewartha and Zelinsky

MILES
0   200   400   600

KILOMETERS
0   200   400   600

CYLINDRICAL EQUAL-AREA   MKB-PC 1962

MAP 1

(Map 1). Major population clusters occur in each of the three tropical zones, as do areas of very sparse population. In general, however, the zone labelled E seems to have the highest density, when account is taken of the large populations in Southern Nigeria, Rwanda and Burundi, and around the shores of Lake Victoria, although this zone includes the thinly-populated Congo rainforest. It might be inferred, then, that warm areas with high rainfall and without clearly marked dry and rainy seasons are best able to maintain human populations in the African tropics.

Comparison of population distribution with other attributes of the natural environment would undoubtedly suggest additional relationships between economic performance and resource base. M. R. Bloch's map showing the availability of salt in precolonial Africa, for example, suggests a possible connection between the high cultures of the West African savannas and the salt deposits of the central Sahara, although it is hard to accept his statement that because of the scarcity of salt "inner Africa was able to support only a thin human population."[3]

Examination of the major population groupings makes it clear that more than climate and more than natural environment are at work. These other determinants are of two kinds: technical knowledge, and allocative or organizing efficiency. The dense populations of the Guinea coast result from a combination of both, employed in a physical environment not too dissimilar from the relatively empty lands along the Congo. Similarly, although the physical environment of Zone C permits the establishment of a heavy human population like that of Northern Nigeria, it is necessary to turn to consideration of technology and of political and economic organization to understand how in fact such a large community came into existence at this place.

THE REVOLUTIONS IN TECHNOLOGY AND ECONOMIC ORGANIZATION

Present-day distribution and density of population in tropical Africa reflect the influence, among others, of two profound changes in the determinants of economic productivity--one, a change in technology; the other, a change in economic organization. The greatest technical change of modern times almost certainly was the introduction of a complete new set of food crops from the Americas. Perhaps the ultimate effect of improved medical and hygienic knowledge may be greater, but this knowledge still is narrowly shared, whereas experience with the New World crops has long since spread throughout the continent.

We can only conjecture how the new crops altered human populations and their physical environment, but enough is known about the characteristics of the food plants to make conjecture plausible. In manioc the African farmer found a crop that gave

him more food calories per acre than any crop he had known. Furthermore, it cost no more in labor effort--perhaps less--than the
traditional crops. In areas where irregular rainfall and drought,
or plagues of locusts, were an ever present threat to food supply,
manioc afforded protection against hunger and famine. Its general
adoption throughout the equatorial belt must certainly have saved
many lives and resulted in a rapid increase in population. Maize
provided a new cereal, often the only cereal, to forest-dwelling
populations, and its superior yield and ease of processing permitted it to displace the traditional sorghums and millets over
much of the eastern and southern grasslands. The New World beans
and peanuts supplied high quality protein to supplement dwindling
supplies of animal protein as increasing populations hunted out
the areas near their villages. Peanuts, too, brought a major
source of vegetable oils in the fat-poor regions of the savannas.

If the conjecture is right that manioc, maize, beans, peanuts, and other American crops permitted a considerable increase
in the population of tropical Africa, this added population in itself must have altered the natural landscape and the non-human
population profoundly. Some of the new crops may have affected
the environment more directly. Because manioc will produce economic yields on land so depleted in plant nutrients as not to be
suited to other crops, its adoption in a foodcrop complex may
cause land to be held under cultivation longer than before, requiring longer fallow periods to bring fertility back to previous
levels. When combined with the increased populations that manioc
makes possible, the result may be almost continuous cropping, as
in southern Togo and parts of Northern Rhodesia; it may also, by
guaranteeing a supply of calories but not of proteins, substitute
protein hunger for true hunger, so that larger populations survive
but at lower levels of health and vigor, as in some parts of the
Kwango. Maize cultivation may lead to somewhat analogous results.
Although this crop will outperform the millets and sorghums when
rainfall is ample and properly distributed, it suffers much more
from deficiencies in moisture supply; farming communities that
have shifted heavily to maize frequently find that the incidence
of hunger and famine, or its severity, has increased. Cultivation of maize in pure stand can also result in heavy losses of
soil through erosion.

This particular widening of natural limits on economic
production, following the introduction of the New World crops,
has essentially been completed. It was achieved by the opportu-
nistic transfer of techniques developed elsewhere into a similar
and congenial environment. The technical changes now possible in
tropical Africa have a different genesis: they result from the
purposive, rational application of the massive scientific knowledge and methodology of the twentieth century to the alteration
of environment to suit man's ends. This technical revolution,
which is only beginning to have its impact on the economic prob-

lem, spreads so wide the bounds that resource endowment places on production as to make them a matter of little technical concern. To the new technician it must almost appear as if man could mold his environment into any form he wishes. Investigations of the efficacy of commercial fertilizers when applied to African soils and of the possibility of higher yields from improved plant varieties provide some intimation of the possible impact of the new technology on African economic production.

The story of the early misinterpretation of lush tropical growth as evidence of great soil fertility is familiar to most students of tropical Africa. When attempts to bring African lands under cultivation by methods that had been used elsewhere failed, because these soils were in fact low in plant nutrient content and susceptible to rapid degradation, the period of enthusiasm over the apparently boundless prodigality of nature was followed by one of equally exaggerated discouragement. Results obtained by applying barnyard manures and cover crops were disappointing, and it was widely believed that because of the peculiar nature of tropical soils--in particular, their acidity--it would be extremely difficult, if not impossible, to increase their fertility by the application of mineral fertilizers. It was not until after World War II that extensive investigations of fertilizer response were undertaken. The results were exciting: crops grown on tropical African soils reacted to the addition of nitrogen, phosphorus, and potash in the same fashion as crops grown elsewhere. The same principles that had led to greatly increased outputs in Western Europe and North America could serve as the basis for similar achievements in Africa. The danger now may be that the pendulum of opinion will swing too far again in the opposite direction, and that a second period of excessive enthusiasm may follow the one of excessive pessimism. It is hard not to share this enthusiasm when one hears reports of five- to ten-fold increases in cocoa yields achieved in Ghana by moderate applications of fertilizer combined with reduction in shade cover.

Just as important as the new findings by soil scientists are the new products of the plant breeders, and, in fact, each reinforces the other, for increased supplies of plant nutrients can be more effectively exploited by new plant varieties, and many of the new varieties need increased nutrient supplies in order to realize their full potential. Research leading to the development of higher yielding varieties of export crops is of long standing and has had notable successes. In 1951, for example, well-managed oil palm plantations in the Belgian Congo were producing 800 to 1,000 kilograms of oil per hectare (perhaps three to five times that obtained by smallholders); improved crosses then undergoing field trial were yielding 1,500 kilograms, and higher yields were in sight. By 1962 field-tested varieties were producing three tons of oil per hectare, with much higher yields possible.

Domestically consumed foodcrops have so far received less
attention than export crops, although maize hybrids developed for
some localities display much higher yields than the strains now
cultivated. A new synthetic hybrid now being multiplied in Kenya,
for example, has yielded up to 140 bushels per acre in field trials,
compared with typical yields in the area of about 18 bushels.[4]
Their optimum utilization, however, will come only with the general use of mineral fertilizers. One of the most interesting new
developments in plant breeding is the establishment of programs in
East and West Africa for improvement of the millets and sorghums
by scientific breeding and selection. These important food grains
of the grasslands have been largely neglected by African research;
their improvement could have a sizable impact on productivity in
the savanna regions.

If the greatest technical change in Africa in modern times
was the introduction of a complete foodcrop complex from the Americas, the greatest organizational change, and closely interrelated
with the technical one, was the introduction of the agricultural
and mineral products of Africa into the markets of Europe and North
America. It is this change that has enabled the people of Africa
to increase their economic productivity far above subsistence
levels, and to provide a basis in wealth, organization, and skills
for the construction of modern economies. It of course has a
technical component in improved methods of transporting goods
from hinterland to port, but the more important part was the development of a market trading system to assemble the produce of
thousands of small producers, bring it out to the coast, and em-
bark it on ships for distant markets.

Adoption of the New World crops led to horizontal or dupli-
cative expansion of existing societies and caused only minor alterations in social structure, but the development of export industries required and provoked more profound social changes. They
were probably least severe in areas where farmers were able to
engage in production of small amounts for sale as an additional
agricultural activity, employing labor previously idle or engaged
in non-agricultural activities. Sometimes this meant a reduction
in domestic manufacture of products now become available through
the market, but in general, the production of export crops seems
not to have been at the expense of foodcrops. Even this minimum
alteration in the economic order, however, required a basic change
in the producer's willingness to trust unknown producers to supply
him with part of his consumption requirements through the anonymous working of the market. Farmers like those of southern Ghana
and Western Nigeria who made the production of export crops their
principal economic activity became more deeply immersed in the
market mechanism and learned to accept increasing depersonalized
provision of consumption goods, even to the extent of obtaining
a large part of their food supply by purchase. All these changes,
however, were essentially minor when compared to the alteration

in values and personal relationships experienced by those who took
up wage employment in the cities, plantations, and mines.

These were major changes indeed, but they have opened the
way for even greater ones which may eventually permit the same
sort of revolution in allocative efficiency that seems to be in
store in the technical realm. In fact, realization of the technical potentialities depends in large part on further refinement of
the economic organization itself.

The technical revolution makes it possible to overcome almost any environmental limitation, but at a cost. High among
these costs are those incurred in improvement of the human agent.
The critical role of technology as a widener of the perceived
resource base implies a need for research to identify new techniques and for training to put them to use. It is not enough to
know that the research methodologies of the Western world are also
applicable in Africa: they must now be employed to yield solu-
tions to peculiarly African problems.

Earlier experience with the blind transfer to Africa of
production techniques that had been successful elsewhere led to
recognition that the traditional agricultural methods had evolved
in harmony with the physical determinants of production. The agricultural development schemes of the Congo, for example--the
paysannats indigènes--largely bypassed changes in techniques to
rely primarily on changes in organization in achieving increased
output. Research and development of the kind now required to release economic production from the confining bonds placed on it by
environment are costly, but the potential benefits are great
enough to warrant a considerable expansion of the present effort.
The situation in agricultural research in Africa today is made
particularly critical by loss of expatriate scientists; without a
special effort to reinforce the existing organizations, research
facilities may actually decline, as they have in the Congo, and
much of the progress made after World War II may be lost.

The lag between knowledge and practice is usually long,
but in some parts of Africa it has seemed to be infinite. The
value of research findings, however great, remains potential only,
until they are transmitted to men who will use them in productive
practices. Agricultural research stations in many parts of tropical Africa are now the repositories of knowledge that could profoundly alter productivity, but they have encountered continuing
difficulty in putting this knowledge to work. Both continued research and expanded and more imaginative educational programs will
be required if the new technology is to achieve any part of its
possibilities.

WILLIAM O. JONES

THE QUALITY OF THE HUMAN AGENT

Economic production is the exploitation by man of his environment. At the present stage of knowledge the quality of the human agent appears to be a more important limitation than the quality of natural resources. The individual's efficacy in production depends upon his will, his knowledge, and his physical capacity. The will to produce more can be stimulated by knowledge and by health, but its basic strength, however conditioned by culture, probably varies more within a society than between societies. Knowledge has economic significance both as it includes knowing how to produce efficiently and knowing how to employ effectively the proceeds realized from the sale of one's products. Health is basically determined by nutrition and pathology.

The impact of endemic disease in tropical Africa can be sharply reduced by known techniques, many of which do not require the conscious participation of the population. The incidence and seriousness of others can be reduced only through education and individual action. Nutrition, on the other hand, is primarily a matter of total productivity--of income--and of consumption habits. Technical knowledge enters both in increasing available income and in using this income to improve nutrition. The nature of the relationships between resource base, knowledge of production techniques, economic organization, consumption habits, and child health has recently been studied in a set of Western Nigerian villages by Collis, Dema, and Omololu,[5] and in Pankshin Division of Northern Nigeria, by Collis, Dema, and Lesi.[6] In the western villages they found the "nutritional standards of the various groups studied [to] reflect their agricultural prosperity, the quality of their land, and the influence of climate and economic factors."[7] Particularly interesting are their comments on two cocoa villages. West African cocoa farmers are typically prosperous and relatively healthy individuals (cf. notes 5 and 7), but in these two villages "the people were apathetic to a marked degree, seeming hardly to have the energy to come forward and talk to us, but rather sat or lay about while their children looked sickly, weak, and undernourished."[8] Whether the poor quality of diets in these villages was due to general poverty or to ignorance and improvidence is not clear; certainly the value of foods consumed was low as compared with other healthier villages. The authors of the study find the cause in the social disorganization of the cocoa villagers, which they attribute essentially to imperfect adjustment to the market economy:

> The reason for this is that it is not enough to introduce a highly paying cash crop to an illiterate peasantry and expect them to profit by it. What happens is that it tends to kill their traditional life, merely putting money in their pockets for a short period in the year, during which time they enjoy themselves. When the money

gets scarce, months before the next harvest, they find
themselves short of everything. . . . [W]ith money running out they can only buy the cheapest food, e.g., cassava and yams. Also the cocoa season is short and the
cocoa farmer has very little to do for the remaining
part of the year but sit around. Such idleness is not
the refreshing rest that comes after labor, but sterile
boredom in which man's mind and body degenerate, leaving him unhappy and discontented.[9]

Not all cocoa growers are like the inhabitants of these
two Nigerian villages;[10] when they are, the fault would appear to
lie not in nature but in man. (Most surveys of West African
cocoa-growing villages reveal a remarkably complete adjustment
to the modern economy.)

In the northern villages on the Jos Plateau the investigators found nutritional status to be good, but an "appalling
child mortality" of 54 per cent in the sample taken, which they
attribute simply to lack of medical care. They state that "modern
medical science has almost all the answers to the ills these people suffer from. If this knowledge could be brought to the people
in such a way as not to disrupt their traditional life, in other
words with sympathetic understanding, their health and particularly the health of their children could be improved more than
100 per cent."[11]

GROUP ORGANIZATION AND ECONOMIC PLANNING

Implicit in the concept of economics and economic organization is that it deals not with individuals but with organized
groups; the Robinson Crusoe model, so popular in earlier years
with teachers of elementary economics, does not in fact touch the
core of economics at all. The objective of economic organization,
it is true, is to allocate limited resources among various uses so
as to achieve the greatest possible total of human satisfactions,
but this allocation is conceived of as occurring within a group,
or an economy, and as involving greater or less specialization of
economic roles among the group's members. In discussions of economic development the group may be a community or a region, although it is most often thought of as comprising all members of a
nation-state, primarily because the nation is the decision unit
capable of reconciling or choosing among the manifold economic
goals of its members and of implementing its decisions.

When economic organization is viewed in terms of national
economies, even economies as small as some in tropical Africa, it
is at once apparent that it is concerned with the mobilization of
diverse resources and diverse skills. Within Togo's 22,000 square
miles are to be found deciduous rainforests suitable for cocoa,

saltwater swamps and lagoons, relatively dry short-grass plains, and tree and grass savanna; and the nature of foodcrop production varies systematically from north to south. Within its boundaries, too, are to be found at least 18 distinct tribal groups. In Rwanda and Burundi, with a combined area about equal to that of Togo, no less than 25 "natural regions" are distinguished according to elevation, temperature, rainfall, terrain, and soils, and at least four major foodcrop zones. Such variety of natural resources and the inevitable variety of individual talents to be found in populations of a million or more--even within relatively homogeneous cultures--produce variations in the ease and cost with which individual commodities can be produced in specified localities, the comparative advantages in production that are the first basis of economic exchange. The dramatic effect on total productivity of the opening of trade between previously isolated communities, or of the sudden reduction in transport costs when a road, railway, or river route is opened to traffic, is familiar to all students of economic change. With trade, no community need be limited to the resources present in its immediate vicinity; instead, it can employ resources available any place in the trading network. To these increases in output which result simply from more efficient utilization of the endowment of resources and talents that exist at the time when trade is opened must be added those which result from the impact of economic intercourse on the existing technology and even on the resource base. Economic isolation usually means cultural isolation as well; once broken, technical knowledge flows with commerce, enlarging the total pool of information available throughout the trading area. At the same time, the encounters between different techniques frequently result in innovations that are improvements on both. The changed economic environment may also create new technical problems as well, thus adding a further spur to productive inventiveness.

If the natural environment itself is not changed, certainly man's perception of it is. When refined salt is available through trade, salt-yielding plants cease to have economic value; when meat, as well as hides and skins, can be sold at a distance, the economic character of livestock alters; when iron ore can be brought in to be smelted near coal deposits, minerals take on new values; when fertilizers can be carried to farmlands at a reasonable price, the site value of worked-out lands becomes more important and natural fertility less.

Economic intercourse may also intensify man's willingness to produce by widening the variety of goods he can obtain with productive effort, and by reducing their cost. The converse of this proposition was demonstrated frequently enough in the periods of shortage during and immediately after World War II to make argument unnecessary.

The importance of economic organization in implementing

technical achievement is apparent when we consider ways of increasing the economic production from agriculture, tropical Africa's principal industry. Present output is limited essentially by the size of the labor force and by the number of crops that can be taken before yields fall so low that it is more economical to bring new land under cultivation than to continue cultivating the old. The soil scientists have demonstrated that, by appropriate addition of plant nutrients, yields per acre can be increased, and, at the same time, the period under cultivation can be extended and the time in fallow shortened, thus reducing the labor input required to clear new land. The technical solution is at hand, but application of it awaits the time when the value of the increase in yields becomes significantly greater than the cost of the fertilizers which will make it possible. (This might be considered as equivalent to saying that the increased output will be forthcoming when there is need for it, but this will be true only if need for product and real cost of input are accurately reflected in prices. Under present conditions they probably are not.)

Very little has been done to learn how efficiently farm products, particularly foodstuffs destined for domestic consumption, are distributed in Africa; it is highly probable, however, that costs could be reduced by provision of some of the services generally available in the advanced economies and by state intervention to reduce uneconomic restraints on trade. Similar opportunities undoubtedly exist for reducing the costs of purchased inputs; their marketing is further complicated by the insistence of some governments on themselves supplying farmers with fertilizers, pesticides, and improved seeds. These state monopolies, although set up from motives of service rather than of profit, have all too frequently impeded the flow of products rather than facilitated it. (A frequent complaint of agricultural officers is that after having persuaded farmers of the merits of fertilizers or pesticides, they find that through administrative error adequate supplies are not available when and where they are wanted.) Without attempting to pass judgment on the relative merits of private and state enterprise, it can be stated with confidence that reduction of distribution costs is now the essential condition for bringing many technical innovations effectively into play.

The rearrangement of productive agents that is the object of economic organization is not restricted to natural resources; in numerous instances the distribution of human population too is far from optimum--in some places too thin, in others too dense. For the distribution of African populations in 1960 still reflects in large part the technology and economic organization of 50 or 100 years ago, as well as the influence of historical circumstances and other non-economic factors. Rearrangement of these populations is underway, but major permanent migrations may be necessary to achieve optimum combinations for production. Areas of severe land shortage still exist side by side with under-uti-

lized lands; population in many areas is too dispersed to make
modern transport and communications economic; and it is still possible to say of some areas, as one of my students did recently of
the Sudan, "The Sudan has a population problem. It is too sparse-
ly populated. The five persons per square kilometre constitute
an inadequate source of labour for the rapid development of a country that depends on irrigation agriculture."[12]

The redistribution of resources and persons, the development of improved economic links throughout the economy, the acquisition of new skills, and the establishment of new industries can
profoundly alter the patterns of comparative advantage existing
when trade began. New technology flowing in along trade lines,
development of new service and supply industries, opening up of
mass markets to take the products of large-scale industries--all
reduce the importance of the original resource endowment. When
Arthur Lewis made his recommendations for industrialization in
Ghana in 1953, he provided what has come to be regarded as a classic example of the application of the law of comparative advantage
to economic planning, employing as his basic criteria the relative
costs of transporting the raw and finished product, the cost (not
wages) of labor, the size of the market, and the economic environment, by which he meant essentially the availability of supporting
services, from telephones to machine shops.[13] On the basis of
these criteria he classified the prospects for 38 industries as
favorable, marginal, or unfavorable.

Several industries which Lewis put in the marginal or in
the unfavorable category, however, are included in the Ghana
Seven-Year Development Plan that was approved ten years later.[14]
Although some appear to have been included for non-economic reasons, the selection of others illustrates two ways in which comparative advantages may be altered: one, technical; the other,
economic. (Lewis was considering immediate choices and was little
concerned about industries that might become profitable after certain alterations in the economy were completed.)

Lewis placed soap manufacturing in the doubtful category,
despite the large domestic market, because Ghana produced neither
vegetable oils nor caustic soda in quantity; paper-making was
specifically rejected because Ghana's forests contain only hard-
woods; and sugar-refining was rejected until an irrigated sugarcane plantation could be established. All three of these industries are in the Plan. Oil for soap manufacture will come from
oil-palm plantations to be established for this purpose--in effect, this is an alteration of the economic organization; Lewis's
proposed sugar plantation will be developed, presumably, in part
at least, with water from the Volta Dam--again a change in the
economic environment; and an attempt will be made to develop a
paper industry using pulp from sugarcane fibers, rice straw, or
sorghum straw--a change in the contemplated technology. Another

manufacture, candles, which Lewis placed in the doubtful category
because Ghana did not produce the raw material, presumably think-
ing of paraffin from petroleum, might have been included in another technology in which candles were made from tallow.

The way in which changes in economic organization may
affect production decisions apparently dictated by technical considerations may be illustrated by developments in some of the major
tropical export crops. V. D. Wickizer, in an article published in
1960, discussed the relative suitability of eight major tropical
export crops for production by smallholders or by estates.* Of
these eight, only tea appeared to him to be essentially a crop ill-
suited to smallholders, but he also cites sisal as a type of minor
export crop that is best produced by plantations. He named cane
sugar, bananas, and coffee, however, as crops for which "productive advantages for export are generally considered, under today's
conditions, to lie with the plantation."[15] Crops in which the
large operations have an advantage are those requiring expensive
capital equipment for primary processing and high technical skills
for growing and harvesting. Specifically, "if a tropical export
crop must be planted on a large scale to provide a marketable bulk
or quantities sufficient for economic quality processing, it is
clearly better suited to large-scale plantation enterprise than to
smallholder production. . . . Fermented 'black' tea [the principal tea in international commerce] requires machine manufacture
and this, together with the strict requirements of successful cultivation, makes the crop eminently well-suited to plantation production."[16] Large capital investment in processing is necessary
because technical considerations dictate that minimum unit costs
can be achieved only with plants of large capacity; large volume
is required to permit full utilization of this capacity and because the economic organization cannot market small quantities
efficiently; and inadequate dissemination of technical knowledge
and farming skills makes it desirable to distribute these scarce
skills possessed by only a few managers over as large an output as
possible. The case for plantation production seems strong. In
fact, however, there is no absolute reason why the individual or
organization that owns the large plant must also engage in farming; large-volume production can be obtained through the market
mechanism,** and smallholders can be educated to become as skill-

---

*These products were sugar, bananas, coconut-palm products,
oil-palm products, cocoa, coffee, tea, and rubber. Rice and maize
were excluded because exports are a small part of total output,
cotton, tobacco, and citrus because exports come chiefly from non-
tropical countries.

**It is at least possible that consumer preference for black tea
is also a result of the market mechnism, i.e., of the promotional
and marketing efforts of black-tea producers.

ful producers as European managers. Wickizer tells us that "direct cultivation of the soil by the owner of the [sugar] central is exceptional in the Philippines,"[17] and recent experiences in improving the farming techniques of cocoa growers in Ghana and coffee growers in Kenya demonstrate the success of education in disseminating technical knowledge. Black tea is now being produced successfully by smallholders in the Nyeri district of Kenya, where 1,200 small farmers deliver the leaves to a central factory.[18]

In agriculture most advantages arising from technical economies of scale probably can be achieved by a variety of farm organizations; the farm need not be large because some necessary machines are large. In manufacturing, however, economies of scale still make large operations preferable in many industries, and the economic organization must accept limitations placed on it by technical considerations until technology is able to produce small processing units that are just as efficient as large ones.

NATIONAL GOALS: PLANNING FOR THE FUTURE

Most countries of tropical Africa have adopted economic development plans of one sort or another, varying in complexity and resoluteness of planning from little more than multiple-year governmental budgets to elaborately detailed schemes for achieving national goals. The objectives of these plans are mixed. They include the preservation of national security, the establishment and maintenance of national unity, the legitimization of new national governments, and national prestige. Prominent among the goals of all plans, however, and of principal importance in most, is a rapid rise in the economic well-being of the population. To increase national product is the first necessary step, but it is also necessary to decide how the increment in product, or in fact the total product, will be shared among the members of society. This involves decisions not only about who will benefit, but about when they will benefit. It is not enough to agree that steps will be taken to raise national product to higher levels; the problem involves agreement on the way in which this increased product is to be distributed over time.

As caretakers of a communal, or national heritage--ultimately as guardians of the species--the national planners' responsibility extends to distant future generations. By specifying what population is to be maintained at what level of living, it might be possible to formulate rational plans for utilization of perceived natural resources over periods of centuries--it might be possible, that is, if technical and economic knowledge were assumed to be unchanging. Fortunately they are not. The impending technical revolution is the most recent manifestation of an

expanding perception of the world that is certain to continue, bar-
ring nuclear war or other global disaster. Economic knowledge has
achieved much less than technical knowledge, but it is not unrea-
sonable to hope that the future will see breakthroughs in this and
other social sciences similar to those that have already occurred
in the natural sciences. A planning model for the future, therefore, must allow for changes in our knowledge of the composition
of the earth, of ways in which its constituents can be transformed
into things useful to man, and of ways to allocate resources and
products to maximize their social value. Each kind of knowledge
is changing and will continue to change; each is influenced by
changes in the other.

If we are to judge from historical experience, the continuing expansion of technical knowledge will make the future value of natural resource assets less than the values assigned to
them on the basis of present information, either because additional resources capable of fulfilling the same functions will be identified, or because more efficient ways of employing the present
resources will be worked out. This in itself suggests that the
present value of future availability of many resources should be
discounted in order to allow for changes in technology and economic organization. If this were the only reason for shifting
emphasis from future to present use, however, it would be a san-
guine economist who would counter the macaber pronouncements of
some conservationists with Micawber's promise that "something will
turn up." In fact, much more compelling reasons may persuade the
economist to accept seemingly reckless exploitation of nonrenew-
able resources. In the growth process, it may be necessary to
consume one resource in order to build the capital plant and economic organization or to create the human population capable of
further exploitation of the environment and construction of an
economy of high productivity. Just as the depletion of the forests of the old American Northwest made possible the rapid construction of dwellings and other structures needed by a growing
middle western population,[19] so the devastating cutting of firewood along African rivers and railways may be preferable to long
delay in improvement of transport. To export the resources of the
ground in the form of mineral ores, or in the form of coffee, peanuts, and cotton, may not be improvident if this is the only way
to obtain rapidly the capital goods and the skills required for
economic development. This kind of exploitation may sometimes be
a matter of survival, too, involving the unavoidable gamble that
if the present danger is met, some way may be found to overcome
the future one.

On the whole, it is probably best to tend toward optimism
rather than pessimism. It is still not good practice to live on
capital unless that is the only way to survive into a period when
the creation of new income may be possible. On the other hand,
it is folly not to employ capital in new productive ventures, even

though some may fail. For the new countries of tropical Africa this may mean a prodigal expenditure of natural resources in order to obtain the means for rapid economic advance. If our science were less imperfect than it is, we might be able to determine which of this mining of resources is essential, which fruitless. In any event, we should make every effort to identify and explain the possible costs of destruction of forests, of erosion and soil depletion consequent on large-scale exploitation of grasslands, of destruction of aquatic life and loss of recreational areas because of pollution of lakes and streams, of the loss of mineral resources because of quick pay-off mining and pumping of oil, of the destruction of irreplaceable herds of wild animals, of smog, of slums, of flimsy dwellings, and of inflammable towns. We should at the same time remember, however, that every one of these costs results from an attempt to create income, and that the present value of this income may be incomparably more important to the long-term economic welfare of the society than the future value of the costs entailed in generating it. Only if we do can man effectively exercise his dominion over the fish of the sea, and over the fowl of the air, and over every living thing that moves upon the earth.

NOTES

[1] G. T Trewartha and Wilbur Zelinsky, "Population Patterns in Tropical Africa," Annals of the Association of American Geographers, June, 1954.

[2] "An Agroclimatic Mapping of Africa," Food Research Institute Studies, III, 3, November, 1962.

[3] "The Social Influence of Salt," Scientific American, July, 1963.

[4] B. F. Johnston, "The Choice of Measures for Increasing Agricultural Productivity: A Survey of Possibilities in East Africa," Tropical Agriculture (Trinidad), April, 1964, p. 101.

[5] W. R. F. Collis, J. Dema, and A. Omololu, "On the Ecology of Child Health and Nutrition in Nigerian Villages," Tropical and Geographical Medicine, XIV (1962).

[6] W. R. F. Collis, J. Dema, and F. E. A. Lesi, "Transverse Survey of Health and Nutrition, Pankshin Division, Northern Nigeria," West African Medical Journal, August, 1962.

[7] Op. cit., p. 226 (see note 5).

[8] Ibid., p. 221.

[9] Ibid., pp. 223-24.

[10]Cf. R. Galletti, K. D. S. Baldwin, and I. O. Dina, Nigerian Cocoa Farmers (London: 1956), and Polly Hill, The Migrant Cocoa Farmers of Southern Ghana (Cambridge: 1963).

[11]Op. cit., pp. 152-53 (see note 6).

[12]Seth LaAnyane, "Some Reflections on African Economic Development" (unpublished manuscript, 1964).

[13]W. Arthur Lewis, Report on Industrialization in the Gold Coast (Accra: Gold Coast Government, 1953).

[14]Seven-Year Plan for National Reconstruction and Development: Financial Years 1963/64-1969/70 (Ghana: Office of the Planning Commission - 1964).

[15]"The Smallholder in Tropical Export Crop Production," Food Research Institute Studies, I, 1, February, 1960, pp. 52-53.

[16]Ibid., p. 63.

[17]Ibid., p. 71.

[18]The Economic Development of Kenya (Baltimore: 1963), p. 122. [International Bank for Reconstruction and Development.]

[19]Op. cit. (see note 1).

THE AFRICAN SAVANNA CLIMATE AND PROBLEMS
OF DEVELOPMENT

by

Benjamin E. Thomas

One of the most pervasive ecological elements on the continent of Africa is that of climate. In one way or another it affects, or is associated with, most of the problems of development. It is necessary to emphasize that most Africans are farmers and that African climates, almost everywhere, present problems. There are no extensive areas in Africa where rainfall is sufficient for many kinds of crops, well-distributed throughout the year, and reasonably dependable as to amount and time of occurrence. Western Europe and eastern United States, by way of contrast, have large regions where the distribution and amount of rainfall are much more favorable. Even the humid forested areas in equatorial Africa have places where there is a short and troublesome dry period in addition to high temperatures and other conditions which lead to soils that are often infertile.

The type of climate and vegetation association that is most typical of Africa is tropical savanna. The major purpose of this paper will be to point out some of the complicated relationships of climate to vegetation, of climate and vegetation to local economic and health problems, and of climate to transportation. These are only a few of the aspects of the savanna which are intimately involved with other savanna conditions and with problems of economic development.

We have had general information on the main elements of savanna climate for many years. General information, however, is not accurate enough to solve the many ecological problems which are involved. Until we have a reasonably exact knowledge as to the distribution of the various natural elements of the savanna and can explain the detailed relationships of these elements to each other and to economic development, we cannot proceed with assurance towards solving some of the problems. For example, it is not sufficient to know that drought causes difficulty for farming. Each particular species of plant has its own growing requirements, and these are related not only to climate but to soils, drainage, water supply, and, of course, to the culture of the people, who may or may not possess techniques and the cultural system which will cause them to turn a wild plant into a useful resource.

To keep my discussion brief, my remarks will be restricted

to some of the advances that are being made in knowledge regarding
the relations of the physical nature of the savanna zone to health,
to vegetation, and to transportation, with emphasis on the last
item. Let us look first at the general nature of the savanna zone
and its distribution in Africa.

THE SAVANNA AND STEPPE ZONES

     For our purposes we may combine the savanna and steppe
zones and define them as the areas which have tropical temperatures, seasonal rainfall, and too much vegetation to be desert and
not enough to be considered woodland or forest. The general causes
of savanna and steppe climate are well known. There is one zone
south of the Sahara that extends from Senegal across Mali, Upper
Volta, Niger, Northern Nigeria and Chad to the Republic of Sudan.
In this area the intertropical convergence zone moves northward
and brings rainfall during the summer months. There is another
zone south of the equatorial forest in Angola, southern Congo
(Leopoldville), Zambia, Rhodesia, and southern Tanzania. Here
again a major cause of summer rainfall is the shift of the intertropical convergence zone. During the summer of the southern hemisphere the zone is located farther south than at other seasons,
causing summer rains.

     In East Africa the situation is more complicated. This
part of the continent is affected by monsoon winds which are related to the pressure systems of Africa and Asia. In general, the
southwest monsoon blows toward Asia during the summer of the northern hemisphere because of the high temperature and low pressure in
interior Asia. The northeastern monsoon blows from Asia towards
South Africa during the winter of the northern hemisphere because
of cold and high pressure in interior Asia. Between these two
periods of monsoons, there are periods without monsoon winds.
Where moist monsoon winds are forced to rise along plateaus or
mountains, rain may result, but if the air masses descend, drought
results. Thus, the monsoons are critical elements in East African
rainfall. Often there are two rainy seasons during the year, but
these vary from place to place.

     The areas outlined above, when combined, form a broad zone
of savanna and steppe climate which extends across Africa south
of the Sahara, southward in East Africa, and then westward across
Zambia, Rhodesia, and Angola--a sort of horseshoe-shaped zone
covering most of tropical Africa. The only areas in Middle Africa
that are excluded are the deserts, the forest areas, and the mountains and plateaus which are too high to have tropical climates.
(Further information on African climates may be found in the standard reference by W. G. Kendrew.)[1]

     Within this great savanna and steppe zone there are crit-

ical differences in rainfall and temperature which have important
consequences for economic development. The season of rainfall may
be short or long, may consist of steady rain or intermittent show-
ers, may vary from year to year, and even fail to materialize in
dry years. The exact time when rain begins in a given area is
often of prime importance to the farmer. Timely rain may result
in good crops and a good year, but late or light rains may result
in famine. Vegetation, of course, is closely related to these
elements of rainfall as well as to slope, drainage, and soil types.

Another element that varies significantly within this zone
is temperature. In general, the higher elevations have lower temperatures, but the nature of air masses and their movements are also of importance. In the western savanna, for example, it makes
a great difference to the farmer whether the wind is a hot dry one
from the Sahara or a cooler and moister air mass from the Atlantic.
Meteorologists and climatologists are still studying air mass movements, variations in rainfall from year to year, and similar elements in an attempt to discover why a particular area receives the
exact amount of rainfall it does. One purpose is to gain enough
knowledge and experience so that future rainfall may be predicted
with a reasonable degree of accuracy.

A surprising feature of the savanna and steppe zone in
West Africa is that there are two irregular east-west bands of
very light population, separated by a discontinuous band of heavier
population. Even small-scale atlas maps show this unusual population distribution.[2] A partial explanation for the band of
heavier population appears to be that it has sufficient rainfall
for grazing and some farming and, therefore, attracts more people
than the desert to the north.

The denser savanna and light forest farther south have
slightly more rainfall, but they are still not moist enough to
provide a dependable base for farming. In fact, the heavier rainfall and slightly less hot summers result in suitable temperatures
and vegetation for tsetse flies which carry nagana (sleeping sickness in animals). This disease prevents the raising of most types
of cattle and other forms of domesticated animals. Climate, vegetation, and disease are closely associated and are important factors in the population picture, but there are also many unknown
elements. Warfare, slave raiding, and migration, as well as a
rise in tsetse flies and sleeping sickness when an area reverts
from farmland to unused bush, are some of the known cultural and
physical elements. But the accurate evaluation of the various
physical and cultural influences, and the discovery of new factors, will require more research along several lines.

THE AFRICAN SAVANNA CLIMATE AND PROBLEMS OF DEVELOPMENT

CLIMATE, DISEASE, AND HEALTH

It has been known for a long time that certain areas within the savanna belt are more unhealthy than others. When the early explorers and geographers travelled in Africa, they often wrote observations on the prevalence of fever in swampy areas, and of sleeping sickness in the tropical bush. This was the beginning of the research field that is now called medical geography. Another type of observation made by those early investigators was on the debilitating effects of heat and humidity upon man and on the refreshing effects of cooler breezes or of less humid periods of weather. Such observations based only upon history, experience, and conjecture were useful but, of course, they could not form the basis for research work to solve the health and behavior problems involved. This aspect of geographical study, under the influence of modern medicine, physiology, and climatology, has become the research field of physiological climatology.

Medical geography may be defined as the study of the areal distribution of disease and its relation to the environment. Although the viewpoint and organizing themes are geographical, most of the content is substantially medical. A major problem of the field has been to replace a collection of unverified impressions and shaky hypotheses about the relations of diseases to their environment with theories which can be tested in the light of reliable data. The line of research usually runs from the diseases themselves to the organisms which cause the diseases and on to the environmental circumstances which affect the organisms. Research involves the mapping of diseases, and the determination of causative agents, vectors, intermediate hosts, and reservoirs for the disease. These may be related to climate and the natural environment in either obvious or very obscure ways.

Most of the important discoveries in medical geography have been made by workers in sciences such as bacteriology, biology, and entomology. The disciplines of medicine and geography have then made use of this knowledge. As an example of progress that is being made along these lines, one may cite Studies in Disease Ecology, edited by Dr. Jacques May, the former head of the Department of Medical Geography of the American Geographical Society of New York.[3]

Physiological climatology is the study of the effect of atmospheric conditions on the functioning of the normal human body. Geographers in the early days often philosophized about the effects of climate on man. Often this line of reasoning was used to support the theory of environmental determinism. But recent research supports only some of the earlier opinions. Physiological climatology was established as a new field of research during and following World War II, with scientists in the United States and Canada playing leading parts. Climatologists, physicists, physiologists, and geographers contribute to the field.

The heat balance of the human body provides a focus for quantitative studies in physiological climatology. Physiologists can study and measure the effects of thermal conditions on this heat balance along with the adaptations which are made by the normal body to meet these conditions. Thermal stress is calculated for the conditions of physical activity and type of clothing worn as well as for temperature, humidity, air movement, and radiation. These last four items bring in climatologists or physical geographers to assist in measurement and mapping. This type of research, of course, is a great advance over mere theorizing about the effects of climate on man. Practical applications of physiological climatology lie in the planning of work regimes, clothing, and housing for tropical areas, elements which are related to both climate and economic development. Dr. Douglas H. K. Lee has done pioneer work on physiological climatology as well as on the general effects of climate on development in the tropics.[4]

As an example of the influence of climate on disease, and of the indirect effects of climate on disease through vegetation, let us take a quick view of the complicated situation of tsetse flies and sleeping sickness in Tanzania and malaria in Somalia.

Trypanosomiasis, or sleeping sickness, is caused by trypanosomes which are carried by tsetse flies of the genus Glossina. A tsetse fly lives on blood and may bite an infected animal or person, and transmit the disease to another which it bites later. Many animals, especially antelopes, serve as reservoirs for the disease. Both the larger animals and the tsetse flies require certain types of vegetation in order to exist. The antelope requires grass or other plants for forage, and the tsetse flies have particular vegetative requirements for breeding areas and for shade during the heat of the day. The kinds of animals which can serve as hosts for one type or another of trypanosomiasis range from eels to elephants. And the various species of tsetse flies have different requirements for shade, moisture, and temperature.

There are at least eight known species of tsetse flies in Tanzania. Two or perhaps three of these carry the highly fatal type of human trypanosomiasis (trypanosoma rhodesiense); one carries the less virulent form of human sleeping sickness known as trypanosoma gambiense. There are at least two species of tsetse flies that spread nagana, or animal trypanosomiasis. The flies that carry human trypanosomiasis require denser types of vegetation, and therefore it is not surprising that the outbreaks of human sleeping sickness have been in the moister western part of Tanzania and in scattered areas of forest or denser savanna vegetation. The tsetse flies that carry nagana, however, are found throughout the vast expanse of dry savanna in Tanzania. The only areas free of them are the cool highlands, arid regions without trees, and farmlands, towns, or cleared areas where man keeps down the number of flies.

Tsetse flies decrease in number and then disappear as one enters a desert, but the reasons are not fully understood. Apparently the flies cannot live in grassland or barren areas because there are no trees or shrubs to provide shade. Several species of Glossina cannot survive exposure of one hour at 110° to 112°F. or three hours at 104°F. When temperatures reach these figures in the hot summer of the savanna and steppe, either the high temperatures or the lack of shade or both may be responsible for the absence of flies. But within the savanna, at slightly lower temperatures, some species require the trees found only along river courses, others prefer certain species of acacia, and some have a wide range of adaptation. The removal of certain favored types of bushes, without complete clearing, is effective in eliminating some species of flies.

Low temperatures slow down the activity of the tsetse fly, sometimes to the extent that they prevent the fly from going after food, so that it dies from starvation. But the lower temperatures in some places, may be associated with greater humidity and a denser vegetative cover and animal life, so that the fly can exist without the necessity for much activity. Also, the critical point both high and low temperatures, probably vary with different species. Examples of research to provide some of the needed answers are the publications of J. P. Glasgow[5] on the distribution and of L. van den Berghe and F. L. Lambrecht[6] on the control of tsetse flies.

On the physical and biological side, it should be noted that climatic and vegetative conditions in Africa are suitable over much wider areas for the tsetse flies which carry nagana than for those which spread human sleeping sickness. The presence of the tsetse fly, in spite of efforts to control it, hinders economic development in many parts of Africa, because domesticated animals cannot be kept. The lack of domesticated animals results in a series of problems: no animal power for farm work or transport, an absence of mixed farming or grazing, and a shortage of protein in the human diet.

Malaria, of course, is carried by several species of the anopheles mosquito. The mosquito requires moisture in order to breed and live, and in most parts of the African savanna there is a close correlation between climate on the one hand and outbreaks of malaria on the other. The mosquito requires reasonably warm temperatures, and within the areas of suitable temperature, malaria is endemic in areas where moisture is always available. In other places, outbreaks usually occur after the rainy season has started, and continue afterward for a month or two because there is still available moisture in stagnant pools and in spots protected by vegetation.

In the Somali country of East Africa, malaria is rare in the few areas that are high and cool, and it is also rare in the desert. But in the warm steppes and savannas there is summer rain near the Ethiopian highlands, winter rain near the Gulf of Aden, and spring and fall rain in southern Somalia. In each case malarial outbreaks occur about one month after the rains begin and persist for a few weeks after they stop. The Somali Republic, therefore, has the problem of malaria in addition to the primary economic disadvantage of light and irregular rainfall.

CLIMATE AND VEGETATION

The relations of climate to vegetation are extremely intimate and complicated. There are many types of savanna vegetation, and the traveler in Africa is often more impressed with the variety of vegetation from place to place than with the similarities. There are still many mysteries about the relationship of climate to vegetation that have not been solved. We may cite, however, an example of a notable advance along this line. In the Republic of Sudan, the distribution of species of acacia was so repetitious, as well as varied from place to place, that for some time it was believed that the distributions were somewhat arbitrary or unpredictable. For example, a particular species of acacia would occur on hills in central Sudan, and then not be located again until one moved several miles farther south. But in the southern area, when the same species reappeared, it was sometimes found on hills and sometimes found in valleys in areas that had more rainfall than in areas farther north. Also the other plants with which it was associated varied from place to place.

Dr. John Smith worked on the problem for years, and finally discovered a method of explaining the relationship.[7] He observed, for example, that a particular species of acacia might occur where the rain falls on comparatively level land. If, however, there is drainage to the area, or run-on, a species of acacia which requires more moisture could exist. On the other hand, if there is drainage away from the particular area, or run-off, a species of acacia which requires less moisture might grow. If run-off and run-on were the only factors, the problem would be simple. However, the local type of soil in these semi-arid areas is also critical. The general rule Smith discovered is that more moisture is required for a given species of acacia growing in clay soils than in sandy soils because the clay holds the moisture, and it is not available to the plant as readily as in sand. Therefore, in an area where rainfall generally increases from north to south, there may be one zone of a species of acacia in a dry area with sandy soils and another belt of the same species of acacia many miles farther south in a wetter area with clay soils. Thus, acacia senegal, from which gum arabic is collected, occurs in two belts. One of these is on sandy soil with about 16 inches of rainfall and another on clay soils with 24 inches of rainfall.

Dr. Smith studied the species of acacia in selected areas with heavy clay soil where there was neither run-on nor run-off and listed them in order, from the most drought-resistant to those which require the greatest total rainfall. His list, as given in K. M. Barbour's geography of the Sudan,[8] is as follows:

Acacia Species	Approximate Mean Annual Rainfall
(1) Acacia flava	100 mm. (4 in.)
(2) " orfota	
(3) " tortilis	
(4) " raddiana	
(5) " mellifera	200 mm. (8 in.)
(6) " fistula (syn. A. seyal, var. fistula)	
(7) " senegal (syn. A. verek)	
(8) " seyal	
(9) " drepanolobium	
(10) " campylacantha	
(11) " sieberiana (syn. A. verugera)	
(12) " albida	
(13) " hebacladoides	
(14) " seyal var. multijuga	
(15) " abyssinica	1,200 mm. (48 in.)

CLIMATE AND TRANSPORTATION

As is well known, the savanna climate in Africa often makes dirt roads impassable during the summer wet season and that the winter dry season may result in dry streams which are, of course, not navigable. From this simple statement of facts it would at first glance seem logical to assume that water transportation would be at its height during the summer wet season and that transportation on roads would be at its best during the dry season. Once again we have the familiar story of an apparently simple relationship that is in reality very complicated. For example, warm season rains begin near the equator and gradually spread northward in West Africa and then gradually retreat southward. The pattern of soaked and impassable roads, therefore, is in almost constant change for the warmer months of the year.

The writer, on field trips to interior West Africa, was surprised to note that roads were flooded and impassable in a few areas during the middle of the dry season. Also, he discovered that the Niger River is actually navigable for greater lengths during the winter season, when there is no rainfall, than it is during the rainy summer. This can be explained by a lag in the drainage, including the slow filling of one segment of the Niger for many weeks before the water is raised to a level where it will flow over falls and rapids to raise the next segment downstream. This lag in drainage explains the high level of the Niger River during the dry season, and the flooding of nearby areas at that time can account for impassable roads even though there has been no rain for several months.

In the Sahara-Savanna borderlands it is often so hot during the summer months that the operation of motor vehicles over long routes is discouraged. In some places motor traffic comes to a halt. We can observe, therefore, that one aspect of the summer climate--the very high temperature--can partly cancel the otherwise desirable aspect of summer savanna climate for motor traffic--the dry season.

These conditions lead to several questions. What is the total direct effect of climate (including excessive heat, flooded roads, and dry stream channels) on usable roads and waterways in interior West Africa? How can this effect of climate be measured? And how can one eliminate subjective judgment in determining when the sun is too hot, a river too shallow, or a road too flooded for one to travel?

The writer came to the conclusion that a practical method of finding whether it was too hot, too wet, or too dry for a given mode of transportation was to discover when the major forms of commercial transportation, such as river boats, truck lines, or bus companies, actually suspended operations. The routes that were usable on the fifteenth of each month could then be mapped for a large area. Former French West Africa was chosen because comparative data could be obtained from reports of the several territories. Data was collected from the three navigation companies operating on the Senegal and Niger Rivers, and from the half-dozen companies that operate commercial truck and bus lines over the main routes. Finally, secondary roads were mapped by using the reports on impassable roads from each of the 114 minor civil divisions or cercles in former French West Africa. The resulting patterns have been shown on monthly maps of usable roads and waterways and published by the author in a monograph.[9] We may observe, by describing the transportation situation for each month, that the changes through a yearly cycle are both numerous and complicated.

It is convenient to start with May 15th, at the end of the dry season for most parts of the savanna in West Africa. Roads are usable almost everywhere. Dry and usable routes extend from Senegal in the west across Mali, Upper Volta, and the Niger Republic. Such places as Kayes on the Senegal in western Mali and Kabara and Timbuktu in north central Mali are on usable routes.

River navigation during May, however, is restricted to the lower Senegal, from St. Louis to Podor, insofar as large boats are concerned. All of the Niger River in the interior savanna zone has drained so low that no segments are used by steamers. It is true that canoes can operate in certain ponds and portions of the river, but they do not form part of the long distance freight system.

On June 15th the situation for river navigation is the same as in May: only the lower Senegal is usable. But the summer rains have started, and are sufficient to make many road segments unusable, such as those running south from Matam in Senegal, south from Kayes, and east from Mopti in Mali. Temperatures have risen also, and travel from northern Nigeria across Niger to Algeria is suspended because of the summer heat. In short, several routes near the Sahara are not used because the wet areas are impassable and the dry areas are too hot.

By July 15th the lower Senegal River has risen until it is navigable from its mouth upstream to Matam. Also, the upper Niger River in Guinea and western Mali has filled with water from the summer rains until two long segments are usable--from Kankan in Guinea to the falls at Bamako in Mali, and below the falls from Koulikoro to Mopti. Meanwhile additional roads have become impassable over a wide area--none are usable between Matam in Senegal and Mopti in Mali, and summer heat discourages travel into the Sahara.

In August both the Senegal and the Niger rivers continue to rise. The former becomes usable from Matam upstream to Kayes. And the Niger becomes navigable from Mopti downstream to Kabara, the port for Timbuktu. Roads in the northern savanna are still impassable because of flooding, or unused because of summer heat. But the intertropical zone of rainfall is so far north in August that some areas near the Guinea coast experience a short period of less rain. Roads in western Ivory Coast near the Liberia border are usable on August 15th, but are flooded in July and become impassable again in September.

On September 15th the Niger River is navigable for the additional distance from Kabara to Gao, and the Senegal River is still usable to Kayes. The pattern of usable roads is still almost as fragmentary and restricted as it was in August. This is the month in which the combined Senegal and Niger waterways come closest to providing a complete route from west to east. With the exception of the land gap between Kayes on the Senegal and Koulikoro on the Niger, there is a water route in September all the way from St. Louis in Senegal to Gao in eastern Mali. It should be noted, however, that navigable depths on the Senegal spread upstream from the mouth, whereas navigable levels begin near the headwaters of the Niger and move downstream as additional segments are filled.*

On October 15th, we find that water has drained from the upper Senegal, making it unusable from Kayes to Matam. But on the Niger River, water is still draining into the lower segments from upper ones. The river becomes navigable from Niamey in the Niger Republic to Malanville in northern Dahomey. Meanwhile, temperatures have fallen, and it is cool enough so that roads are used across the Niger Republic into the Sahara. Also, the southward retreat of the rains permits a number of routes, such as some of those in eastern Senegal and central Mali, to dry to usable condition.

On November 15th the pattern of navigable water routes is the same as in October. The dry season has started, and more roads in the savanna zone become usable, including many in western and central Mali.

In December, the Senegal River is still navigable from the coast to Matam, but along the north side of the stream roads are often flooded by water from the river. The upper Niger is draining into the lower segments, and there is no rainfall to replenish the supply. The Niger becomes unnavigable from Kankan in Guinea to Bamako in Mali, whereas the long segment from Koulikoro to Gao and the short one from Niamey to Malanville continue at usable levels. Additional roads dry to a usable condition, even around the swampy inland Niger delta region near Mopti.

By January 15th the Senegal has fallen until it is navigable only from its mouth to Podor, and the lower level ends the period of flooded roads along the north bank near Matam. A portion of the middle Niger River, from Bamako to Mopti, drains until it is unnavigable. Roads are usable almost everywhere. For the first time in many months there is a complete network of usable routes from coastal Senegal to eastern Senegal and onward to cen-

---

*This long water route, although usable only seasonally, formed an important part of the French colonial transport system. Before World War I a railway was built to connect Kayes with Bamako and with Koulikoro below the falls. Another line was constructed from Conakry on the coast of Guinea to the inland town of Kankan on the upper Niger River. A railway was later completed from Dakar to Kayes. This made it possible for goods to be shipped from the Middle Niger through Koulikoro and Kayes to the port of Dakar, avoiding the problems of seasonal navigation on the Senegal. Also shipments could go from the Upper Niger to Bamako and Dakar. This avoided the problems of navigation of the shallow Upper Niger to Kankan and the high operating costs of the winding mountain railway from Kankan to Conakry. These and other factors led to the rise of Dakar as the greatest port and rail center in West Africa.

tral Mali. But part of the middle Niger River, from Kabara to Gao, has received so much water from upstream that it floods some of the nearby roads and makes them difficult to use or impassable. This is the strange case of flooded roads in an area where it has not rained for many months.

In February the patterns of usable roads and waterways remain about the same. But by March 15th enough water has drained from the middle Niger so that it falls to unnavigable levels between Mopti and Gao. In the entire area of former French West Africa this leaves only two short usable river segments: from St. Louis to Podor in Senegal, and from Niamey in Niger to Malanville in Dahomey. Roads in the savanna zone, of course, suffer no handicaps from either rainfall or high temperatures at this time.

The same situation continues in April. Then, by May 15th, the segment of the Niger River from Niamey to Malanville drains until it is no longer navigable. Soon afterward summer rains begin, move northward, and cause another cycle of changing conditions for transportation. The flood water from the Niger River in Mali and the Niger Republic runs into the lower Niger River in Nigeria in May, just at the beginning of the savanna rainy season. This explains a seemingly miraculous condition in Nigeria. If the savanna rains in central Nigeria come at the expected time in late May and early June, the Niger River rises rapidly to flood stage; this is natural and normal. But if the rains fail to arrive, the Niger River rises anyway, to about the same height as if it had rained! The explanation, as can be seen by following the flooded and therefore navigable portions of the Niger River, is that it takes a year for the river to transmit the flood crest of the summer run-off from the highlands of Guinea to the plains of Nigeria. The flood of water from the previous summer in Guinea and Mali arrives just in time to start the flood from the summer rains in Nigeria.

The complicated and changing pattern of transportation in the savannas of West Africa is the combined result of climatic conditions in association with landforms, soils, and drainage, insofar as natural conditions are concerned. The focus in this paper has been on natural conditions, but it should be emphasized that there are economic, social, and political influences which determine whether or not people will choose to have goods to transport, where roads will be built, etc. The patterns of usable roads and waterways, however, help to show the many and varied effects of climate and reveal a problem which adds to the difficulties of economic development in the savanna and steppe zone.

ECOLOGY AND DEVELOPMENT: A SUMMARY

By way of conclusion, it seems appropriate to underline

three features of ecology that have importance not only in respect
to climate but also in regard to other aspects of ecology.

(1) The effects of climate are so widespread and persistent that they extend, in direct or indirect fashion, to almost
all types of economic development which deal with man's use of
natural resources in tropical Africa.

(2) General information on climates, or on other ecological factors, and their relations to other conditions, is not enough.
One must understand the reasons for the relationships and just how
the ecological influences operate. Often there is a lack of pre-
ciseness or a mystery about a relationship which is not eliminated
until the underlying mechanism is discovered, examined, and explained. Examples of relationships requiring explanation include:
the circulation of the atmosphere and the causes of precipitation,
the soil forming processes and their relations to changes in vegetation, the life cycles of the hosts and vectors for tropical diseases, the supply and demand situation for particular tropical exports, and the relations of the value systems of indigenous peoples
to their agricultural practices. There can be many mechanisms at
work in an ecological system, as well as ecological systems within ecological systems.

(3) A study of ecological conditions often crosses the
traditional borders of the sciences and involves many disciplines.
For example, an attempt to explain the importance of temperature
and rainfall, which are primarily elements in physical science,
soon leads to biological matters, like vegetation and animal life,
and then to transportation, agricultural economics, and cultural
practices, which are elements in social science. An investigation
of the suitability of the climate and soil of a particular area
for a particular crop must be associated, in one way or another,
with a study of pests and diseases, and a consideration of the
economic system, cultural practices, attitudes, and food habits
of the people involved, along with other factors. Otherwise, the
ecological picture is not complete. Africa is noted for the failure of many grandiose plans for economic development which neglected to consider all the pertinent ecological factors--physical,
biological, and human.

NOTES

[1]The Climates of the Continents (5th ed., Oxford: Clarendon
Press, 1961), pp. 29-146.

[2]See, for example, Philip's Modern College Atlas for Africa
(2nd ed., London: George Philip and Son, 1961), p. 40.

[3]New York: Hafner Publishing Co., 1961. [Studies in Medical Geography No. 2, American Geographical Society.]

[4]Climate and Economic Development in the Tropics (New York: Harper & Bros., 1957).

[5]The Distribution and Abundance of Tsetse (New York: Macmillan, 1963).

[6]"The Epidemiology and Control of Human Trypanosomiasis in Glossina Morsitans Fly Belts," American Journal of Tropical Medicine and Hygiene, XII, 2, March, 1963, pp. 129-64.

[7]The Distribution of Tree Species in the Sudan. Ministry of Agriculture Bulletin No. 4 (Khartoum: 1950).

[8]The Republic of the Sudan: A Regional Geography (London: University of London Press, 1961), pp. 62-63.

[9]Transportation and Physical Geography in West Africa (Washington, D.C.: National Academy of Sciences, 1960).

MINERAL RESOURCES

by

Bernard W. Riley

As geological survey of the continent progresses, it is becoming common knowledge that vast reserves of mineral resources exist in Africa. Simply to describe these reserves and to list the contribution that Africa makes to the rest of the world economy in minerals is not the writer's intention. Nevertheless, we must acknowledge not only the dimensions of the African mineral reserves, but also that throughout most of recorded history, and possibly much earlier too, the main stimulus to contact with the interior of Africa has been the desire for some share of this mineral wealth. Whether we focus on West, Central, or South Africa at their respective periods of historical exploration, we cannot dismiss as irrelevant the impetus which mineral wealth, particularly the metallic suite, gave to the search for trade contacts with the interior.

The search by Europeans had its beginnings in the fifteenth and sixteenth centuries, with the Portuguese, Dutch, and English voyages for trade in gold which preceded the slave-trade era.[1] (This sea-borne trade in gold had been preceded by an overland trade in the precious metal, now known to have been virtually the sole prerogative of the "Moors," as E. W. Bovill has shown.)[2] The discovery of widespread mineral sites and the exaggerated legends their discovery generated were responsible for stimulating Portuguese trade inland from Sofala to outposts at Sena and Tete (all in Mozambique), as well as for the making of contacts through the Sabi River valley with the Karanga of Rhodesia. The interest of the Dutch was also aroused. In 1600, Jan van Riebeeck, then Governor of the Dutch Cape of Good Hope station, sent an abortive expedition inland to find the "empire" of Monomotapa.

The once secure European notion of the Sahara as a barrier to the economic and social accessibility of lower Africa must give way in the light of recent scholarship, which has shown both the antiquity of the exploitation of mineral resources in Africa and its extent. Workings of considerable antiquity and of undoubted pre-European date were seen and described in the late nineteenth century by F. C. Selous and the young German geologist Karl Mauch in what was then Mashonaland and Manicaland (Rhodesia). These workings lent credence to the legends of the empire of Monomotapa in central Africa (as did the copper, gold, and iron-working sites which have since been found in the tribal lands of native inhabitants who have no adequate explanation of their origin).[3]

The early European exploitation of the African mineral reserves was often merely an exchange by barter of salt for gold.[4]
Admittedly, this exploitation did not reach the proportions which
industrialized society and usage now demand, nor was it followed
by wholesale migrations of non-indigenous populations (as it was
in the case of America and Australia), except in the case of the
Republic of South Africa. By the nineteenth century, however, the
exploitation of mineral resources had become so significant to
the central and southern areas of Africa that revival of the search
for the legendary King Solomon's mines was suggested and indeed
their actual existence was claimed.[5] The second half of the nineteenth century saw the birth of a somewhat shotgun pattern of mineral exploitation, which has continued throughout Africa and has
made a very considerable contribution to the continuing growth of
the Western economy during the last hundred years. This exploitation has resulted from massive capital development in a few favored
locales, such as the Witwatersrand of the Transvaal and the Katanga
and Zambia copperbelts.

No one can deny either the overwhelming contribution of
African minerals to the world economy or that the continuance of
this contribution is vital to keep the wheels of industry turning
both inside and outside the African continent. Not only the present African sovereign states, but also the former colonial powers,
have come to depend upon, in their several ways, this storehouse
of gold, diamonds, copper, manganese, cobalt, nickel, antimony,
chrome, vanadium, and uranium. Of none of these minerals do African sources account for less than 40 per cent of the free world's
annual supplies, and in all cases this contribution could become
larger.[6] These minerals can be produced in Africa more easily
and economically than elsewhere, and thus Africa is able to compete
successfully with other sources which may have the advantage of
proximity to markets, but which have not the prodigious reserves
which Africa enjoys. Without African mineral resources both European and North American industry would be in dire straits indeed.

The significant fact which arises from this discussion of
Africa's mineral resources is that Africa's contribution to the
world supply cannot possibly decrease in importance in the foresee-
able future, for the depletion of mineral reserves, with the spo-
liation of surface which this has frequently entailed, has been far
more serious in Europe and North America than in Africa. In Africa many known deposits are not fully exploited, for despite the
recent advance in geological exploration and topographical mapping,
vast areas of the continent remain unknown in anything like the
detail necessary to estimate the mineral reserves with accuracy.
It is unlikely that the extent of these reserves is overesti-
mated.[7]

Thus we may confidently believe the reports that Ghana alone has some 200 million long tons of bauxite awaiting the completion of the Valco Smelter and the acquisition of cheap hydroelectric power from the Akosombo Dam on the Volta River before it can be fully exploited. This is in addition to the advantage the same country enjoys with its manganese ore supplies in the Tarkwa Valley, which are almost the only supplies of this ore in tropical Africa.[8] Gabon, too, has great development prospects with the high quality iron ore it possesses (as high as 60 per cent iron), making it one of the richest sources of iron ore in the world. Estimates are that it has reserves of over one billion tons of iron ore within a 400-mile rail distance from ocean transport.[9]

There is no doubt that Africa is well-favored with mineral wealth. What remains in doubt is whether the economies of many independent African states are yet in a position to take full advantage of their own mineral endowments. This brings us to the topic of the disadvantages involved in the development of mineral resources.

THE DISADVANTAGES OF MINERAL RESOURCE DEVELOPMENT

By definition, the utilization of mineral resources is the exploitation of fund resources; as such, they are beyond the power of man to replenish. The patterns of distribution of these mineral deposits are sporadic and "spotty." This spattering of fund resources is uneven even locally, whether in mineralization zones, in metamorphic aureoles, or in the exposures created by erosion.

Furthermore, there is an analogous sporadic pattern of distribution of the cultural environments necessary to take effective advantage of the mineral resources. Large-scale fund resource utilization requires a level of technology possible only where there is an equally high level of social organization of a particular type. It demands, in the first place, a supply of trained personnel to manage, administer, and maintain expensive capital equipment. This organization, as usually found, requires a social stratification that is internally structured according to social functions which have come to be assigned according to the amount of formal schooling received by the individuals within the community. (At least this is the case within the community that is located close to the point of extraction of the mineral lode.) Any cultural advancement generated by such mining activities is essentially limited to the mine site and processing plant, and the resulting social organization is overwhelmingly urban in character. The resultant social organization (often indeed the mere existence of urban concentrations) is frequently at loggerheads with--and alien to--the social organization of the traditional rural areas of Africa.[10] (The presence of urbanized areas has been a contributive factor to the changing attitudes toward land tenure on the

part of the indigenous inhabitants since the time when mineral con
cessions were first obtained from them. At that time ownership of
land was to them a concept of use rather than possession per se;
certainly it did not extend to the wholesale extraction of mineral
ores from beneath the surface.)

Many African territories are still largely dependent upon
revenues derived from the exploitation of mineral resources, and
it is pertinent to question the wisdom of their including continue
exploitation in their plans for development. Whether the revenues
accruing from mineral exploitation are used for the benefit of the
public or private sector of the economy is somewhat irrelevant,
for overdependence upon mineral resources at their present level
of economic development is perhaps creating more problems than are
being solved in the sovereign states of Africa, and extensive development of the mineral wealth of a state is unlikely to be a
panacea for the economic ills with which it is beset. There have
been several social anthropological studies of the disruption
caused by mineral exploitation--disruption leading to economic and
social disintegration in the tribal areas as a result of the increasing and constant drain of man power from the tribal areas to
the mines. Very real losses of output within subsistence economie
have resulted.[11]

In short, it would seem that the cultural disharmonies
which result within the cultural environment from overdependence
on mineral exploitation in the long run will cost more to mitigate
or eradicate than if they had not been allowed to develop in the
first place.

THE ACCESSIBILITY OF MINERAL RESOURCES

There is a geographical factor involved, however, which
has been only implicit in the foregoing. The accessibility of the
mineral resources presupposes the feasibility of opening the in-
ternal reaches of Africa to some form of heavy transportation--
first, for the installation of the heavy machinery necessary, and
second, for the successful transporting of large quantities of
minerals to markets abroad where they can be sold at competitive
prices. The configuration of Africa--its surface and structure--
has been (and indeed is likely to remain) the greatest stumbling
block to the widespread exploitation of its mineral endowment.

Lack of adequate and cheap transportation is the greatest
African handicap, and it is because of the extent of this handicap
to many of the territories that it remains the fundamental problem
As a consequence of its compact shape, Africa has the greatest per
centage of landlocked area and population of any land surface of
the globe [Landlocked area: 18 per cent; landlocked population:
11 per cent in the independent states as of January 1, 1963].

Fourteen African political units are dependent upon the goodwill of their neighbors (some being dependent on more than one) for their communication with the outside world.*

In such a situation, there will be a harmonious passage of mineral export products through a neighboring country only where the means of outlet is not used to any major extent for an export product which is in direct competition with a mineral product of the neighbor concerned. It is indeed fortunate for Zambia, therefore, that neither Angola nor Mozambique can produce copper so cheaply or so prodigiously that it would want to deny Zambia rail access to Lobito Bay (Angola) or Beira (Mozambique), both 1500 rail miles from the Zambian copperbelt.

Whatever is achieved in the improvement of heavy transportation facilities, the part such improvement will play in cultural accessibility cannot be too highly emphasized. A transportation network is not a static phenomenon, for it functions as an artery of cultural exchange, and facilitates population concentrations at nodes and termini. It encourages people to migrate, creates heterogeneous populations in the urban centers, and fosters the settlement of substantial non-indigenous minority groups. Nor do the effects end simply with this admixture, for this in turn creates a demand for goods and a need for utilities, services, and labor in the population centers and along the lines connecting them. Thus, the required lines of communication to mineral utilization sites produce important cultural effects. These are best described as metropolitan and centripetal.

Higher population concentrations require a greater per capita expenditure by the government than less densely populated areas, for the concentration of urban life requires safeguards for health (purified water supplies and sewage treatment), welfare facilities (hospitals, clinics, and recreation centers), and educational institutions (schools and training establishments). The equipment and machinery necessary for the efficient operation of these services are costly as well as are the administrative organizations and maintenance which they demand. It is possible that the rising expectations for services and utilities in the urban centers will get out of hand, in that more will be demanded than the revenues available will permit. It has long been apparent in the copperbelt, for example, that the only effective way to stabilize the labor force in the mine labor compounds is to increase the provisions of accommodation for married men, together with their dependents, adding costs for services not required for their mi-

---

*These fourteen states are: Basutoland, Bechuanaland, Burundi, Central African Republic, Chad, Malawi, Mali, Niger, Rwanda, Rhodesia, Swaziland, Uganda, Upper Volta, and Zambia.

grant "single" predecessors.[12]

If stress has been laid so far on the effects of wholesale mineral exploitation, it is well to remind ourselves that these are an innovation in Africa and contrast with the consequences of flow resource development. Flow resource development, especially cash crop and subsistence agricultural cultivation, operates over fundamentally larger areas than mineral development; its effects are rural, dispersive, and centrifugal in character. (Perhaps the best evidence of this has been provided by the series of studies by Polly Hill on the effects of cocoa cultivation in Ghana.)[13] What is implied here is that, in contrast with the effects of mineral fund resource utilization, the effects of flow resource development are such that social change is less obligatory, and the desires for conservation and preservation of the physical landscape remain to act as brakes upon any dislocative processes, and thus smooth the transition from rural to urban concentrations. In flow resource development, the gradual transition of the physical environment is frequently well-nigh imperceptible.

The most serious hindrance to present utilization of flow resources is their vulnerability to climatic vagaries, but fund resource utilization is not wholly immune to such hindrances. For example, it is obvious that the demands for adequate facilities, such as an abundant water supply for operation of equipment and for the labor force involved, must temper the enthusiasm which the quality of an ore-body may generate should the mine site require a water supply derived from a distant, difficult to reach, or otherwise expensive source. Conversely, there may be the difficulty of overabundance of water, as when the pumping dry of seepage during an inordinately wet period may prove an economic handicap sufficient to force abandonment of a mining operation, as happened at the Kanshanshi and Bancroft mines in Zambia in 1957.

What appears from the foregoing, therefore, is the conclusion that for economy of operation and successful exploitation of mineral resources, consideration of both physical and cultural factors is a prerequisite. It is pertinent to mention in this connection that many of the world's most successful development schemes have involved the creation of "supra-regional" authorities to integrate the local political administrative units. Perhaps it is significant that these schemes have been directed mainly toward the successful utilization of water--the only mineral flow resource of significance to an economy at large. Generally they have involved hydroelectric power development and coordinated flood control and irrigation plans. In addition, such authorities have been responsible for concomitantly encouraging cultural changes. At the risk of stating the obvious, this is the signal achievement of the Tennessee Valley Authority in the United States, perhaps the most widely known pioneer scheme of this type. The TVA scheme had the responsibility for the implementation of conservation policies which were intimately connected with cultural adaptation of the old into the fabric of the new, and the necessary resettlement of people and the relocation of their cultural foci.*

This type of development is what Africa has yet to see, either in actuality or (and this is a regrettable admission) as a clearly stated integral part of a long-term planning scheme. The Katanga and Zambia copperbelts, though they are significant and undeniable foci of fund resource development in Africa, have not been fully integrated with the great changes for which they have been mostly responsible. These copperbelts are the areas (with the exception of the Witwatersrand of the Republic of South Africa) where the contrasts between "haves" and "have-nots" are perhaps the greatest on the continent.**

MINERAL RESOURCES AND THE FUTURE IN AFRICA

Perhaps it is possible to put forward some tentative conclusions at this point. It is the main thesis of this paper that the ecological aspects of mineral development have never been fully recognized anywhere in the world. Wherever wholesale mineral utilization has taken place, dysfunctional processes have operated to make its effects apparent. Its worst consequences have been recognized and studied, so that preventive (if not curative) programs to mitigate similar ravages in other areas are now under way. However, there is a difference between the possibility of success being achieved by such programs in North America or Western Europe and the chances of similar success in the fund resource utilization areas of Africa. The "advanced" Western countries are able to bring to bear the full weight and strength of a vastly more integrated technology (with all that this implies in the way of modern scientific knowledge and administrative machinery) and can bear the considerable financial costs involved.

Yet the need for the implementation of such programs, in terms pertinent to the underdeveloped areas of the world, has

---

*Perhaps more important, the electric power from the water flow resource permitted the introduction of air-conditioning in the cotton textile factories of the Southern states, thus giving new life to the cotton industry.

**Given this imbalance in the Katanga province within the Republic of the Congo, it is difficult to believe that the outcome could have been anything else but unfortunate economic disruption and a secessionist policy in Katanga during the early months of political emancipation.

never been more necessary than in the case of Africa. Indeed, in the light of the strategic importance of certain minerals found in Africa (uranium and "rare earth" metals) to the present world situation, the need for such programs has become most urgent. But this need is overshadowed by the urgency of planning future mineral resource development in a manner consistent with the economic and political situation of the independent African nations.

As has been indicated, mineral wealth in Africa is sporadic in its placement; thus we are forced to fall back on the knowledge of the geographers and the geologists--and the sociologists--in our assessment of what is likely in the mineral development of the African states. It would appear that there are two extremes in the successful utilization of fund resource mineral deposits. On the one hand, there is the happy case where the quality and quantity of the mineral deposit are such that its exploitation can easily finance the overcoming of any obstacles. In Africa these obstacles include such things as distance from markets and lack of trained personnel and labor force among the indigenous people. Successful exploitation also requires a social climate permissive toward the immigration of sufficient entrepreneurial personnel to make up for deficiencies and toward the installation of the necessary capital equipment to get the enterprise working. On the other hand, there is the case of the poor quality mineral deposit, where the economic hazards and the lack of social integration are great, but can be sufficiently reduced to make successful exploitation possible.

Specific examples of each type of case may be cited. As an example of the first type, there is the Wankie colliery in Rhodesia, where ease of access to good quality coal seams (lenses of coal up to 30 feet thick at moderate depth) made possible coal production cheap enough in terms of pit-head price to overcome the obstacles of the conspicuous remoteness of the mines from the markets in Rhodesia's Zambezi valley as well as an inadequate rail transportation network. (This situation maintained at Wankie until the Kariba Dam provided cheap power to the area.) As an example of the second type, we can cite the shift of production from wasteful small operations in the alluvial diamond production areas of Ghana to larger operations where economies of scale which derive from mechanized methods begin to operate, which have thereby successfully overcome the vagaries of output which the inconstant labor force once imposed.

Finally, this evaluation of African mineral development cannot possibly end without at least a nod of recognition toward the social and political factors now involved in such development. There is, in many independent African nations, an attitude of "industrialize or perish," which we must examine in the light of the possibility of its achievement, and from which policy statements about the future development of mineral resources cannot be sepa-

rated. As stated previously, because of its size and its compact
shape, Africa has a great landlocked area which is its greatest
stumbling block to economic and political development. Partition
has further complicated its problems, for there are now more territories in Africa which are dependent upon good relations with
their neighbors to maintain access to overseas markets and transportation arteries than in any other continent. Furthermore, many
of these territories are handicapped by a lack of fossil fuels and
a lack of water resources which can be utilized to develop power
to be used for large-scale industry. Even where hydroelectric
power development is possible for the increase of mineral output,
there are still difficulties. Ability to compete with other world
sources is involved, and the special problems involved in being in
competition with a coastal neighbor.

Thus it must be concluded that economic planning for mineral resource development in Africa will not in the future be less
susceptible to the consequences of political fragmentation (super-
imposed upon the obstacles of the physical environment) than it
has in the past. Indeed, it will most certainly be more sensitive
to and constrained by them. All in all, it is clear that, for future mineral resource development, international cooperation and
planning between African states, with the advice and goodwill of
international agencies which are cognizant of the ecological consequences of whatever plan is proposed, will be their only sound
course of action.

NOTES

[1] For an account of the earliest recorded gold shipment, see
A. W. Lawrence, Trade Castles and Forts of West Africa (London:
1963), p. 31.

[2] The Golden Trade of the Moors (London: 1958), chap. 7 and
chap. 19, pp. 191-202.

[3] For a detailed account of the location of these sites and a
chronology of their discovery, see J. Desmond Clark, The Prehistory of Southern Africa (London: 1959), pp. 281-313.

[4] Bovill, op. cit., chap. 19 (see note 2).

[5] For a discussion of this claim, see W. R. Dunlop, "Is Modern
Rhodesia Ancient Ophir?" Canadian Geographical Journal, VII (1933),
pp. 189-98.

[6] The best statement of this contribution will be found in
G. H. T. Kimble, Tropical Africa (2 vols., New York: Twentieth
Century Fund, 1960), I, pp. 289-369.

[7]See the statements on mapwork in progress in Rumeau A. Uneko, "Topographic Mapping in Africa," in A Review of the Natural Resources of Africa (New York: UNESCO, 1963). See also A Geological Map of Africa (New York: UNESCO, 1963).

[8]Kimble, op. cit., pp. 306-7 (see note 6).

[9]Ibid., p. 300.

[10]The best collection of studies made of these changes in social organization will be found in D. Forde, ed., Social Implications of Industrialization and Urbanization in Africa South of the Sahara (London: 1956). [Prepared for UNESCO by the International African Institute.]

[11]Though there have been many studies on this theme of late, perhaps the two pioneering works are Audrey I. Richards, Land, Labor and Diet in Northern Rhodesia (London: 1939) and I. Shapera, Migrant Labor and Tribal Life (Oxford: 1940).

[12]For results of investigations by sociologists of the attitudes and expectations of urban living in the copperbelt, reference should be made to J. Clyde Mitchell, The Kalela Dance (Manchester: 1956) [Rhodes-Livingstone Paper No. 27] and Hortense Powdermaker, Coppertown (New York: 1962).

[13]The two most important of her studies are The Gold Coast Cocoa Farmer (Oxford: 1956) and The Migrant Cocoa Farmers of Southern Ghana (Cambridge: 1963).

RANGELAND DEVELOPMENT IN EAST AFRICA

by

Harold F. Heady

The objectives of this paper are to review briefly rangeland development programs in East Africa, to examine problems associated with keeping rangelands productive while they are being
used, and to analyze the interdependency between economic growth
in East Africa as a whole and increasing the products and services
from rangeland. In total, rangeland development in East Africa
is concerned with approximately 680,000 square miles, roughly 20
million people, over 40 million domestic animals, and a rich but
uncounted complex of wild animals.

Perhaps 90 per cent of the land area in East Africa is
grazed by ungulate animals and is referred to as rangeland or pas-
ture land. A small part of the high mountains and dense forests
is not classed as range, although a few grazing animals may be
found there. Rangelands in East Africa, as elsewhere, are uncultivated because they are too sloping, shallow, rocky, sandy, or
because the soils have too high a content of salts or clay for
efficient crop production. Two rainy seasons and two dry seasons
each year plus high evaporation reduce the effectiveness of precipitation to below that needed for cultivated crops.* Therefore,
the use of land for range livestock production is based on understanding and manipulation of natural ecosystems with relatively
little control by traditional farming practices. Normally, however, as technology improves in the cultivation of crops and as
increasing populations require more food, the better rangeland is
converted to growing of agronomic crops. Most East African cultivators raise some domestic animals, intermingling grazing lands
with the planted acres.

RANGE MANAGEMENT PRINCIPLES

The principles that are presently suggested for rangeland

---

*L. H. Brown estimated that 75 per cent of the total land area
in Kenya is semi-arid, with less than 30-35 inches of rainfall,
the lower limit of cultivation.[1] On these semi-arid areas live
one-sixth of the population and nearly 40 per cent of the domestic
animals. In Uganda and Tanzania, the percentages of semi-arid
lands, as well as the percentages of people and domestic animals
living on them, are approximately the same as in Kenya.

73

development in East Africa come mainly from four areas: the United States and Canada, England and Western Europe, Australia and New Zealand, and the Republic of South Africa.   All are temperate areas.   Applications of these principles, such as control of livestock numbers, alternating periods of grazing and nongrazing, control of undesirable woody plants, development of water, and seeding desirable forage plants, are as effective (with minor changes) in tropical semi-arid East Africa as they are in the temperate regions.[2]   Though the species of plants seeded on East African rangelands are different, the necessity for removing competing vegetation, planting and covering the seed, and protecting the young plants from grazing are the same the world over.

The major purpose of range management is to promote and to maintain the most efficient production of animal products.   In some areas, this major purpose is modified to provide water for downstream use, game preservation, timber products, and recreational opportunities.   Implicit in this purpose are such goals as arresting soil destruction caused by improper grazing practices and increasing forage production beyond that of the natural vegetation by planting desirable forage species, by fertilization, and by control of undesirable plants.   The aim is to prevent the destruction of natural ecosystems in areas of extensive use and to increase productivity through intensive management, where it is justified by economic needs.

CONDITION OF RANGELAND RESOURCES

Vegetational zones of East Africa listed in order from high to low elevations and roughly from high to low precipitation effectiveness are as follows: alpine grassland, bamboo forest, broad-leaved and narrow-leaved evergreen forests, woodlands of deciduous small trees and large grasses, bush and small grasses, and ephemeral annual grasses with scattered shrubs in the deserts. Since grasses are the primary forages, all of the region has been mapped on the basis of existing grasslands and potential grassland types.[3]   Also, reconnaissance surveys of geology, soils, and water have been made.   These and a number of highly valuable research accomplishments draw attention to the wide variety of range resource conditions in East Africa.

Substantial gaps exist in the ecological knowledge concerning the different vegetational types and how to manage them.   Two-thirds of the approximately 350 publications pertinent to range management in East Africa prior to 1960 appeared in the decade 1950-1960.[4]   Potentials of livestock, game, and water production have not been determined, nor are the changes in vegetation caused by grazing, fire, and climate adequately documented.   However, enough has been learned recently to show that East African rangelands can be made to produce more than they are now yielding.

Many of the papers published between 1950 and 1960 concentrate on the results of improper land use. There are more published photographs of land which is badly eroded because of severe overgrazing by livestock and devastating fires than on any other subject. In the past, control of livestock, game, and man by disease, predation, war, water unavailability, and drought maintained animal pressures for forage well below the potential carrying capacity of the land. In the last 50 years, we are told, a process of insidious decline had been underway on the rangelands. Veterinary care has permitted animal populations to increase beyond forage production capabilities; water facilities constructed in formerly unused range areas have resulted in the destruction of vegetation and soil; unnecessary killing of wild animals and changes in their habitats have resulted in serious game losses; cultivation has led to soil erosion; nature's system of checks and balances has been upset; on grazing lands there is overstocking in the wet years and starvation in the dry years. Vegetation improvement in the years of favorable rains is evident, but former productive capacity is not quite reached even at these times, so that averaging across the climatic cycles shows a cumulative decline.

This commonly heard indictment of land use in East Africa does not recognize positive results obtained in several land management programs. It does not acknowledge man's ability to create better conditions for his animals and himself than nature originally provided. The tendency is to concentrate on failures, such as the Ground Nut Scheme in Tanzania, and to overlook positive efforts, like those to rebuild part of the Ground Nut Scheme area into a crop- and livestock-producing location.

Trouble spots exist and should not be ignored. Perhaps extreme statements are justified and needed to obtain support for improvement programs, but they leave exaggerated impressions of the gravity of the problems. Three points will help to clarify the situation. First, not all the natural heritage has been destroyed, nor is there imminent danger that it will be. A recent map of Kenya's Masailand shows well over half the area with reasonably good grass cover and no more than 10 per cent denuded. Three years after close control of livestock began in a grazing scheme in the Rift Valley Province of Kenya, abundant grass of high quality had returned on formerly denuded soil. Near Machakos, soil conserving crops, barnyard manure, and hand constructed bench terraces have made productive land where gulleys had cut deep trenches. Survey, problem analysis, and farm planning resulted in contour farming, crop rotation, fencing, and cooperative use of heavy implements for plowing and harvesting on farms of the Elgeyo Tribe in northern Kenya. (After approximately 20,000 miles of travel in East Africa in 1958-1959, which included visits to the worst and the best areas in terms of land management, the author concluded that land destruction was not as widespread as commonly described.)

Second, agriculturalists, veterinarians, wildlife managers, range managers, foresters, and administrators have tended to work narrowly in their own disciplines. Efforts are sincere, and each field can point with pride to successful projects, but interpretations of land conditions are frequently flavored with biases and objectives of the individual fields. For example, for the agriculturist or forester, bush is undesirable and is to be eliminated if the tsetse fly is to be controlled or the land used for forest crops. On the other hand, bush produces forage for certain game species, so the wildlife manager does not enthusiastically advocate woody plant control. The range manager takes an intermediate approach because livestock ranges with certain palatable species of bush are often better than those with pure grass. When the land owner or user is presented with the different recommendations of these specialists, he becomes confused, when what he is seeking is clarification. But, though difficulties arise in the application of the available biological knowledge, hope for immediate progress in rangeland development exists because of an increasing awareness of the political and economic aspects of the problems it raises. (This point will be discussed further in a later section.)

Third, there are situations where success in one field results in problems in another. Veterinarians in East Africa have done a splendid job in disease control under adverse circumstances. Rinderpest is all but eliminated, except in game populations. Application of tick control techniques has reduced losses from East Coast fever. Foot-and-mouth disease is checked in many areas. Examples of successful programs could be listed in all the technical fields, and each is a triumph and a contribution to progress. Yet, these programs are criticized as being destructive. For instance, disease control is criticized because it has allowed animal numbers to increase and the ranges to become overgrazed. Obviously, the solution lies in increased production of feed and sale of animals rather than in reduced disease control. Similar conflicts in interests between wildlife and livestock production, between planned and unplanned use of fire, etc., draw attention to rangeland problems. They have contributed unnecessarily to the belief that East African rangelands are being destroyed at a rapid rate. Successes in rangeland development are seldom described outside technical journals.

RANGE IMPROVEMENT PROGRAMS

Several rangeland improvement programs have been attempted in East Africa, and descriptions of a few, such as water development, bush control, and wildlife preservation, are warranted. Development of domestic water supplies has been a popular project because people need the water, and a government can point with pride to new water establishments such as wells, dams, and pipelines. This is visible progress that is limited principally by available development funds.

Failures in water development are seldom the result of physical causes, but are due frequently to human shortcomings. Permanent water in specific areas often fosters year-long concentration of people and their animals, which destroys vegetation and accelerates erosion. Water development without planned land use, therefore, is to be avoided, because one aim in water development is to obtain even distribution of grazing over large areas. Two examples illustrate some of the other difficulties. First, a number of years ago, windmills were used to pump water in northern Uganda, but they could not be maintained because the fan blades made excellent shields and were often appropriated for such use. Second, at one well in south central Kenya, which had been constructed at government expense for free use by the people, four operators had to be replaced in the space of 18 months because each was unlawfully charging for the water and pocketing the money.

In addition to programs of water development, there have been attempts to control the bush. The African bush is a widespread complex of vegetation that is composed of many shrub species. Increased bush density in recent years has lowered livestock and grazing values. Reduction of woody species has been attempted in dozens of areas throughout East Africa in order to promote grass forage for livestock and to eliminate tsetse flies. Three moderately successful control areas are the Athi-Tiva scheme southeast of Nairobi, the Mara ranch in western Masailand, and the Rift Valley area north of Nairobi. The bulldozer and fire were the principal tools used, but other methods included selective chemical herbicides and heavy grazing by goats. While these schemes were labeled successful at the beginning, they have since shown signs of failing because the bush is the natural plant climax and will return unless a maintenance program is continued. A recent report on the bush problem and control methods began with the thesis that, unless responsibilities for long-term proper management and maintenance were provided and planned from the beginning, bush control should not be attempted.[5]

Little specific information is available on physiological activity of bush plants in relation to weather conditions, on responses of the plants to the time and kind of chemical treatments, and on methods of preparing fuel for effective burning. The techniques for controlling woody plants need to be refined. Initial successes with bush control indicate that the rangelands of East Africa have a high potential grass productivity and livestock carrying capacity. Nevertheless, much remains to be learned about bush control, and an effective widespread program has not been pushed.

Costs of bush control in East Africa do not appear to be

materially higher than the costs in temperate areas, but low returns from livestock sales reduce the possibilities of economical
conversion from bush to grass. The profit margin cannot be rapidly increased without additional facilities for transportation,
processing, marketing of animal products, and increased consumption
of meat locally. In one respect, successful bush control contributes to economic progress through increased livestock production;
in another, it is dependent upon progress throughout the region's
economic structure. This interdependence, perhaps more than any
other factor, determines the success or failure of bush control programs, as well as other range improvement efforts.

Another range improvement program has been directed toward
wildlife preservation. Recently, wildlife managers have made considerable effort to preserve wildlife populations in East Africa
and other areas of Africa. The values of wildlife in the tourism
industry and as a unique resource are unquestioned in terms of
Western values. If game is to continue in abundance, game values
must be enhanced, perhaps through harvesting game for meat. Studies
show that some game animals produce more protein per acre and at a
faster rate than domestic livestock, and that they can live in
tsetse fly areas where livestock cannot be grazed.[6] It is clear
that game cropping should replace meat production by domestic animals, at least in certain places. Successful regulated game cropping programs occur on a limited scale in East Africa. For it to
become a major industry will require economical methods of harvesting, processing, and transport, but these do not exist. As
these problems are solved for either game or domestic livestock,
both types of animals will benefit, but traditional raising of
livestock and the relative ease of harvesting and processing domestic animals are likely to maintain cattle, sheep, and goats in
the dominant position as meat producers.

Overgrazing is damaging to populations of wild species before it becomes harmful to domestic animals. For example, the
plains species, such as gazelles, wildebeest, and zebra, which
live together on grasslands, have different and specific diets.
Each does not normally feed upon the whole flora, but only on certain species. Domestic animals graze on a wider range of plants.
Overgrazing, which results in changing the type of vegetation, as
well as in reducing the density of plants, has immediate effect
on those animals with specific diets. Wild ungulate animals generally decrease in areas grazed intensively by domestic animals.

The wild animals, too, can cause material change in the
habitat. The hippopotamus has overgrazed areas in Queen Elizabeth
Park in Uganda, and elephants have been an important factor in the
elimination of forests in Uganda's Murchison Falls Park. These
situations have developed from animal protection--a form of land
management which aims to maintain a large picturesque population.
It is self-defeating, as it leads to habitat degradation followed

by decline in animal numbers. Clearly, the solution is maintenance of animal numbers within the ability of the habitat to produce food. This requires harvesting of game, which places game in direct competition with livestock at the market place.

Basically, the solution to the rangeland problem is to increase the consumption of meat,* to increase the quality and sale of all kinds of animals from the range areas, and to lower the numbers of range livestock. Smaller numbers would allow more feed for each remaining animal and improve meat quality. However, simply replacing meat from domestic livestock with game meat may well contribute to further overgrazing by domestic animals and to further encroachment upon game habitats, because less demand for meat from domestic livestock will result in fewer being marketed and more on the range.

HUMAN FACTORS IN CONTROL

Although many biological questions need answers before rangeland development in East Africa can go forward with certainty, examples of improvement schemes indicate that considerable success can reasonably be expected from application of current knowledge. The major causes for failure are lack of control of animal numbers and livestock movements. Without these, disease control, more water, bush clearing, reseeding, tsetse control, and other husbandry practices cannot succeed either in East Africa or in highly developed areas. Control of livestock numbers is mainly dependent upon economic, sociological, and political factors and has little chance of being attained if only the biological aspects of range development schemes are taken into account.

For example, persuading people to sell livestock is difficult. The custom in many tribes is to reckon wealth in terms of numbers of cattle. A few animals are traded for necessary goods and services, but raising animals specifically for market is uncommon. Deep-seated customs such as this are difficult to break. Education in its broadest sense, with efforts directed toward adults as well as children, will probably provide the best solution to land management problems.** When people in the hinterland

---

*A second good reason for increasing the consumption of meat is to raise protein consumption within the region. For this purpose, greater average earning power is required. Average family income is unknown, but 50 dollars per year seems to be a fair estimate. Little opportunity exists for buying meat when the few available pennies must cover all the necessities in life.

**East African governments are active in providing and directing

become knowledgeable concerning efficient use of their biological surroundings, the relation of their social customs to those of others, and their own economic potential, they will participate more adequately in land management programs. When the desire for a better life is developed and means for its attainment clearly found effective, efforts to push forward will also be more effective.

In addition to tribal customs, economic factors also affect the numbers of range animals. Sale of no more than 10 per cent of the herds each year probably would be sufficient to bring the numbers of animals into balance with feed supplies within a few years. Given present numbers, this would mean selling four million animals annually in East Africa. However, there is no market for such a large quantity. Foreign trade takes only a few thousand cattle through the canned and refrigerated meat trade. (One processing plant exists in Tanzania and another in Kenya.)

Further development of all exportable agricultural products in East Africa can raise income per family and is, in fact, necessary before any single segment of agriculture, such as rangeland development, can progress materially. The importance of agriculture in East Africa is indicated by the fact that four-fifths of Kenya's wealth comes from the land.[*] Oil has not been found, mineral resources are of minor importance, and industrial development has proceeded at a slow pace. Agriculture is the first and tourism the second major source of outside funds in East Africa. They are likely to remain in high positions. Both depend upon land management and upon such things as advertising and well-developed transportation for favorable market positions.

---

higher educational opportunities in cooperation with other nations. In 1963, the Institute for International Education reported that slightly over 5 per cent of the East African students in the United States were specializing in Agriculture. A more rapid increase in the number of trained personnel in Agriculture and the relevant sciences is vital, since East Africa is largely an agricultural area.

*Kenya's agricultural exports (mainly coffee, tea, sisal, fruits, pyrethrum, and meat) in 1958 amounted to approximately 75 million dollars from the European-managed farms and 16 million dollars from native African sources. Excluding areas below 10 inches of rainfall, Europeans were operating on 20 per cent of the best cultivated land, 25 per cent of the fair cultivated land, and on 10 per cent of the better rangeland. These data suggest that a potentially great economic development exists for agriculture in East Africa, and that the land resources can be used by Africans to further develop profitable export trade in agricultural products

National leadership has played and will continue to play a key role in the economic growth of these two industries. Nowhere in East Africa can change in the way of life be separated from the practice of government, because government leadership sustains inflow of capital, fosters development of skills, and urges hard work--the principal ingredients of economic growth. During periods of rapidly changing government, when economic uncertainty, possibilities of land reform, and changing administration dominate, people's attitudes toward their work are wavering. Certain programs may be lost or temporarily set back in time. One example in rangeland development will illustrate.

By 1959, over a million acres in Kenya had been placed in a number of grazing schemes. Some were relatively new, and few results had been obtained, but others were five to six years old. They had shown outstanding results. Vegetation had returned to denuded land, water had been developed, seeding and brush control were under way, and established boundaries had permitted grazing on a planned basis with stipulated numbers of animals. People had been persuaded--and forced, to a degree, at the beginning--to allow the work. Later they recognized the benefits and were requesting new schemes faster than agriculturalists could be found to initiate them. In 1959, the outlook for continuing range programs was good. An unprecedented drought that ended in 1961 reduced the benefits of the grazing schemes because it forced overuse of all the ranges. Excellent range conditions at the beginning reduced the severity and shortened the critical period of feed shortage. Unfortunately, grazing control and improvement efforts were discontinued after the drought. During the height of the period that culminated with Kenya's independence in 1963, technical people left because of uncertainty about tenure, compensation, and their physical well-being. Lacking trained personnel among their own people, Kenyans were not able to resume the programs after the drought.

Thus it is evident that, though politics are normally outside the biologist's interests, political events affect the application of biological knowledge. Rarely do politicians actively push scientifically-preferred biological programs in developing countries, because these are slow to show results. Experience and education are probably necessary so that the 80 to 90 per cent of the population who are agriculturalists in East Africa will be reoriented to appreciate long-term programs, stable economic enterprise, and an improved quality in rural living.

Progress comes first and moves fastest in the city because it is the center of industry, communications, education, and government. This paper has analyzed the extension of reform to the rural areas, especially the rangelands, of East Africa, where steps toward reform have been short, meager, and not always forward. Perhaps it is unnecessary to repeat that all parts of a society can best develop together--that city dweller and farmer and nomad have a stake in each other's well being. The rural East African is a productive part of the economic whole, but he has been largely overlooked in the headlong rush toward new political systems.

NOTES

[1]The Development of the Semi-arid Areas of Kenya (Nairobi: Ministry of Agriculture and Animal Husbandry, 1963). Mimeo.

[2]H. F. Heady, "Range Management in the Semi-arid Tropics of East Africa According to Principles Developed in Temperate Climates," Proceedings of the Eighth International Grassland Congress (1960), pp. 223-26.

[3]H. F. Heady, Range Management in East Africa (Nairobi: Kenya Department of Agriculture and East African Agricultural and Forestry Research Organization, 1960).

[4]Ibid.

[5]J. R. Bentley, Brush Control in Kenya (Nairobi: Ministry of Agriculture and Animal Husbandry, 1963). Mimeo.

[6]G. G. Watterson, Conservation of Nature and Natural Resources in Modern African States (1963). [International Union for Conservation of Nature, No. 1.]

MEDICINAL PLANT HUNTING IN TANZANIA

by

Mildred E. Mathias

THE HISTORICAL BACKGROUND

Our first written records of plants describe the use of
herbs as cures and give information on their collection and preparation. These records are found in a Chinese pharmacopeia of the
twenty-eighth century B.C., on Sumerian tablets of the twenty-
second century B.C., in the Indian Reg Veda, and on Egyptian papy-
ri before 1600 B.C.[1] However, it was not until the third and
fourth centuries B.C. that the Greeks began to stress the importance of careful observation of the effects of plants on certain
diseases. Although some of the early lists of medicines include
hundreds of kinds of plants, comparatively few of these plants
have played an important role in modern medicine. We have, for
example, strychnine, emetine, curare, quinine, and cocaine from
South America, and digitalis, atropine, and opiates from the Mediterranean areas. We have almost forgotten that these medicines
are derived from plants which may have been used by man for thousands of years. Man in an urban civilization has become more and
more removed from the natural environment and as a result has neglected plants still used medicinally by primitive peoples. These
plants may have been noted and studied occasionally by the field
botanist, they may be listed in compilations of poisonous plants,
they may appear in cultural studies, but until recent years their
potential has been largely ignored.

It had long been thought by botanists and medical men that
we had exhausted our store of inherited information on plant drugs.
Many of the plant uses of our forefathers had been found to be
based on superstition, and through the years the plant names have
disappeared from the pharmacopeia. Any presumed uses were passed
off as "old wives' tales."

One such plant was Rauwolfia serpentina, the Indian Snake-
root, known from the Indian Reg Veda since the seventeenth century
B.C. and still prescribed in the Ayurvedic system of medicine.
The isolation and examination of its most important alkaloid--
reserpine--in 1952 revealed its importance to modern medicine as
a tranquilizer and a blood pressure depressant.[2] Earlier in 1935
the alkaloid d-tubocurarine had been isolated from the curare
plant, Chondrodendron tomentosum, and adopted in surgery as a
muscle relaxant. The recognition of the value of these two plants

has given impetus to extensive surveys of plants and plant products. Not only have collections been made of plants still used in
primitive medicines, but a general screening has been initiated of
all plant materials. Certain plant families have received special
attention because of their drug potential. From these searches
have come such new drugs as vinca leucoblastine from Catharanthus
roseus. We have now the technology for establishing the scientific
basis, if any, for many ancient cures, and may find applications
for the drugs far beyond the original use.

As a result of this increased interest in medicinal herbs
and primitive medicines, an active field of plant exploration and
experimentation has developed.[3] In 1950 the search for possible
sources for the drug cortisone by official United States' agencies
was initiated by a presidential decree. This has been a joint
project of the United States Department of Agriculture and the
National Institutes of Health.[4] A second cooperative program has
been one searching for possible alkaloidal bearing plants with
alkaloids useful in treating hypertension.[5] The Department of
Agriculture has been attempting to bring such plants into cultivation and thus eliminate dependence upon animal sources and the
erratic exploitation of wild plants. In more recent years there
has been inaugurated an extensive program of screening large numbers of plant extracts for fungicidal, bactericidal, anti-viral,
and anti-cancerous activity. The large drug companies as well as
government agencies throughout the world have been involved in
this search for and study of plant drugs. Modern scientific techniques have replaced less refined methods. Drugs as valuable as
reserpine or curare may not be found, but our knowledge of the
chemical composition of plant products, of the use of plants by
many peoples, and of the variation and distribution of world floras
will be increased immeasurably.

METHODS OF COLLECTION AND STUDY

A study of plant drugs is initiated by sending trained collectors to promising floristic areas to make mass collections of
plant parts for standard chemical analysis and pharmacological
screening. Plant parts are carefully collected from a single individual plant whenever possible and thoroughly dried for preservation. From the field this material is sent to a laboratory as soon
as possible to avoid excessive loss of volatile substances. Extractions are prepared in a uniform manner, and screening tests
are conducted, using standard laboratory animals. If the tests
show promising results, they may be followed by identification and
isolation of the active principle in the plant extract; its chemical structure may be determined and may be altered to make its
action more favorable. Eventually, after two to ten years, a new
drug may be released to the trade.[6]

Each specimen for analysis is accompanied by a voucher
herbarium sheet, a dried pressed specimen, from the same individual. For each sample there are field notes on date of collection,
precise locality, local uses and names, and any pertinent data,
such as size or flower color, which may prove helpful in identification. The documentation of each collection with herbarium
vouchers makes it possible to duplicate the collection even to the
stage of maturity of the plant originally obtained. The herbarium
specimens are sent to an herbarium where they are studied and identified. Even though the chemical and pharmacological screening
may prove negative for potential drug use, the herbarium specimens
still have a real value in adding to our store of knowledge. They
are a record both of occurrence and of variation of plant forms.

PLANT HUNTING IN TANZANIA

The choice of a locality in which to collect plants is
often fortuitous. It was a contact with an anthropologist which
led us into the field in the Southern Highlands Province, Tanzania,
during the summer of 1963. A team of anthropologists from the University of California had returned from an extended stay in East
Africa with a few plant specimens and a small collection of prepared medicines. The former were mostly plants known to be useful, and had been recorded in the literature, but the plant sources
of the latter could not be identified. This was particularly surprising since each sample had a native name and since an encyclo-
pedic compendium had just been published on the poisonous and medicinal plants of East Africa.[7] Probably no other area of the world
has comparable accounts of such detail and with such extensive
listings of native plant names.[8] Documentation was needed for the
prepared medicines as well as more adequate quantities of material
for pharmacological and chemical study. The best solution was to
visit the original collection site and attempt to collect the
plants from which the preparations had been made.

Once the decision was made to go to Tanzania, a series of
problems had to be solved. We would be working with a tribal group
whose language we could not hope to learn in the time available, so
an interpreter was essential. Plant collecting equipment is bulky
and heavy, and arrangements had to be made for securing it by loan
and purchase in East Africa. Transportation suitable for all roads
and adequate for transport of specimens had to be secured. In the
solution of each of these problems we were helped immeasurably by
the anthropologists who knew the area. They introduced us to a
trustworthy and competent native interpreter; they gave us names
of contacts--local medicine men, suppliers of field equipment,
etc. (The East African Herbarium in Nairobi is unique in the
directory of the herbaria of the world in that it offers the loan
of collecting equipment to expeditions.)[9] With such experienced
advice and assistance we were able to organize our program and get

into the field within a few weeks.

The next hurdle was to establish rapport with the local
authorities and medicine men in southern Tanzania. We had been
warned by our advisors that the latter might not be easy, since
information on medicinal plants and their uses is usually a family
secret. The few weeks we had might not provide sufficient time for
overcoming cultural barriers. However, the local African civil
authorities promised full cooperation, and our medicine men could
not have been more helpful. It was a source of both surprise and
pleasure to be able, within a few hours' time, to assure success
of the expedition. The medicine men not only agreed to go into
the field with us to assist in the plant collecting, but also
agreed to tell us their formulae and methods of treatment.

The two medicine men we consulted represented quite different types. One spoke his native tribal language and a bit of
Swahili; he lived in a rural environment, had had little or no
formal education, and his plant lore included ancient superstitions
The other was reasonably fluent in English as well as Swahili; he
lived in town, read widely, was well informed on world affairs,
and told us none of the superstitions of the first. These two
individuals represented opposite ends of a spectrum, and as a result we gained an insight into native culture and plant use which
was unusual in the time available. Both men had learned their
medicinal plant knowledge from their parents. At first neither
wanted money for the information they were to give us, since they
thought the plants might not prove effective in the United States;
after being assured that we must pay them for their time, they then
wanted to be certain that proper credit would be given them and
that additional financial benefits would accrue if the plants
proved valuable. The urban medicine man told us that, although
the cures had been family secrets, now that Tanzania was an independent nation, they owed this medical information to the world.

The medicinal plant lore of the rural medicine man contained many ancient superstitions. Certain plants to be effective
required special collecting techniques--the roots must be gathered
only at midnight in the dark of the moon by a naked man who drags
himself prostrate across the stony ground to the shrub or tree.
The extractions must be made by boiling the segments of root in the
abdominal cavity of a black chicken. Certain preparations must
be taken while facing specified points of the compass. (These superstitions are very similar to those described by Theophrastus in
the fourth century B.C., who even then expressed doubt concerning
their validity.)[10] Diagnosis is accomplished by a Ouija Board technique with special wooden wedges rubbed on a wet flattened branch.
To this ancient lore of collecting techniques and diagnosis there
has been added a modern touch--a white powder mixture purchased
from a town supplier. This compound, however, still carries with
it the taint of magic, since one component, copper sulphate, is

blue-green when purchased, and turns white when heated, a color
change which doubtless adds to its psychological effectiveness.
Superstitions such as these may well influence the choice of plants
included in some of the medicinal mixtures. Certain plants may be
collected and used by the medicine man solely because the shape of
the fruit or some other unusual characteristic seems to give it a
special power. The modern collector, however, must be careful to
get specimens for analysis of all plants used, even those which
superficially seem valueless.

It is always possible that an openly cooperative attitude
by a medicine man may be a cover and that he will give a collector
plants which he knows are useless. This would be easy to do when
the collector knows neither the region nor the language. However
we feel that our informants were sincere and honest, since independently we got the same plants from each.

Our collecting areas were all in the Southern Highlands
Province in the vicinity of Iringa. The native vegetation is
largely Brachystegia woodland, but the medicine man in this area
has exploited the total environment, often travelling miles on
foot to get a particular plant. We were taken to a number of habitats, from pools along the Little Ruaha River, with a typical riv-
erine vegetation, to thorn scrub on dry rocky hillsides, woodland
of Brachystegia and Julbernardia, and open savanna dominated by
Parinari. There was no micro-habitat without its medicinal plants.

We concentrated our efforts on collecting plants which affected the central nervous system--plants used in the treatment of
epilepsy and insanity. We collected herbarium material of each
plant, material for pharmacological and chemical screening, information on methods for preparation of the medicines, and dosages.
Since some of the prepared medicines were from combinations of as
many as eleven different species of plants, it was necessary to
collect samples of each species, and it may be necessary in screening to check not only the pharmacological activity of each component but of the total product.

In studying treatments for epilepsy and insanity there are
special problems. Primitive man often did not recognize the natural causes of disease and particularly of mental disease. The
patient was presumed to be bewitched by some supernatural power or
by another person. The obvious cure was to thoroughly purge the
patient of all foreign influences, and, consequently, medicines
which produced violent reactions were assumed to be the most effective. Our collections and formulae indicate that our medicine men
have inherited this type of medicine and the superstitions on which
its use is based. The plants we obtained contain violent purga-
tives and emetics, and some of the plants would produce death in
overdose. The question then arises if, among the 37 plants obtained, there is one with a unique property affecting the central

nervous system. The 37 species represent 35 genera in 26 plant
families. None of them is in the list of alkaloid-bearing plants
prepared by J. J. Willaman and Bernice G. Schubert.[11] Even one of
the families is not in the Willaman and Schubert list. However
four important alkaloid-producing families are represented--Rubi-
aceae, Leguminosae, Verbenaceae, and Loganiaceae.

These collections will add a significant number of new
plants and new uses to the records of medicinal plants. Of the
37 species collected by us only ten are cited by John M. Watt and
M. G. Breyer-Brandwijk for a similar use,[12] none by P. R. O. Bally,[13]
five by G. R. Williams,[14] seven by J. Hutchinson and J. M. Dalziel,[15]
and only two by Thomas S. Githens.[16] This collection obviously indicates the need for more localized studies and collecting. Each
group of peoples, each community, may have its own secrets, and
each is a potential source of new plant information.

There are not enough trained botanists to visit and study
the plants of every area of the world. In this study other field
workers--the anthropologist, the linguist, the geographer, the
zoologist, etc.--can assist by recording information, always docu-
menting it with the essential herbarium voucher specimen and accurate field notes.[17] The specimens collected should be pressed
and dried and sent to a recognized herbarium or specialist for
identification and subsequent storage. For example, a complete set
of our collection is on file at the East African Herbarium in
Nairobi, and identifications have been made by the staff there.

MEDICINAL PLANTS IN THE AMAZON BASIN AND EAST AFRICA COMPARED

Our previous studies of primitive medicines have been in
the upper Amazon Basin of Peru and Ecuador. Thus both of our collecting areas have been within the tropics, the one dry and the
other wet tropics. The tropics still constitute a frontier for the
botanist: the environment has been occupied by flowering plants
since Permo-Triassic,[18] the floras are still poorly known, and they
abound, particularly in the wet tropics, in large numbers of still
undescribed species. The latter is true despite the fact that in
the tropical zone of East Africa man has had a long residence. (The
Isimila site in our collecting area dates from the Paleolithic.)[19]
Here man has had some 100,000 years for the testing of plants for
their medicinal values.

One of the interesting and thought-provoking outcomes of
investigations in these two hemispheres has been a comparison of
attitudes and methodology. The medicine man--the brujo--of the
Amazon is usually operating outside the law, and, consequently,
information from a legitimate brujo is not easy to obtain. He may
never admit his abilities to cure, and he may refuse to share his
knowledge of plants. The medicine man of Tanzania is a respected

member of his community and, as mentioned previously, does not hesitate to assist in plant collecting and give information of the uses he makes of plants.

Of particular interest is the development of a stem culture in the Amazon and a root culture in East Africa. This may reflect the difference in composition and structure of the flora and man's solution to a difficult collecting problem in each area. Medicines in the rain forests of the Amazon are obtained from stems which are certainly more easily cut and more readily available than the roots. However, in the thorn scrub of East Africa, the spiny, rigid stems above ground are far more formidable than the roots (even in a stony soil), and the majority of the medicines are extracted from roots.* In the seasonal flora of southern Tanzania there are notable differences in the above ground portion of many plants, depending on whether it is the dry or wet season. In the Amazon rain forest seasonal changes are inconsequential.

MAJOR OBJECTIVES

We have two major objectives in these investigations: botanical and pharmacological. The botanical objectives are not only the documentation of medicinal plant uses and the occurrence of plant products but also the addition to our knowledge of variation in plants and the composition and distribution of floras. There is an urgent need for recording this information. Modern culture is invasive,[21] and ethno-botanical lore passed down through generations is being lost; modern transportation is making even the most remote parts of the tropics accessible, and the original flora is being exploited and destroyed before a record of it is obtained or any knowledge of its past use or potential value.

The pharmacological objectives are the discovery of new drugs and the discovery of new variants or new sources of known drugs. Ideally these objectives should be those of a team of field workers--the botanist, the pharmacologist, the anthropologist, the linguist, and the organic chemist. A concerted cooperative study by such a group of specialists is a much desired interdisciplinary approach which would be mutually profitable to all participants.**

---

*On the other hand, the root culture of Tanzania may represent an ancient heritage derived from the same sources as those recounted by the Greeks, who even recognized a special group of medicinal plant collectors--the rhizotomi or root-gatherers.[20] They believed that when the top parts of the plants die all of their properties are concentrated in the roots.

**One of the critical areas in an investigation of native medi-

The economic potential of such a study is difficult to predict. The discovery of an important drug source can lead to exploitation and extermination of a plant by foreign and native collectors, to temporary or permanent cultivation to provide ready sources of plant material, or to eventual synthetic production of the chemical first manufactured by the plant. Sales of drugs from plants have increased markedly in recent years, and the market for medicinal plants is rapidly approaching $300,000,000. Investigations of natural products are world-wide, and probably less than five per cent of the plant kingdom has been analyzed. There is always the hope of discovering a new and valuable product, which makes the search for medicinal plants one of the exciting fields of investigation today.

---

cines is the need for extended studies of their uses, including accurate diagnosis of ailments and reports on long-term effectiveness of purported cures. A medically trained field worker could supply much needed information if he had the opportunity for extended study in an area.

NOTES

[1]George Sarton, A History of Science: Ancient Science through the Golden Age of Greece (Cambridge: Harvard University Press, 1960).

[2]Robert E. Woodson, Jr., H. W. Youngken, E. Schittler, and J. A. Schneider, Rauwolfia (Boston: Little, Brown and Co., 1957).

[3]Robert F. Raffauf, "Plants as a Source of New Drugs," Economic Botany, XIV (1960), pp. 276-79; Richard E. Schultes, "Tapping Our Heritage of Ethnobotanical Lore," ibid., pp. 257-62; Margaret B. Kreig, Green Medicine (Chicago: Rand McNally and Co., 1964).

[4]D. S. Correll, B. G. Schubert, H. S. Gentry, and W. O. Harvey, "The Search for Plant Precursors of Cortisone," Economic Botany, IX (1955), pp. 307-75.

[5]J. J. Willaman and B. G. Schubert, "Alkaloid Hunting," ibid., pp. 141-50.

[6]H. B. Macphillamy, "Drugs from Plants," Plant Science Bulletin, IX, 2 (1963), pp. 1-5.

[7]John M. Watt and M. G. Breyer-Brandwijk, The Medicinal and Poisonous Plants of Southern and Eastern Africa (2nd ed., Edinburgh: E. & S. Livingstone, 1962).

[8]Walter Busse, "Uber Heil- und Nutzpflanzen Deutsch-Ostafrikas," Deutsche Pharmazeutische Gesellschaft Berichte, XIV (1904), pp. 187-201; P. R. O. Bally, "Native Medicinal and Poisonous Plants of East Africa," Bulletin of Miscellaneous Information (Kew: 1937), pp. 10-26, and "Heil- und Giftpflanzen der Eingeborenen von Tanganyika," Repertorium Specierum Novarum, Beihefte 102 (1938), pp. 1-87; P. J. Greenway, A Swahili-Botanical-English Dictionary of Plant Names (Dar es Salaam: Government Printer, 1940); Thomas S. Githens, Drug Plants of Africa (Philadelphia: University of Pennsylvania Press, 1949); G. R. Williams, Dictionary of Native Plant Names in the Bondei, Shambaa and Zigua Languages with Their English and Botanical Equivalents (Nairobi: 1963), mimeo.

[9]J. Lanjouw and F. A. Stafleu, Index Herbariorum (5th ed., Utrecht: 1964).

[10]Theophrastus, Enquiry into Plants and Minor Works on Odours and Weather Signs, trans. Sir Arthur Hort (2 vols., New York: Putnam, 1916). [Loeb Classical Library.]

[11]Alkaloid-Bearing Plants and Their Contained Alkaloids. U.S. Department of Agriculture Agricultural Research Service Technical Bulletin 1234 (Washington, D.C.: Government Printing Office, 1961).

[12]Op. cit. (see note 7).

[13]Op. cit. (see note 8).

[14]Op. cit. (see note 8).

[15]The Useful Plants of West Tropical Africa (London: Crown Agent for the Colonies, 1937).

[16]Op. cit. (see note 8).

[17]F. R. Fosberg, "Plant Collecting as an Anthropological Field Method," El Palacio, LXVII (1960), pp. 125-39.

[18]Daniel I. Axelrod, "A Theory of Angiosperm Evolution," Evolution, VI (1952), pp. 29-60.

[19]H. N. Chittick, Short Guide to the Isimila Paleolithic Site (Bagamoyo, Tanzania: Department of Antiquities, 1959).

[20]E. L. Greene, "Landmarks of Botanical History," Smithsonian Miscellaneous Collection, LIV (1909), pp. 45-51.

[21]Schultes, op. cit. (see note 3).

MEDICINAL PLANT HUNTING IN TANZANIA

The author wishes to acknowledge support from Contract No. DA-04-495-AMC-791(A), Army Chemical Center, Edgewood, Maryland, to the Department of Pharmacology, University of California, Los Angeles.

BENEFITS AND COSTS OF WATER CONSERVATION

by

Harold E. Thomas

The interdisciplinary character of this paper is indicated in the title, for water is a physical resource, but costs, benefits, and conservation are all ideas of man--ideas that vary from individual to individual, from one society to another, and from time to time within the same culture. It is my thesis that in the evolution of culture there is also an evolution in attitudes toward conservation. Although modern Africa is the prime concern of this paper, I have found it necessary to document these evolutionary trends by citing examples from the past and from other parts of the world, notably several localities in the United States, where both the water development and the attitudes toward conservation may be portents of things to come in some localities in Africa.

I have long felt that conservation should refer to more than mere preservation, and that it should embrace the "wise" use of natural resources. As thus defined, conservation can be universally accepted as good, and in the interest of mankind. Also, for those who write about conservation, and for those who are "conservation-minded," this definition provides that comfortable association with wisdom. The principle of conservation is indeed widely accepted, sufficiently so that conservation movements have broad popular support, but human ingenuity is such that, for many things that are favored by one group in the name of conservation, the antitheses are favored by other groups--also in the name of conservation.[1] Thus, though there is general agreement on the principle, there is wide diversity of opinion as to the means to be employed and ends to be achieved.

In September, 1963, at a meeting in Nairobi of the International Union for the Conservation of Nature and Natural Resources (IUCN), I had opportunity to see the overall comprehensiveness of conservation, and the diversity of interests in various aspects of the natural resources.[2] Of major concern at that meeting was the population explosion that is currently rocking the world, and the corollary pressure for increasing exploitation of natural resources, which will inevitably place many member organizations of IUCN on the defensive. A defensive role is nothing new to those conservationists who have been concerned with the preservation of individual species or isolated stands of animal or plant life, or with the preservation of certain areas for their

scenic, recreational, wilderness, historic, or scientific values.
But IUCN represents a composite of many of these separate interests, whose combined objectives are to preserve all natural life
and natural resources in all environments, including forests,
grasslands, deserts, mountains, plains, lakes, rivers, and oceans.
Here there is danger of resisting the population pressure at all
points, hoping to maintain the status quo, and thus developing a
sort of conservation Maginot line, which becomes increasingly in-
defensible in the face of the overwhelming numbers of people in
the world.

AGE DIFFERENTIATION OF CONSERVATION ATTITUDES

As I listened to the discussions at this IUCN meeting, I
felt that I was hearing a representative sampling of attitudes toward conservation the world over, and that I could differentiate
those attitudes according to the human generations represented.
The age of senility was of course not represented--persons in that
age group would be too old or too uninterested to attend such a
conference. The generation of maturity was well represented--my
age group, whose members had achieved the half-century mark and
were old enough to be grandparents. The generation of youth was
fairly well represented--the age of active parenthood, between the
quarter-century and half-century mark. The generation of dependents and generations still unborn were not represented, but they
did not lack for spokesmen.

My "mature" generation includes many of the leaders in
government, in science, in education, and in other areas of our culture. So far as years are concerned, we have more of a "past"
than we can anticipate for a "future." Our social and economic
position is approaching a steady state, and our living is essentially made. Our ideas of conservation are likely to reflect our
knowledge of the past and to emphasize preservation of the natural
resources for the future benefit of mankind. In the world population, ours is a minority group.

The "youthful" generation includes the principal working
force, who by farming or industry or other services support the
economy, form the "taxpayer" group, and, in a democratic system,
have an important voice in governmental policy because they probably constitute a majority of the voters. They are the aggressive
generation, for they must make a living, acquire social and economic status, and support the younger dependent generation as well
as those of the older generation whose incomes are at a bare subsistence level. Their ideas of conservation are likely to reflect the ever-present problems of growth, and to emphasize development of the natural resources for the benefit of mankind.

This distinction between "mature" and "youthful" genera-

tions of participants at the IUCN conference could also be applied
aptly to the nations from whence the participants came. More than
half of these participants hailed from Europe and North America,
and most of these represented private conservation groups, societies, and foundations; generally they were mature individuals, but
even those who were chronologically young had the mature outlook
of an affluent society whose resource base provides far more than
mere subsistence. The conference being held in Nairobi, the next
largest contingent was from the developing African nations; most
of these were younger as individuals, and most of them were representatives of governments with responsibilities for a burgeoning
population whose economy is at a meager subsistence level. Although the IUCN participants from these governments were primarily
concerned with conservation, they had a strong awareness of their
countries' needs for resource development. A third major contingent at the conference included representatives of universities or
colleges (especially those in Africa)--institutions that have long
provided leaders of thought in conservation as well as economics.

The dependent generation enters the economic picture at
present only as consumers of commodities and wealth, and unborn
generations do not have even that status, although they can eventually be far larger numerically than the living population. Because they are to be the recipients of most of the benefits of
conservation, whether by preservation from the past or by present
development and use of the natural resources, these future generations cannot be forgotten in discussions of conservation.

Can we not find a unifying point of view that will harmo-
nize the diverse objectives of the several generations--a diversity that pits those seeking to use natural resources (even "wise-
ly") against those who oppose any form of exploitation? I believe
Teilhard de Chardin has provided such a unifying point of view in
his definition of culture:

> By human culture, I refer to the manifold process
> according to which any human population, whenever left to
> itself, immediately starts spontaneously to arrange itself
> at a social level into an organized system of ends and
> means, in which two basic components are always present:
> First, a material component, or "increase in complexity,"
> which includes both the various types of implements and
> techniques necessary to the gathering or the production
> of all kinds of food or supplies and the various rules
> or laws which provide the best conditions for an optimum
> birth rate or for a satisfactory circulation of goods
> and resources within the limits of the population under
> consideration. Second, a spiritual component, or "in-
> crease in consciousness," namely, some particular out-
> look on the world and life (an approach which is at once
> philosophical, ethical, aesthetic, and religious), the
> function of which is to impart a meaning, a direction,

and an incentive or stimulus to the material activities and development of the community.

For the many fragments of mankind that have become isolated or have gained their independence in the course of time, just so many tentative technicomental systems of the world as a whole--that is, just so many cultures--have gradually come into existence. This is one of the major lessons taught by the universal history of man, from the earliest known stages until the present time.[3]

In stating that both material and spiritual elements are essential to a culture, Teilhard de Chardin does not, and cannot, attach greater importance to one than to the other. Biologically and historically, however, the material needs have come first. These are the needs most readily satisfied by exploitation and development of the natural resources.

EVOLUTION IN CONSERVATION ATTITUDES

The history of our American culture provides indications of the evolution of conservation attitudes. So far as conservation was concerned, the American pioneers lived in an age of innocence, and exploited the natural resources without restraint. They cleared forests to provide shelter, firewood, and farmland, they attacked the grasslands with plow and livestock, and they destroyed wildlife for food, security, or amusement. Extensive areas were despoiled for usable minerals and fuels, and the wastes of civilization were dumped into streams or on vacant land. The chief urge toward preservation of the natural resources for future generations was a selfish interest, readily satisfied by the acquisition of land, mineral, and water rights as private property.

In the meantime, the long-range results of exploitation began to show up in many places--in soil that had lost its fertility, rangeland that had lost its grass, water that had lost its quality, forests that had disappeared, "dust bowls," lands that had been laid waste and abandoned. Some of the exploitations had yielded quick profits, permitting a few people to retire at an early age to sunnier climes. But to "successors in interest"-- communities, the nation--many of these pioneer enterprises have been overall economic losses.

In the past 30 years, research by scientists, especially in universities and in government, has told us much about how to sustain the yield of renewable resources, and how to develop the non-renewable ones in an orderly manner without undue waste. Analysis of costs and benefits shows that in the long run many such "conservation practices" have a sound economic basis. (For new developments of resources, cost-and-benefit analyses are essential, if significant funds are to be invested, in order to estimate the security of the investment.) This has led to an evolution in conservation attitudes.

In California, for example, as elsewhere in the American West, there has been intense exploitation of the resources--by hydraulic mining for gold along many streams, gold-dredging of numerous plains, cutting of virgin forests for timber, cattle ranching, intensive irrigated agriculture--but these operations have dwindled or they are approaching a steady state. In recent years of rapidly increasing population, the chief exploitation of the natural resources has been for living space. Much of this exploitation has occurred in areas of natural beauty, and it has produced damage, scars, and unsightliness in many places, but with this difference from earlier exploitations: the people for whom the resources are exploited--home owners--are planning a future in the environment and are determined to preserve its natural beauty, while yet providing for additional increments of population. By community action, planning commissions, and zoning ordinances, some have been remarkably successful in their efforts.

I consider that these communities express a mature conservation attitude, in that they reach beyond Teilhard de Chardin's "material component," which can be evaluated solely by a cost-and-benefit analysis, and embrace a "spiritual component" or "increase in consciousness" which cannot be evaluated in dollars. Since the preservation of natural beauty and other aesthetic values almost inevitably leads to increased costs of real estate development, this "spiritual component" does involve an immediate dollar cost for an intangible long-range benefit. Such a choice can be made in an affluent society, but is not available to one on a meager subsistence economy.

As attention to aesthetic values increases, problems multiply for public agencies and others responsible for the services that are an essential part of our modern civilization--roads, electricity, telephones, gas, water, sewage. These are "material components" provided to all on demand and at minimum cost, and therefore traditionally with scant consideration for aesthetics. The attitude has been changing in recent years. For example, this statement was made at a recent conference of civil engineers:

One of the major problems engaging the attention and the efforts of electric utilities today is aesthetics: the urgent need to improve the appearance of the facilities that are used to distribute electricity to urban and suburban areas. At almost every industry and professional meeting where electric distribution engineers come together, this is the No. 1 topic of conversation. New techniques are being developed, and the art of electric distribution is undergoing a major revolution.[4]

One agency affected by this changing attitude is the California State Highway Commission, which has responsibility for construction of a network of freeways to permit automobiles to range throughout the state continuously at high speed. In recent months the Commission has encountered strong opposition to proposals for freeways along the west shore of Lake Tahoe and through state parks in the redwood forests along the northern coast. One of its major problems at present is San Francisco's "freeway revolt": after a network of freeways had been constructed to connect the San Francisco-Oakland Bay Bridge with the San Francisco Civic Center and the peninsula south of San Francisco, the San Francisco Board of Supervisors reacted disapprovingly to a Commission proposal for a tie-up with the Golden Gate Bridge, and resolved that if the Golden Gate Bridge were to be connected with the rest of the system, it must be by some other route than that proposed by the Commission, which would have destroyed part of the Golden Gate Park and many city blocks of residential areas.

The peninsula south of San Francisco is the scene of several similar conflicts between forces stressing their short-range interest in maximum development at minimum cost, and forces concerned with the preservation of prized resources for future generations. The eastern half of this peninsula is becoming an intensively urbanized area extending from San Francisco to San Jose. In the western half (west of the famed San Andreas fault), however, there is a continuous greenbelt in mountainous terrain, relatively unoccupied and unused except for recreation. The people of the peninsula, and therefore the cities and counties that speak for them, see this greenbelt as of great spiritual value for the expanding population of the future, and they have become exponents of the long-range objectives of conservation. Opposed to these long-range objectives are the short-range benefit-cost analyses of the numerous agencies responsible for providing utilities within the urbanized areas. It was cheaper and quicker, for instance, to loop a major power transmission line on towers over the unoccupied greenbelt than to bargain with multitudinous landowners along a more direct route within the urbanized area. It will be cheaper to run an overhead line from this tower line to the Stanford linear accelerator now being constructed by the Atomic Energy Commission--no matter how ugly the line may appear to millions--than to place it underground through the scenic greenbelt. The utility agencies, created to serve the public interest, can use their power of eminent domain to achieve their objectives, but the cities and counties who oppose their present plans also represent the public interest. The conflict is thus one between public interests: on the one hand, short-range but national, and on the other hand, long-range but local--or at the most, regional.

In summary, conservation may have various meanings, reflecting the economic position of an individual or a culture. To an individual or a culture operating at a meager subsistence level, conservation may appear to be something to be undertaken in the future, after the urgent needs of the moment are satisfied. Above this poverty level, an increasing "material component," or accumulated wealth, gives increasing opportunity for choice in methods of resource development and use. Hopefully, the choices made are ones that will lead to greater wealth, i.e., the benefits will exceed the costs. Many such choices may lead to long-range benefits that will extend to several succeeding generations, and may be supported by conservationists as constituting a wise use of natural resources. But the choices made are directly related to the society's economic position. With increasing affluence, a society can give increasing weight to the social (aesthetic, ethical, philosophical) values that Teilhard de Chardin includes in his "spiritual component" of culture. These cannot be quantified as dollar values, and therefore cannot be evaluated in the same terms as the "material component." They may, however, require some dollar cost for their achievement, and to that extent irk the economy-minded.

MAN AND WATER RESOURCES

Water is literally the most abundant substance on earth, but about 97 per cent of the estimated total of 326 million cubic miles of it is salt water in the oceans.[5] This salt water is unsuitable for the life processes of terrestrial plants and animals, including man, and it restricts their living area to about one quarter of the surface of the globe. The fresh water needed for terrestrial life is produced naturally by a world-wide, sun-powered purification plant, which maintains about 3,100 cubic miles (liquid measure) of water as vapor in the atmosphere, from which fresh water is precipitated as rain or snow, and to which water is evaporated from the land masses and especially from the oceans. Although the atmosphere's water-holding capacity is small, it has produced sizable accumulations of fresh water over the eons--about 7 million cubic miles of polar ice caps, and 2 million cubic miles of liquid water in or on land areas. Of this liquid, 30,000 cubic miles is in fresh-water lakes and streams, 16,000 is soil moisture, and all the rest is ground water.

The quantity of water that is precipitated upon land areas each year is many times as great as the volume of water in the atmosphere at any one time. Some of this contributes to soil moisture, making up for depletions by vegetation-absorption and by evaporation. Some of it contributes to ground water, replacing that which has been discharged by springs or by seepage into lakes, streams, and marshes. Any residuals from precipitation that are not consumed by plants or animals, or otherwise evaporated from the land masses, are discharged to the oceans by rivers or streams or underground flow. Thus the fresh water of the continents is a resource replenished by precipitation, and the discharge to the oceans--averaging perhaps 9,000 cubic miles a year (in gallons, 10 followed by 15 zeros)--is an indication of the amount that might be salvaged from the world's rivers for uses beneficial to man.

However, the precipitation and therefore the renewable fresh-water resources are distributed very unevenly. Several areas receive more than 200 inches of precipitation a year, several others less than 200 inches a century. On each continent there are extensive areas where the precipitation is less than the potential for evaporation--these are the arid and semi-arid regions that rarely have surpluses to contribute to the oceans. About one third of the fresh water discharged to the oceans is from the 12 rivers of largest volume.[6] Generally the amount of recoverable fresh water is greatest where people don't need it, and least where they do.

Throughout most of prehistory, man's relations to the water resources, like those of other large mammals, were chiefly adaptations to the environment, and he was forced to live near water sources. The obvious sources for man's daily water needs were lakes, rivers, small streams, and springs, including those that form oases in deserts. When ephemeral streams ceased flowing, water was obtained from holes dug in the streambed. Eventually, however, wells were dug to obtain shallow ground water in many places relatively remote from streams and springs, giving man considerably greater freedom in his choice of residence.

In regions where rainfall was deficient for crops, several prehistoric agrarian societies flourished by irrigating--on a small scale by carrying water from streams, and on a large scale by diverting it in canals. As pointed out by K. A. Wittfogel, where there were large water-deficient areas, and large rivers constituted a substantial source of water, "man had to create large-scale enterprises that usually were operated by government. The emergence of big productive water works (for irrigation) was frequently accompanied by the emergence of big protective water works (for flood control), and at times the latter even surpassed the former in magnitude and urgency."[7] The resulting agrarian economy, which Wittfogel has called "hydraulic agriculture," required the effective cooperation (or corvée) of large numbers of people in maintenance of control structures and ditches, and in the irrigation and intensive cultivation of crops; for this there had to be planning, record-keeping, communication, and supervision--organization in depth, and thus a massive and permanent bureaucracy and a monolithic society. Having only a minimum of labor-saving tools and animals, the hydraulic farmer lived a life of unending drudgery. Nevertheless, the great hydraulic civilizations of Egypt, India, China, Mesopotamia, Peru, and Mexico maintained themselves for several thousands of years. Wittfogel considers that, prior to the commercial and industrial revolution, the majority of all human beings lived in hydraulic civilizations.

Especially in the past half century, however, with developments in equipment and technology, man has been able to modify the water environment with progressively increasing thoroughness and complexity. By dams, he creates reservoirs that can provide dependable water supplies as he needs them, in spite of fluctuations in natural sources. By deep wells and turbines he withdraws large quantities of ground water. By pipelines and pumps he transports water over distances of hundreds of miles. By various processes he treats waste waters so as to make them reusable, and he demineralizes sea water or other saline water. By drainage systems he reclaims swamps and waterlogged lands, and by levees or barriers he prevents water from entering places where it is not wanted. By landfills he has made dry land out of natural water bodies, and by various techniques he has prevented erosion by water. Today we can state that water of a specified quality can be made available at any point on earth, provided someone is able and willing to pay the cost.

The cost of water is related to other considerations--its value to the user, and the uses to which it is put. Many uses are consumptive: water is boiled away, evaporated, absorbed and transpired by plants. Many other uses are nonconsumptive, so that the water remains after its use, but polluted with dissolved, suspended, or floating materials, and thus deteriorated in some quality by its use. Different water uses do not all require water of the same quality: one can flush toilets with water unfit to bathe in, bathe in water unfit to drink, and drink water that would be unsatisfactory for use in boilers. On the other hand, one can purify water until a fish can't live in it, or soften water until it is poorly suited for irrigation. However, the consumer generally has far less choice as to quality of water than he has as to gasoline and oil for his car. For reasons of economy, all the water comes into a consumer's house in the same pipe, so that he drinks the same water that he uses to flush toilets--it all must meet the drinking water standards of the Public Health Service. Also for reasons of economy, our culture does not adequately provide for treatment of water that has deteriorated from nonconsumptive use. Many of us count on nature to take care of our raw sewage and industrial wastes, and even where we have sewage treatment, it generally removes only 85 to 95 per cent of the suspended solids and 90 to 98 per cent of the bacteria.

So far as most users are concerned, water is a commodity whose value depends upon its peculiar properties: its heat capacity, its surface tension, its density, its mobility, and its capability as a universal solvent.[8] Quality of the water supplied is important to the user, but the source of the supply is not: it is immaterial whether the water comes from a well, spring, lake, cistern, stream, or demineralization plant, nearby or remote. Thus, for most users, water is a utility comparable to electricity, and their concerns with water are those having to do with the supplying of it in the quantity and quality to meet their needs.

Other users depend upon water in its natural environment, perhaps without using the water as a commodity, as in fishing, hunting, bird-watching, boating, painting, photography, skiing on snow or water, touring, or camping or housing in a scenic area. These users are especially concerned with conservation of the water and its natural environment.

WATER ECONOMICS

A cost-and-benefits analysis of water use is likely to be somewhat subjective, depending upon who is to pay the costs, who is expected to receive the benefits, and their relation to the analyst. Even with rules, checks and balances to assure a maximum of objectivity, there may not be true freedom of choice concerning water uses, because of limitations in funds or other capabilities. Also, in weighing the various plus and minus factors, the scales may be tilted by traditions, rights, and taboos--the conventional wisdom that we have inherited from the past.

Present water laws and customs vary considerably from state to state and from nation to nation, but many of them reflect the environment in which they originated.[9] Where water is most abundant, as in rivers, the commonly accepted doctrine is as expressed by Justinian in 534 A.D. in his "Classification of Things," where he asserted that, by natural law, air, running water, the sea, and the shores of the sea are common to all. In humid regions, water is commonly recognized as appurtenant to the land, and therefore available especially to the landowners to use if and as they desire. By contrast, in arid regions, the first to discover water and use it is commonly protected from encroachment by others, although, in recognition of the essentiality of water to life, the "right of thirst" may be paramount. Much of the Moslem world is in arid regions, and for it the prophet Mohammed declared that free access to water was the right of all in the Moslem community.

Today there are still numerous regions where fresh water is sufficiently abundant that it can be treated as a commodity whose only cost is the small charge for delivery to the user; it is also sufficiently abundant that it can dilute human wastes and make them harmless to others, or so that others can find pure sources and avoid polluted waters. But there are many other places where, because of increasing population and increasing per capita use, water abundance has become water scarcity, while the traditions of abundance linger on in the minds of the people.

The oceans represent an inexhaustible resource of water, particularly for the millions of people who live in coastal areas, but the salt must be removed if it is to be usable. Man has made considerable progress in this, and can now, by any one of several processes, demineralize water at a cost of about $1.00 per 1,000 gallons. For gasoline, milk, cooking oil, or whiskey we would consider one-tenth of a cent per gallon to be a negligible charge for purifying so that it is suitable for our use. But fresh water has everywhere been so abundant and so cheap that demineralization seems economically infeasible. But as we hear the cry "water shortage" increasingly in the future, we may find that the shortage is more truly in our ability or willingness to pay the costs of purification, whether of sea water, inland brackish water, sewage, or industrial waste, than in any actual lack of water. Economics thus becomes a dominant factor--whether the value of a product or service that depends upon the use of water of a specified quality is sufficient to compensate for the cost of providing it.

In water matters we might mark our present culture as a period of adolescence for mankind. No longer "children of nature" closely controlled by our environment, we are now attempting increasingly to control the environment, but have not fully accepted the responsibility for our modifications. By careful observation of our environment through the ages, confirmed in recent years by scientific research, the balance of nature has been well documented: individual species of plants and animals are in balance with each other and with their environment, although admittedly the balance depends in part upon climatic factors, which may make it rather delicate and even precarious. However, insofar as water is concerned, the natural balance seems to be chiefly a creation of man. Whether considered at a specific time over a geographic area, or at a specific point during a longer period of time, nature shows fluctuations in temperature, humidity, precipitation, wind velocity, and other factors that control the water supply. In many parts of the world, a century of record shows series of wetter years (readily accepted in the popular mind as "normal") and intervening series of drier years (popularly labelled "droughts"). All that nature maintains is its right to be unpredictable, as shown by these fluctuations and the variety of climatic conditions. It is man who measures these fluctuations, computes averages, identifies the "balance," and thus can conclude, for instance, that he is working in a "20-inch rainfall zone." But his actions speak louder than his words: many of his activities are directed toward changing the "balance" of nature, and achieving a regular supply of water, as befits his continuing needs.

Water occurs in flow systems which under natural conditions achieve a dynamic equilibrium. Each flow system may include surface water, soil water, and ground water, and it has definable physical boundaries. Each continent has many independent or quasi-independent flow systems of this kind. (In addition, there is an atmospheric flow system, which is world-wide.) In each system there are short-period changes in water storage, because of climatic fluctuations, but over sufficiently long periods these changes become insignificant, and there is an overall balance between inflow and outflow--in other words, a "steady state" is achieved. Anything man does to a flow system upsets this balance and induces an "unsteady state" that changes with time. An "unsteady state" can be induced by artificial storage of water, diversion, drainage, consumptive or nonconsumptive use, and especially by pumping from wells. Eventually--if sufficient time is allowed--the flow system will achieve a new equilibrium, but necessarily different from that existing prior to the artificial development, because that developmental feature has become incorporated in the flow system.

It would appear that the general goal of water development for the public good can be achieved by salvaging water that is naturally wasting to the ocean or to the atmosphere, and making beneficial use of it. But an adequate analysis of water development projects involves far more than a comparison of the costs of the structures, land, and labor involved in the projects with the benefits derived from the water that is made available. A dam, for instance, may regulate the flow of a river and create a reservoir that provides dependable water supplies on demand. But the reservoir also collects the sediment and dissolved salts and organic nutrients that the river naturally might have discharged into an ocean; there may be substantial water loss by evaporation from the reservoir; the land occupied by the reservoir is lost to other uses such as forests and wildlife, as well as to agriculture, even though it may have fertile, alluvial soil; and use of the water for irrigation may create problems such as water-logging, accumulation of soluble salts in the soil, or shallow ground water. Clearly, a thorough analysis should include an evaluation of the effects of a water development program upon an entire flow system over a period of many years or decades.

Fortunately, we are learning, from experience and especially from research, how to predict the long-term effects of proposed modifications in the existing equilibrium. Admittedly, we need far more information than we now have about most flow systems if we are to make accurate predictions of the effects of proposed developments, and, undoubtedly, a couple of decades from now our successors will look back on our present understanding as primitive and elementary. Nevertheless, our present capabilities for long-range predictions are great enough that they should not be neglected or ignored, but in making policy directed toward the distant future, we should recognize the need for more basic data, and foster the research needed for more detailed and accurate analysis.

A complicating factor in our analysis of flow systems, and the one that we know least about, is the ground water in storage, and its relation to the rest of the hydrologic flow system. Our conventional wisdom tells us that, if we are to maintain the "balance of nature," we should limit our withdrawals of ground water to the quantities that can be replaced annually. But the total volume stored underground and available to wells is several times larger than the volume of annual precipitation.[10] In numerous areas throughout the world, but especially within the United States, this accumulated storage is being depleted progressively, and since the withdrawn water is not fully replenished, the withdrawal is an extraction or "mining" comparable to that of petroleum, iron, coal, or other mineral resources. Although such mining of ground water is generally deplored, it has been defended in several areas, notably in Los Angeles, where it was essential in the initial development of an economy that soon became strong enough that it could afford to reach out to Owens Valley and subsequently to the Colorado River for additional water.

WATER POLICY IN TUNISIA

In central Tunisia, bordered by the Mediterranean Sea and also by the Sahara Desert, the use of ground-water resources poses problems in economics and also in public policy and philosophy. L. C. Dutcher and H. E. Thomas[11] summarize the situation as follows: Throughout most of central Tunisia the average precipitation, even during the winter "rainy" season, is less than the potential return of water to the atmosphere by evapotranspiration. Thus the climate is one of prevailing water deficiency. All the water that can be of beneficial use to man must come from the momentary surpluses from rainstorms, and it must be stored somewhere until he needs it. Since soil moisture and all surface waters are subject to loss by evapotranspiration, ground-water reservoirs constitute the prime places for any such storage over long periods. Some ground-water reservoirs have a perennial yield, because there is continuing or intermittent replenishment. Many of these perennial supplies are being used, and have been used since ancient times; others are not of usable water, or are so dispersed that suitable means have not been employed to collect them for use. But all ground-water reservoirs contain stored water in quantities far greater than the average annual replenishment, and several of these, with large volumes in storage, have a rate of replenishment so small as to be negligible.

The prevailing philosophy of water management in Tunisia is that the ground-water resource should not be depleted--that is, the "safe yield" should not be exceeded, and the bilan d'eau should be maintained. The value of this philosophy* should not

---

*The authors realize that any suggestions they might make con-

be questioned in a region that has supported several civilizations
over several thousands of years, and all of them able to rely upon
perennial supplies of water. In this region where mankind has depleted and lost other renewable resources, including fertile soil,
forests, grasslands, and wildlife, these continuing water supplies
are a refreshing contrast.

Nevertheless, it is fundamental that in the development of
any ground-water reservoir the first stage of development involves
some depletion. The water serves no human purpose until it is
pumped out for use. True, once the water is pumped out, it is gone
and unavailable for future generations, but perhaps the present
generation needs it most. Much of the ground water has been unavailable to previous generations because it was at depths too
great for them to obtain it. It may be unwanted by a future generation that perfects the means for economical desalinization of
sea water, which is an inexhaustible supply bordering the Sahel
coastal strip. It is something of value to the present generation,
with its technology in well drilling, pumping, and distribution
facilities, if it helps develop an economy that can eventually afford the costs of desalinization of sea water, particularly in the
coastal communities where the Mediterranean is most accessible.

There is of course an element of risk in thus depleting
ground-water resources: the risk that the economic productivity
of the region will not rise fast enough, or that the costs of desalinization will not fall fast enough, to justify the changeover
before the ground water has been exhausted.

WATER POLICY IN ISRAEL

Israel, also on the Mediterranean, has been one of the
first countries to adopt and implement a comprehensive water policy
based on a nationwide master plan, and for good reason, even though
this policy severely restricts the freedom of action of the individual water user. As described by Aaron Wiener and Abel Wolman,[12]
Israel is semi-arid in the north and arid in the south, and its
arable land and water resources are extremely scarce: about 25
per cent of its land is arable, and the potential water resources
are sufficient to irrigate only about 40 per cent of that. In
the ten years prior to 1961, Israel's economic growth has been ex-
plosive: its population has nearly doubled, its gross national
product nearly trebled, its water use quadrupled, and its area of
irrigated lands quintupled. Similar growth is expected in the

---

cerning modification of this philosophy might be taken as evidence
of the myopic vision of Americans, who have depleted all their resources substantially in less than two centuries.

future, with annual increases of four per cent in population, seven per cent in agricultural production, and ten per cent in industrial production. But against these ambitious economic targets stands the shortage of water.

About 80 per cent of Israel's present water supply comes from wells and springs, and 20 per cent from rivers. Of the average annual ground-water replenishment, an estimated 20 per cent still discharges from the aquifers into the sea, and nearly all the rest is already being utilized. The principal hopes for additional water to meet expanding requirements are: (1) diversions from the Jordan River, a politically hot proposal because the drainage basin of the river also includes parts of Syria, Lebanon, and Jordan; (2) recharging and storage underground of water from flash floods; (3) reclamation, underground storage, and reuse of sewage and industrial waste water; and (4) reduction of ground-water discharge to the sea. Israel's master water plan envisages developments by 1970 that will achieve the full potential of these resources--about a 50 per cent increase over current water use. A major problem will be quality control: the Jordan River water is inferior to most of the ground water, each reuse of water results in some increase of mineral content, and there is danger of seawater encroachment. After the fresh-water resources have been utilized to the fullest, as contemplated in the plan during the present decade, the salt water of the Mediterranean can be demineralized for use, and it is likely that this will be done, even though the cost of water becomes greater than at present. There is also the hope that weather modification techniques will have progressed far enough to increase the rainfall artificially. It is noteworthy that, according to Israel's water law of 1959, all water resources, including ground and surface waters, impounded water, drainage water, and municipal and industrial wastes, are public property and under government control. Thus water service can be operated as an integrated public utility.

The examples of Tunisia and Israel suggest some of the problems of utilization of water as a commodity. These problems involve not only immediate costs and benefits, but the costs and benefits to future generations, and thus may be of especial concern to conservationists. But they are essentially economic problems, and such problems should eventually be solved by the play of forces inherent in the market place. Water will be used in those places and for those purposes which can best afford to bear the cost under prevailing conditions.

WATER CONSERVATION

I have reserved the phrase "water conservation" for part

of what Teilhard de Chardin has included in his "spiritual component" of culture, and for what the rest of us might call "that in-
definable something" which we gain by communing with nature. In
resource development it is sometimes possible to achieve or maintain such benefits by ingenuity and awareness of the possibilities,
at no great monetary cost. I saw a good example of this in Tsavo
National Park in Kenya. Mzima Springs discharge large quantities
of clear water, which forms a beautiful pool for hippopotami and
other wild life, but within a few miles joins a sediment-laden
stream and continues to the Indian Ocean. The springs are the best
source of water for the city of Mombasa on the coast, but to tap
them by means of a dam and diversion works would ruin the springs'
environment. Therefore an infiltration gallery was constructed to
intercept some of the water before it reached the springs, and a
pipeline provides Mombasa with water that had formerly wasted to
the sea, without disturbing the natural vegetation and wildlife
sustained by the springs.

Sometimes efforts at conservation of other natural resources have side effects upon the water resources. Since the
Queen Elizabeth Park was established in Uganda, the hippopotami
have enjoyed the protection afforded, have learned to multiply
rapidly, and have become a major tourist attraction along the Ka-
zinga Channel which empties into Lake George. All day long the
hippos use the waters for bathing and recreation; hence, the nutrients in Lake George have increased significantly, so have the
algae, and the end of the food chain--the tilapia fish--is of major
economic benefit, for Lake George has one of the highest natural
productivity rates known anywhere in the world--about 120 kilograms
of fish per hectare or 135 pounds per acre.[13] However, at night
the hippos go foraging up the small valleys for as far as eight
miles from the water, taking the grasses most desired by the plains
animals, leaving nothing and accelerating erosion. Hence it has
been deemed desirable to "crop" the hippos: several are butchered
each month and sold to the native population, whose diet is otherwise deficient in proteins. Thus, in the conservation of an environment in which water is an important part, we see a variety of
interrelated economic costs and benefits.

According to a recent survey,[14] nutrients may be on the
verge of creating a similar problem in Lake Tahoe in California
and Nevada, but here it is the humans who are multiplying and are
the contributing factor. In many ways Lake Tahoe is unique among
the world's lakes: it is one of the highest (6,225 feet above
sea level), one of the deepest (average 990 feet), and only Crater
Lake in Oregon and Lake Baikal in Russia rival it in clarity of
water. Lake Tahoe is uniquely situated in a climate which makes
possible its year-round use as a recreational center, and is in a
region which has special recreational value. However, as the population increases within the tributary basin, the use of water increases apace, and about 70 per cent of the water will soon be

converted into sewage. Standard ("complete") treatment, or ground disposal (by septic tanks) will eliminate the organic components, but the mineral constituents, particularly nitrates and phosphates, will remain and eventually reach the lake, where they will become the nutrients that could generate a population explosion of algae and other plankton. Already the amount of nutrients produced from human activity is of the same magnitude as the contribution from natural sources. Thus, although present methods of disposal are adequate for protection of public health, the Lake Tahoe Area Council concludes that if the clarity of the water is to be preserved, it will be necessary either to transport the sewage effluents from the watershed, or remove the chemical nutrients from these effluents before they are disposed of within the watershed. Ironically, the nutrients that can be detrimental to the unique quality of Lake Tahoe are tolerable and even beneficial for some other uses of water.

CONCLUSION

In Teilhard de Chardin's "material component" of culture, water serves generally as a commodity or utility, a means to an end. As a natural resource, water flows in well-ordered systems; we can and do modify them to the benefit of mankind. Generally, water requirements can be met by various possible methods of development, and the choice can be made on the basis of analysis of the benefits and costs of each alternative. If we do not limit our analysis too narrowly--if we consider all the area, all the people, and all the time that will be affected by any proposed development--the choice based on economic analysis may be in accord with the aim of conservation to improve the quality of life in our own generation as well as in succeeding generations.

In many places water is in a natural environment that has an aesthetic appeal which adds to the quality of life, or to Teilhard de Chardin's "spiritual component" of culture, and there the water becomes an end in itself rather than a means to an end. Preservation of these environments may be possible even with development of the water for use, but at increased costs. Or the alternatives may be so restricted that one is forced to a choice between beauty and utility. Generally the aesthetic values cannot be quantified and placed on the scale with other costs and benefits in an economic analysis, although this is not strictly true everywhere: in regions whose prime attributes are scenic beauty or opportunities for recreation, such as Lake Tahoe, the aesthetic values can be quantified to some extent, at least by realtors, in increased property values. And if we must in the future be governed by computer logic, we may eventually replace comparisons of dollar values by a comparison of the man-hours spent in aesthetic and philosophical contemplation and general relaxation with the man-hours spent in contributing to the gross national product.

BENEFITS AND COSTS OF WATER CONSERVATION

In any case, the conservation of the intangible values will doubtless depend upon the degree of our affluence. Contemplation of natural beauty is likely to be at a minimum when one is looking for the next meal, after missing several, but such contemplation grows more important, to individuals and to nations, as they accumulate sufficient wealth to permit such indulgences.

NOTES

[1] L. B. Leopold, "Water and the Conservation Movement," U.S. Geological Survey Circular, 402 (1958), pp. 1-6.

[2] Ecology of Man in the Tropical Environment (Morges, Switzerland: 1964). [Ninth Technical Meeting of the International Union for the Conservation of Nature, Nairobi, 1963; proceedings and papers.]

[3] Pierre Teilhard de Chardin, "The Antiquity and World Expansion of Human Culture," in Wm. L. Thomas, Jr., ed., Man's Role in Changing the Face of the Earth (Chicago: University of Chicago Press, 1956), p. 106.

[4] T. A. Bettersworth, Aesthetics in Providing Electric Service to Urban and Suburban Areas (Salt Lake City: 1964). [American Society of Civil Engineers Environmental Engineering Conference.]

[5] R. L. Nace, "Water of the World," Natural History, LXXIII, 1 (1964), pp. 10-19.

[6] L. B. Leopold, "Rivers," American Scientist, L (1962), pp. 511-37.

[7] "The Hydraulic Civilizations," in Wm. L. Thomas, Jr., ed., op. cit., p. 153 (see note 3).

[8] K. S. Davis and J. A. Day, Water: The Mirror of Science (New York: Doubleday and Co., 1961).

[9] H. E. Thomas, Cultural Control of Water Development (San Francisco: 1963), mimeo. [African Studies Association Meeting.]

[10] H. E. Thomas and L. B. Leopold, "Ground Water in North America," Science, CXLIII (1964), pp. 1001-06. See also H. E. Thomas, "Changes in Quantities and Qualities of Ground and Surface Waters, in Wm. L. Thomas, Jr., ed., op. cit., pp. 542-63 (see note 3).

[11] Climate and Surface-Water Features of the Sahel de Sousse, Tunisia. U.S. Geological Survey Water-Supply Paper 1757-E (in preparation).

[12] "Formulation of National Water Resources Policy in Israel," _Journal of the American Water Works Association_, LIV (1962), pp. 257-63.

[13] E. B. Worthington, "Inland Waters," in _op. cit._, pp. 183-89 (see note 2).

[14] _Comprehensive Study on Protection of Water Resources of Lake Tahoe Basin through Controlled Waste Disposal_ (Lake Tahoe Area Council, Board of Consultants, 1963).

SOME PRELIMINARY OBSERVATIONS ON THE ECOLOGY OF A SMALL MAN-MADE LAKE IN TROPICAL AFRICA

by

John D. Thomas

INTRODUCTION

Freshwater systems in tropical Africa have received less attention from biologists than their counterparts in the temperate regions of the world. The majority of investigations in Africa to date have been concerned with the limnology of the great African lakes,[1] the systematics and biology of their fish fauna,[2] and the ecology of the great papyrus swamps in the vicinity of the lakes.[3] Very few studies have been made on lotic habitats[4] and man-made lakes or ponds.[5]

During the colonial era there were few man-made lakes and farm ponds in tropical Africa, but recent emphasis on development has resulted in an increase in the rate of dam construction. In addition to the large-scale impoundments such as the Kariba dam, the Aswan high dam, and the Volta dam, numerous small reservoirs and farm ponds are also being built. The uses for such reservoirs are as follows: (a) source of hydroelectric power for industrial and domestic consumption, (b) source of water for human consumption and industrial purposes, (c) flood and erosion control, (d) water supply for domestic stock, (e) irrigation of crops, (f) fish production, (g) means of transport, and (h) landscape enhancement and sport. Certain of these uses are particularly important in tropical Africa. First, the dearth of locally-produced fuel makes it necessary to harness hydroelectric power to make new industries competitive. Second, the intensity of rainfall in the tropics may be very high (up to 8 inches per hour and 17 inches per day have been recorded in Ghana),[6] and it is therefore important to have dams to control flooding and erosion. Third, being equatorial, the climate has a rainy season with a double or single peak with intervening dry periods when water must be available for both crop and animal production. Fourth, fish production is necessary because over much of Africa the indigenous people suffer from kwashiorkor, a disease caused by protein deficiency which results in ill health and a high infant mortality rate.

No statistics are presently available regarding the rate of dam construction in tropical Africa, but it is noteworthy that in somewhat comparable ecosystems in the United States, reservoirs and farm ponds have become a major feature of the landscape.

Aerial View of Nungua Reservoir

J. S. Dendy estimates that, in Texas and Oklahoma alone, there are approximately 341,000 and 250,000 farm ponds, respectively, and in certain states ponds are being constructed at the rate of about 1,000 a year.[7] Although this rate of development cannot be achieved in Africa at the present moment, it is certain that the construction of reservoirs, particularly large ones such as the future Volta lake, will have a major impact on the ecology of the savanna areas in Africa.

Some aspects of the ecology of such water bodies are of considerable academic importance. These include the kinds of plant and animal community structures encountered, the species diversity, the annual cyclical changes that take place in the physicochemical components, the plant producers, the primary and secondary consumers, trophic structures, and production at the various trophic levels. Information of this kind is clearly necessary for the management of such water bodies for fish production and to enable control measures to be taken against the growth of undesirable aquatic weeds and the vectors of parasites. Water is an essential component of the ecosystem of some of the most important human and animal parasites, some of which are listed in Table 3 (see page 136). It is well known that these parasites contribute to the ill health of man and domestic animals in tropical Africa, and the resultant morbidity and mortality has been one of the major factors in retarding the development of this part of Africa.[8]

The ecological investigation of Nungua reservoir, a summary of which is given below, was initiated in 1958 as a result of the above general considerations, by the declared intention of the Ghana government to proceed with the Volta dam project, and by the need to develop the teaching of ecology at the University of Ghana. The investigation was planned as a general survey to include observations on the cyclical changes in the physicochemical components, the plant producers, the primary consumers, the secondary consumers, and the helminth fauna of the fishes. A full report, including the methods used, will be given in a series of papers to be published later.

TOPOGRAPHY

The Nungua reservoir is situated on the grounds of the University of Ghana agricultural research station at Nungua in the Accra plains of southern Ghana (5.41 N., 0.07 W.) at an altitude of approximately 70 feet. It was completed in March, 1954, by the construction of an earth wall, 1460 feet long, across the bed of the Mamahuma, a small, intermittent stream which drains into the Sakumo lagoon near Tema. Prior to the construction of the dam, the stream was reduced to a few small, discontinuous pools during the dry season.

THE ECOLOGY OF A SMALL MAN-MADE LAKE IN TROPICAL AFRICA

The reservoir, which is triangular in shape (see Fig. 1), is about 4691 feet long and 1525 feet broad at its base when full. At the time of the investigation, its maximum area was about 107 acres (43 hectares) and its maximum capacity was 750 acre feet, but these have since increased. The catchment area of 25 square miles is characterized by soils of three main types, including regosilic groundwater laterites, tropical grey earths, and tropical black earths. Such soils are rich in aluminum and iron and poor in one or another of the biologically important elements, particularly nitrogen and phosphorus.[9] Tall trees are widely dispersed, and the thicket for the most part occurs along the drainage lines or on active or abandoned Macrotermes mounds which are often scattered with some regularity in short or medium-sized perennial grasses. These grasses are tussocky, covering at most about 25 per cent of the soil surface, and are subject to burning more than once a year. Crop production in the catchment area is negligible except in the region of the research station, and the area is used mainly for cattle production.

Three stations--A, B, and C--were selected for detailed studies of the fauna and the physicochemical environment. In the present account, only A, situated on the southern shore of the reservoir, and C, a small fish pond supplied with water from the main reservoir, are considered.

PHYSICOCHEMICAL ENVIRONMENT

(1) Water level, area, and volume: When the dam is at full capacity, the water is 15 feet deep at its deepest point. Changes in volume are, of course, governed by the rates of intake and loss, the former being determined by rainfall and runoff rate. In the coastal savanna, there are typically two rainy seasons occasioned by the northward and southward movements of the intertropical convergence zones. The principal rainy season reaches its maximum in May and June and the subsidiary one in October, although the latter is sometimes scarcely in evidence (see Fig. 2). After the main rains in May and June, the reservoir fills to capacity and thereafter decreases in volume until the onset of the next major rains. Most of the water appears to be lost by evaporation, which is about 6.4 feet per year; little is used for irrigation, and seepage losses are negligible. The small rains in October do not contribute much water to the reservoir, probably because most of the precipitation at this time is used up in ground water recharge and evapotranspiration.

Volume changes in 1958-59 and 1959 to March, 1960, were up to 650 and 370 acre feet, respectively. In consequence of the gently undulating topography so characteristic of much of the savanna, the area of the reservoir varied from 91 to 26 acres (37 to 10.5 hectares) in 1958-59 and from 91 to 57 acres (37 to 23 hect-

116

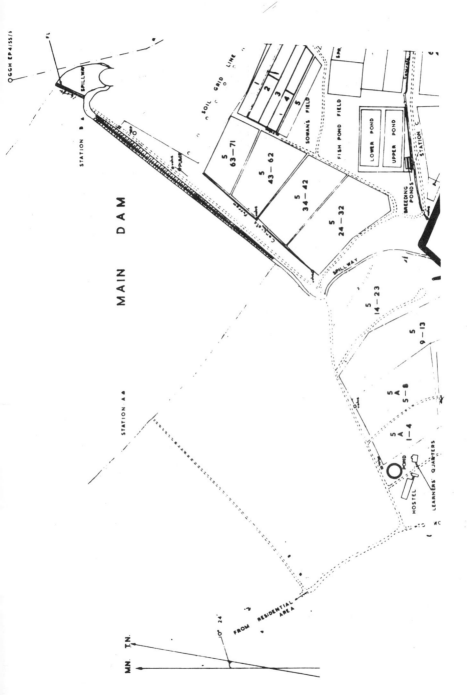

FIGURE 1. Nungua Reservoir, Showing Locations of Stations A, B, and C

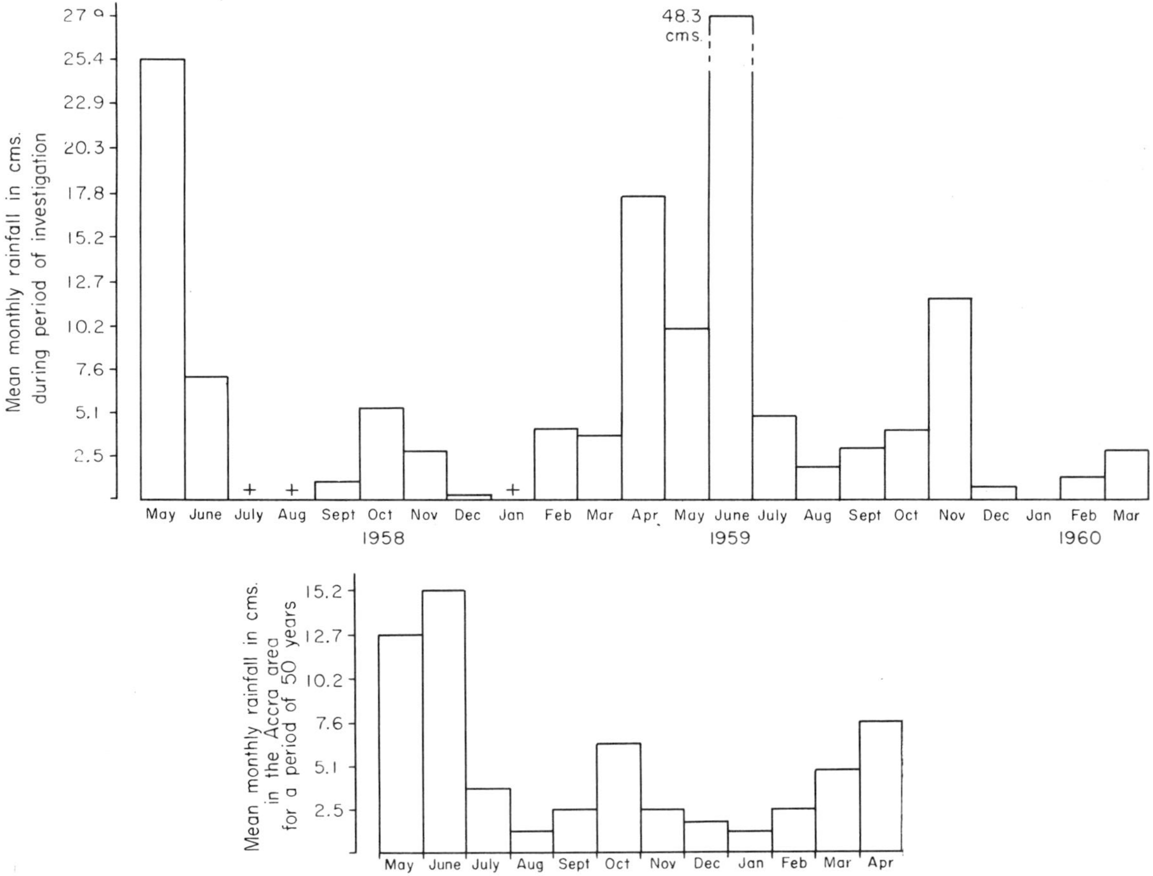

FIGURE 2. Monthly Rainfall Pattern at Nungua Reservoir

ares) in 1959-60. The flood zone is, therefore, very extensive.
(Natural water bodies occurring in areas where rainfall is seasonal
and the evaporation high may also have relatively large flood
zones.)[10] It is clear that a seasonal change of this magnitude
in reservoir area constitutes a major ecological factor.

(2) Chemistry: The result of a chemical analysis expressed
in mg./l., undertaken in April when the water in the reservoir was
concentrated as a result of evaporation, was as follows:

Carbonate (CO_3)	24.6	Magnesium (Mg)	4.6
Sulphate (SO_4)	2.3	Sodium (Na)	8.8
Nitrous nitrogen (NO_2)	0.001	Dissolved iron (Fe)	1.5
Nitric nitrogen (NO_3)	0.25	Alkalinity	41
Chlorides (Cl)	7.5	pH	7.3
Phosphates (P_2O_5)	< 0.02	Total dissolved solids	168
Calcium (Ca)	6.8		

Conductivity values of up to 214 reciprocal megohms were
noted during the dry season. Both the total concentration of dissolved solids and the conductivity, which have been shown to be
close correlates, are useful parameters in assessing water fertility and production. On the basis of these two measurements, it
would appear from data given by G. K. Reid[11] and M. I. van der
Lingen[12] that Nungua reservoir contains an average amount of mineral matter during the summer. Thus, Reid states that most lakes
occupying open basins have 100-200 ppm dissolved solids. However,
much of the conductivity is due to dissolved bicarbonate salts
and, as pointed out by the East African Fisheries Research Organization annual report for 1954-55, the true status of water regarding the biologically valuable nutrients is obtained when the
conductivity due to alkalinity (bicarbonate salts) is subtracted
from total conductivity. One such calculation based on data obtained from the reservoir in December was as follows: conductivity 110, alkalinity expressed as conductivity 64, difference 46.
This value is fairly high, and, of nine African water bodies described by van der Lingen, it was exceeded by only two. It would
appear that, on this basis, a high level of primary production
might be expected during the dry season. The sulphur was unexpectedly high, for as R. S. A. Beauchamp[13] and M. J. Holden and
J. Green[14] have shown, sulphur is often in short supply in African waters. With the exception of phosphorus, none of the other
biologically important components occur in very low concentrations.
It must be noted, however, that the method used to measure phosphorus in the present investigation was not very sensitive, and
it cannot be stated, therefore, that its absence was limiting production. According to F. Ruttner, plankton algae can utilize in-
organic phosphorus in concentrations of less than 1/1000 mg.,[15]
and, furthermore, phosphorus often disappears in a few days after
being added to water in consequence of the ability of plankton
and littoral vegetation to absorb and store it quickly.[16] The fact

that soil and even grasses in the catchment area contain very small quantities of phosphorus[17] suggests, however, that a deficiency of phosphorus might be one of the factors limiting production.

With the onset of the wet season, important changes take place in the chemistry of the water. As a result of the rapid runoff, the water becomes diluted, and between April and May, 1959, the conductivity fell from 214 to 100 reciprocal megohms. During this time, the values of oxygen absorbed from potassium permanganate (in 3 hrs. at 37°C.) increased from 7.5 to 14.9 and those of nitrate nitrogen from 0.09 to 0.25 mg./l. The increase in permanganate values can be attributed to an increase in the quantity of oxidizable organic matter, including that brought in by runoff or trapped in the flood zone. In consequence of the high water temperature, decomposition of the excess oxidizable organic matter is rapid, and by the middle of June, the permanganate values had returned to normal. A much greater increase of from 11.0 to 42.0 in permanganate values was noted by H. Kleerkoper following the flooding of a Brazilian reservoir.[18] The smaller increase in oxidizable organic matter at Nungua reservoir after flooding can be attributed to the activities of farm animals in cropping the herbaceous plants in the flood zones and also to the frequent burning that takes place in the catchment area. Some nitrate may have been brought in by rainwater,[19] but it seems more probable that the increase is mainly attributable to an increase in the rate of nitrification by bacteria following inundation of the flood zone.

(3) Oxygen content: There are some interesting contrasts between the diurnal oxygen curves for Stations A and C. At Station A, after the onset of the big rains in July, there was a deficit of between 27 to 53 per cent in dissolved oxygen at all depths, although there also was evidence of a diurnal swing as a result of photosynthetic activity. The occurrence of a deficit in oxygen, even during the day, can be attributed to the fact that it is being used to oxidize the allochthonous organic matter. Near the shoreline, and in all probability throughout the reservoir, oxygen was present at all depths, and the fact that oxygen values were higher nearer the bottom than at the surface seems to refute the theory that oxygen is removed from the water while it is passing over the bottom mud as a result of wind-induced horizontal circulation. The oxygen deficits at Station C during the wet season (ranging from 74 to 97 per cent) were even greater than those of Station A, but even here there was a slight increase during the day that could be attributed to photosynthetic activity. Although the allochthonous organic matter would be partly responsible for the very low oxygen values at this station, it seems probable that the presence of a dense growth of water lily, Nymphaea, is mainly responsible, for the following reasons: first, a dense growth of such vegetation reduces the amount of light entering the water and, thus, severely limits the photosynthetic activity of the

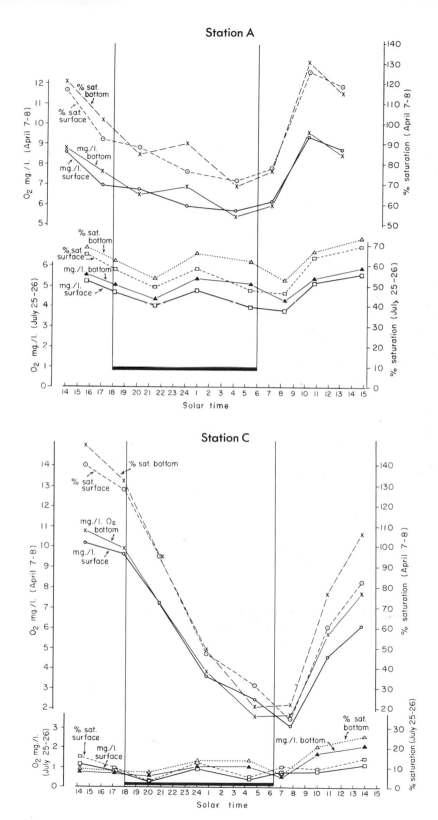

FIGURE 3. The Diurnal Oxygen Curves at Stations A and C in April (Dry Season) and in July (Wet Season)

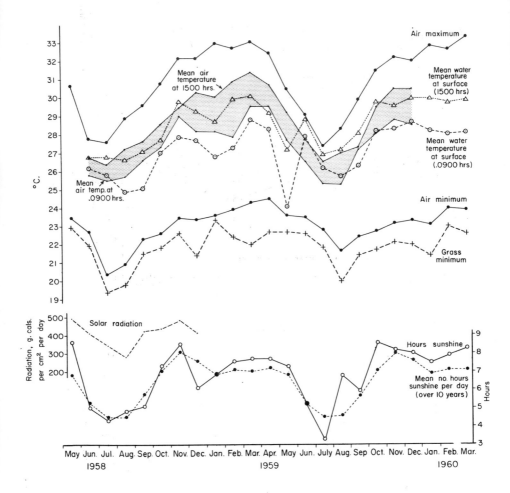

FIGURE 4. The Seasonal Cycles in Air and Water Temperature
and in Solar Radiation

phytoplankton; second, by reducing the effectiveness of wind action, the vegetation reduces the amount of oxygen diffusing in from the surface; and third, such plants would contribute an appreciable amount of autochthonous organic matter which would require oxygen when decomposing. E. M. O. Laurie and G. R. Fish have also shown that aquatic plants reduce oxygen to below the level at which it would stand in their absence.[20]

In contrast to the observations made during the wet season, those made in April during the dry season reveal that the water is supersaturated with oxygen during the day at both stations as a result of intense photosynthetic activity by the phytoplankton. Very little oxygen appears to be used in oxidizing organic matter at Station A during this period, and although some is being utilized at Station C, the values are less than those in the wet season. It must be noted, however, that the dry season values at Station C were obtained after the completion of the faunistic sampling and are atypical, as the pond was drained and fertilizers added shortly before the measurements were made. In consequence, the growth of Nymphaea had been impaired and that of the phytoplankton enhanced.

(4) Temperature: The annual cycle in solar radiation and in the number of hours of sunshine per day is followed fairly closely by the water temperature. This is to be expected, since water is heated mainly by solar radiation, although some heat may be gained by water condensation and by transference of heat from the air or from the bottom. The temperatures are higher during the dry season from November to April or May than during the wet season from June to October. The highest water temperature of 32.8°C. was recorded in March and the lowest of 20.6°C. in April after heavy rain. The highest mean temperature of 30.1°C. occurred in March and the lowest mean temperature of 24°C. in May. After continuous rain in April, the water temperature declined by 10°C. over a two-day period, but after another nineteen days, it had returned to a more normal level. A temperature stratification develops during the day. The stratification does not, however, extend to the north shore of the reservoir, where there is a great deal of turbulence as a result of the action of the prevailing wind. As in other tropical water bodies, the differences between the water temperatures at the surface and at the bottom are small, rarely exceeding 3°C. As a result of nocturnal cooling and wind action, isothermal mixing appears to take place nightly, and the water remains unstratified until about 10.0 hours. Isothermal mixing appears to be a common occurrence in tropical water bodies in Africa. J. F. Talling observed it to take place in 10 m of water in Gebel Aulia reservoir in the Sudan and in 8 m at Pilkington Bay, Lake Victoria.[21] According to E. B. Worthington and F. Gessner, it also occurs in much larger bodies of water to a depth of 20 m.[22] The cooling of the surface water often results in a temperature inversion in areas protected from wind. The diurnal change in sur-

face water temperature follows the air temperature fairly closely, although there is a time lag. The maximum diurnal swing during the dry season was 5.2°C. and 5.8°C. at Stations A and C, respectively. In contrast, the maximum diurnal swing during the wet season was only 1.4°C. and 1.3°C. at Stations A and C, respectively.

(5) Substratum: According to the Revelle system of classification, the substratum at Station A consists of silty sand and that at Station C of sandy silt. The organic carbon content in the sediments at the two stations was very low and declined to values as low as 0.24 per cent at Station A and 0.35 per cent at Station C during the dry season.

FLORA

(1) Macroflora: At Station C, where the water level was kept constant, much of the water surface was covered continuously with water lilies--Nymphaea maculata and Nymphaea lotus. Other plants which occurred on the margin include Jussiaea repens var. diffusa (Forsk), Enhydra fluctuans Lour., Alternanthera sessilis (L.), and various species of sedges. The contrast between Stations C and A during the height of the dry season is very marked. At this time, the shore line at Station A is completely devoid of aquatic or subaquatic vegetation and is frequented by large numbers of waders, including plovers, sandpipers, and black-winged stilts. With the advent of the rainy season and the inundation of the flood beach, a profuse growth of phanerogamic vegetation develops along the shoreline at Station A. Along the water edge the dominant forms are Jussiaea repens var. diffusa (Forsk), Enhydra fluctuans Lour., Alternanthera sessilis (L.), and various grasses and sedges. The shoots of the former species extend for considerable distances along the surface of the water and are frequently found in association with Pistia stratiotes L., the only aquatic plant to develop in abundance at Station A. Azolla africana has occasionally been found but never appears to become established. Cyperus articulatus L. is very patchily distributed in the flood zone, and although it survives the dry season, it has never become widespread. Following the recession of the water during the dry season, the subaquatic vegetation and Pistia gradually disappear. The free-floating Pistia appears to be peculiarly susceptible to wind action, and considerable quantities of the plants are washed onto the southern shore by the prevailing wind where they are dried by the sun. It is possible that the enormous increase in the amount of phanerogamic vegetation during the wet season is induced by the apparent increase in nitrification and by an increase in the exchange capacity of the substratum for cations such as potassium, sodium, magnesium, and ammonium in the presence of the allochthonous organic matter.

(2) Algae: The algae present included representatives of

the Euglenophyta, Chlorophyta, Chrysophyta, and the Cyanophyta.
Genera found to be seasonally abundant were the following: Trach-
elomonus, Stigeoclonium, and Spirogyra; diatom genera including
Melosira, Synedra, Navicula, Cocconeis, Cocconema, Surirella, and
Pleurosigma; the blue-green algae including Croococcus, Anabaena,
Oscillatoria, and members of the Ribulariaceae. The characteristics of the flora support the generalizations made by F. E.
Fritsch regarding tropical algal flora.[23] The majority of the
genera, particularly those in the Cyanophyta, appear to become
abundant only during the dry season, but as no quantitative collections were made, a more detailed investigation would be necessary to substantiate this theory.

(3) Primary production: The primary production of phytoplankton was estimated by the use of the black and white bot-
tle method and also from the diurnal curves of oxygen by using
the method described by H. T. Odum and C. M. Hoskin.[24] (In the
absence of submerged vegetation at Nungua, the diurnal curve is
influenced only by phytoplankton.) The results are given below.

TABLE 1

PRODUCTIVITY EXPRESSED IN mg./OXYGEN/1.^{3}/DAY ESTIMATED FROM
DIURNAL CHANGES IN OXYGEN CONCENTRATION AND FROM LIGHT AND
DARK BOTTLES

Month	Method	Station A	Station C
April (dry season)	Light and dark bottles	6.7	22.6[*]
April	Diurnal oxygen curve	7.2	20.1
July (wet season)	Light and dark bottles	2.1	1.2[**]
July	Light and dark bottles	3.4	1.5[**]
December (early dry season)	Light and dark bottles	1.7[***]	12.6

[*]After use of fertilizer

[**]Pond covered with water lily

[***]In vicinity of Pistia bed

THE ECOLOGY OF A SMALL MAN-MADE LAKE IN TROPICAL AFRICA

When compared with statistics given by B. J. Copeland and W. R. Whitworth[25] and J. L. Baker[26] for Oklahoma farm ponds and other aquatic habitats, the values obtained during the dry seasons are indicative of a high level of production at the surface. It must be noted, however, that in Nungua lake the primary production is confined to the surface half meter as a result of the low transparency of the water. The limit of light penetration as determined by Secchi's disk varied from 21.6 to 45.7 cms. The exceptionally high values obtained for Station C at this time can be attributed to the effect of fertilizer application and are therefore atypical. During the wet and early part of the dry season, the primary production becomes much lower, particularly in the vicinity of _Pistia_ and _Nymphaea_. The low wet season plankton production figures can be attributed to the following conditions: (a) the water is diluted, and there is a possible deficiency in certain minerals, including phosphorus; (b) bacteria and aquatic plants increase in abundance at this time, and they may be competing with the phytoplankton for minerals in short supply; (c) the floating leaves of _Nymphaea_ and the free-floating _Pistia_ plants reduce the amount of light that becomes available for photosynthesis by the phytoplankton.

FAUNA

The fauna was investigated on both a qualitative and a quantitative basis. The number of species occurring in the various taxa was as follows: Tricladida-0, Hirudinea-2, Oligochaeta-1 Mollusca-8, Crustacea-13+, Plecoptera-0, Ephemeroptera-4, Trichoptera-3, Lepidoptera-2, Odonata-33, Hemiptera-38, Diptera-30+, Coleoptera-65, Pisces-7, Amphibia-12, Reptilia-5, Aves-56. The identifications on which the above statistics are based are complete for most of the animal groups, with the exception of the Chironomidae and the Crustacea. No specific determinations of the Ostracoda and Hydracarina were made.

It is well known that tropical habitats can maintain an inordinately high number of species.[27] A comparison of the present data with that from the temperate zone[28] shows that this appears to be the case with the Coleoptera, Hemiptera, Odonata, and Diptera, but not with the Tricladida, Annelida, Mollusca, Ephemeroptera, and Trichoptera.

A consideration of Fig. 5, which shows the percentage composition of the fauna based on the quantitative samples and expressed in terms of the major taxa, reveals, however, that the taxa which are rich in species need not necessarily be dominant numerically. It is also apparent from Fig. 5 that the composition of the fauna changes seasonally at both stations, but in the present paper only seasonal changes in the vectors of parasites, namely, the Tabanidae, Culicidae, and Mollusca will be discussed.

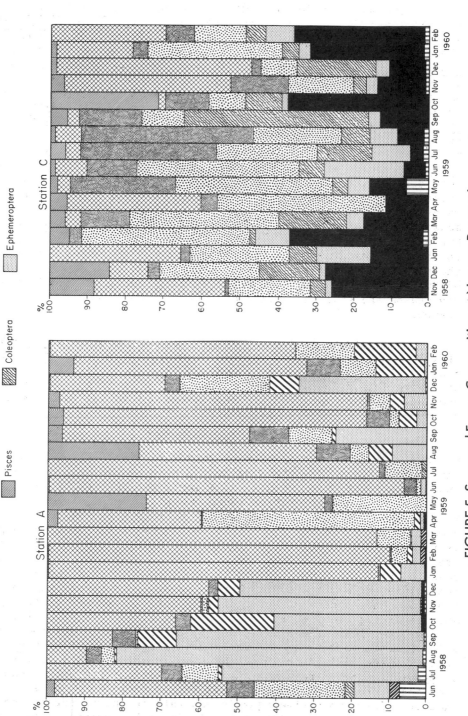

FIGURE 5. Seasonal Fauna Composition at Nungua Reservoir

THE ECOLOGY OF A SMALL MAN-MADE LAKE IN TROPICAL AFRICA

The molluscs found at Station A include Pila africana (von Martens), Melanoides tuberculata (Müller), Limnaea natalensis Krauss, Bulinus (Physopsis) globosus (Morelet), Bulinus forskali (Ehrenberg), Anisus coretus (Blainville), Physa waterloti Germain, Aspatharia (Spathopsis) adansoni (Jousseaume). All the species concerned are rare, seasonal, or patchily distributed and form only an insignificant proportion of the percentage composition of the fauna. In contrast, although only two species, namely, Bulinus (P.) globosus and Melanoides tuberculata, occur at Station C, they form an appreciable proportion of the percentage composition of the fauna (Fig. 5). L. natalensis, B. forskali, A. coretus, and B. (P.) globosus at Station A are normally found only in the presence of aquatic or subaquatic vegetation, either during the wet season or at times during the dry season when the water level remains relatively high. The only molluscs that were not markedly seasonal at Station A were A. (S.) adansoni and M. tuberculata, but as the latter species seemed to be restricted in distribution to the inner margin of the flood zone, it was encountered only in the samples during the dry season. At Station C, the populations of Bulinus (P.) globosus and M. tuberculata declined late in the dry season and started increasing after the onset of the rainy season.

The larvae of insect vectors encountered include Tabanus sp., Mansonia sp., Culex poicilipes, and Anopheles pharoensis at Station A and Culex poicilipes and Mansonia sp. at Station C. With the exception of Chaoborus at Station A, the species of Culicidae and Tabanidae are rare and are found only during the wet season or when the water level remains high.

A comparison with statistics from other aquatic habitats[29] reveals that the standing crop at Nungua reservoir is of a relatively low order. The standing crop need not, however, be a good index of production. Thus, K. R. Allen found that the total annual production of the bottom fauna in the Horokiwi stream of New Zealand was over 17 times that of the average standing crop on a numerical basis, or 100 times on a weight basis.[30] It seems highly probable that the factors involved in Nungua reservoir are appreciably more complex than those in the Horokiwi stream, in consequence of the rapidity with which many animals grow and complete their life cycles at the high water temperatures prevailing in the tropics. Unfortunately, very little quantitative data is available regarding the time required by animals in tropical habitats to complete their life cycles, but it appears that mosquitoes develop from the egg to adults in 10 days, large dragonfly larvae in about 12 weeks,[31] and bulinid snails in from 10 to 14 weeks.[32] It is possible, therefore, that the productivity of the bottom fauna near the shoreline in the reservoir is, in fact, comparable to that of fairly productive aquatic habitats in the temperate zone with a much higher standing crop. It is to be expected that the production of the adjoining savanna would influence that of the

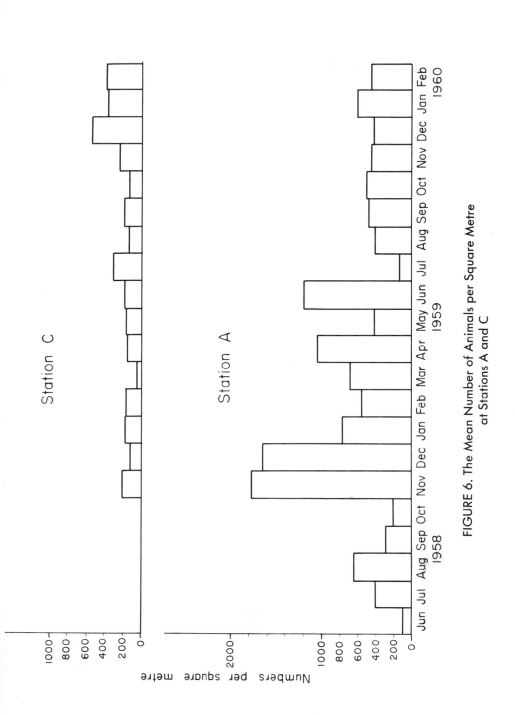

FIGURE 6. The Mean Number of Animals per Square Metre at Stations A and C

reservoir. According to J. D. Thomas, that of the catchment area lies between 0.77 to 1.06 g. of dry matter/m^2/day,[33] which is comparable with production in the tall grass prairies of Oklahoma and Nebraska.[34] The production in terms of cattle of about 20 lbs. per acre per year (approx. kg/ha) is low compared with that of 109-157 lbs. per acre per year of wild life in savanna areas in East Africa,[35] and it would appear that the cattle are not able to utilize the habitat efficiently.

There is evidence of a seasonal change in the biomass of the standing crop at both stations. It begins to increase after the onset of the major rains and eventually reaches a peak towards the end of the dry season before declining again prior to the onset of the next rains. As already indicated, the primary production is at its highest at this time. It is of interest that the seasonal changes in the Bulinus population follow the same course. Although there is some evidence of a decline in the population density per m^2 during the late dry season, these data do not show a well defined trend.

PARASITE VECTORS

(1) Insect vectors: The larvae of insect vectors are rarely encountered either in the lake at Station A or in the fish pond at Station C, and it is possible that aquatic habitats of this kind are not favorable habitats for the Tabanidae or for the Culicidae other than Chaoborus. The habitats in which Culex poicilipes, Mansonia sp., and Anopheles pharoensis occur at Nungua are similar to the ones in which they occur in East Africa. Thus, L. K. H. Goma observed that all three species are found among lake shore swamps in clear water among Pistia and Myriophyllum.[36] Their absence from Station A during the dry season, when the aquatic or subaquatic vegetation disappears, may have resulted from the dearth of organic matter or from the absence of protection given by the plants against predation, or from both of these factors. Goma, in common with many other investigators, has found that aquatic habitats low in organic matter do not contain many mosquitoes. Predators are abundant at both stations and include insectivorous fish such as Clarias senegalensis, Hemichromis bimaculatus, Tilapia zilli, Barbus atakorensis, and Micropanchax gambiense as well as predatory insects belonging to the Odonata, Hemiptera, Dytiscidae, and Gyrinidae. During the dry season, along the shore line at Station A, numerous species of waders also become active. Support to the theory that predation pressure is important at both stations is provided by the fact that the species that commonly occur show adaptations which give them protection against predation. Thus Mansonia species live in close proximity to vegetation. The larva of C. poicilipes, on the other hand, lives close to the bottom, where it lies in an inverted position, resting on modified hairs of the thorax and siphon. Water currents produced by the

labral brushes pass over both the papillae on the head and the anal
papillae. In contrast, the surface feeding mosquito larvae, including those of Anopheles gambiae and A. fenustus, are more susceptible to predation. It is possible, therefore, that their apparent absence from these permanent waters is directly attributable
to predation or to the fact that the females are no longer selecting such habitats as a result of selection pressures. Goma states
that long-standing peripheral pools yield more mosquitoes than do
open waters and that the influence of predation in controlling distribution of mosquitoes should not be underestimated.[37]

(2) Molluscan vectors: Bulinus (Physopsis) globosus is
a vector of the parasite Schistosoma haematobium, Bulinus forskali is a vector of Paramphistomum microbothrium, and Limnaea
natalensis is a vector of Fasciola gigantica. The dearth of
these and other gastropod snails at Station A suggests that it is
not a favorable habitat for such snails. In contrast, mollusca
are more abundant numerically at Station C. It may be suggested
that one of the major factors limiting the mollusca at Station A
is the dearth or absence of aquatic or subaquatic vegetation during the dry season, and the fairly rapid recession of the water
that takes place at this time. Aquatic vegetation (particularly
the broad-leaved varieties) provides a desirable habitat for the
snails because the leaves provide (1) a suitable surface for the
growth of green algae on which the snails feed (2) a suitable
surface for the deposition of eggs, (3) protection against radiation from the sun, water currents, and predators, and (4) a source
of autochthonous organic matter on which the snails feed. It is
suggested in the World Health Organization Technical Report 120
(1957) that the translocation of oxygen to the roots of aquatic
plants might account for the close association of B. forskali with
the root system of such plants. In the absence of vegetation along
the shore during the dry season, the influence of bird predators
may be an important population control mechanism. Forty-five species of birds, including waders, white-faced ducks, geese, herons,
and open-bills, have been recorded along the shore line of the
reservoir, and during the dry season, considerable numbers of
Aspatharia, a large, well-protected bivalve are eaten by birds,
including open-bills.

With the decline in water level, the gastropods which frequent the margins of the water are left stranded, since they make
no effort to migrate with the receding water. As their aestivating
powers are limited,[38] few are likely to survive the dry season.

The seasonal decline in the populations of the gastropod
molluscs, even at Station C, where the water level is kept constant, is of considerable interest. Such seasonal changes are
determined by the mortality and natality rates. In consequence of
the fact that B. (P.) globosus breeds throughout the year in the
tropics and that it has a very high natality rate, it is more

likely that the population changes are mainly determined by a change in the mortality rate. Although there is a dearth of information regarding natality rates, age composition, and mortality rates in population of bulinid snails, there is a strong measure of agreement among conchologists that the population as a whole declines towards the end of the dry season[39] and begins to increase during or immediately after the onset of rain.[40]

Various reasons may be advanced to account for the increase in population density of snails after the onset of rains. First, there is an increase in the growth of aquatic vegetation, possible as a result of an increase in the amount of organic matter and in the nitrification rate. (It is at this time that population explosions in the Pistia occur and the Nymphaea plants put out numerous new shoots.) Second, the decrease in overall temperature, in diurnal temperature range, and in solar radiation at this time may favor survival, but it is generally considered that this is not important, since the change in temperature is not very great, and the molluscs appear to have a wide range of tolerance. Third, the flooding may release aestivating snails such as B. forskali. (In the present study, this cause of increase would apply only to Station A.) Fourth, the increase in the amount of organic matter, including fine particles brought in by the runoff, would favor survival, since the organic matter is an important source of food. (According to the W.H.O. Report 120, young snails are obliged to feed on very small organic particles or on unicellular green algae.)

The decline in the snail population towards the end of the dry season may be explained as follows: First, the increase in solar radiation and temperature may be harmful to the snails. (It is possible that the increase in solar radiation may result in a relatively greater temperature rise on the microhabitat occupied by the snail, namely the Nymphaea leaf, than in the water itself, in consequence of the high specific heat of the latter. So far as is known, this hypothesis has not been tested by field observations, but if the leaves do develop unexpectedly high temperatures, the algal production on the surface and the snails themselves could be harmed.) Second, C. C. Cridland has suggested that the population decline in permanent water bodies is caused mainly by parasitic infections, although this is apparently not the cause of similar population fluctuations in a stream, a temporary body of water, and in B. forskali populations in the permanent body of water studied by him.[41] Third, as already indicated, the decrease in water level results in mortality as a result of snails being exposed to dessication and predation. Fourth, the food may become less abundant at this time. (The aquatic vegetation declines particularly at Station A; hence the quantity of encrusting algae on which snails feed is reduced. At this time, phytoplankton production is at its highest, but even' if the food is normally accessible to the snail, it is possible that the abundance of bluegreen algae may be harmful. It is to be expected also that the dearth of organic matter at this time, especially the particulate material, will be detrimental to the snail population, since it is an important food source, particularly to young snails. As already noted, the seasonal depletion of the organic matter at the end of the dry season can be attributed to the influence of high temperatures on bacterial activity. Organic material is not replenished until allochthonous organic matter is brought in again after the onset of the next major rains.

The seasonal change in organic matter also explains other biological phenomena in the water. First, the decline in total biomass and in population density in the late dry season can be attributed to the fact that many other animals, including species of Chironomidae--numerically the dominant group in the reservoir-- are dependent on organic matter as a source of food. Second, the dearth of organic matter, particularly during the late dry season, may account for the low diversity indices of certain animal taxa, the members of which feed to a considerable extent on decaying organic matter. These include the Tricladida, Oligochaeta, and Mollusca.

If the results of the present investigation apply to many other aquatic habitats in savanna areas in tropical Africa, it may be suggested as a tentative hypothesis that much of the Ethiopian zoogeographical region is relatively unfavorable for aquatic gastropods. In consequence of the fact that snails, particularly aquatic species, are obligatory hosts for trematode parasites, it is to be expected as a corollary that the trematode fauna in the Ethiopian region would not be as rich as in other regions. Although the figures in Table 2 and Fig. 7 appear to support this conclusion, it is possible that the Ethiopian region has fewer trematode genera recorded for it because it has been investigated less thoroughly than other regions. However, the data for the Cestoda and the Nematoda (see Table 2), whose life cycles are enacted, for the most part, in dry, terrestrial habitat, lend no support to the latter possibility. It is clear, however, that before the above tentative hypothesis can be generally accepted, much more data is required.

DISCUSSION

Despite the apparent low species diversity of trematode parasites in the Ethiopian region, man is more heavily parasitized in the African continent than in any other part of the world. According to J. M. Watson, there are on the average two infections per man.[42] Schistosomiasis is the dominant form, affecting nearly half the population. The high incidence and intensity of infection and infestation of the human race in Africa with parasites associated with an aquatic habitat (see Table 3 and Fig. 8) are

TABLE 2

THE NUMBER OF GENERA OF HELMINTH PARASITES IN VERTEBRATE
ANIMALS CLASSIFIED ON A ZOOGEOGRAPHICAL BASIS

PARASITES / ANIMALS	ZOOGEOGRAPHICAL REGIONS					
	Ethiopian	Oriental	Palaearctic	Nearctic	Neotropical	Australi
CESTODA						
Fish	10(13.3)*	12(16.0)	18(24.0)	18(24.0)	15(20.0)	2(2.
Amphibia	5(23.8)	4(19.0)	2(9.5)	6(28.6)	3(14.3)	1(4.
Reptiles	7(18.4)	10(26.3)	5(13.1)	4(10.5)	5(13.1)	7(18.
Birds	77(19.1)	79(19.6)	88(21.8)	61(15.1)	59(14.6)	39(9.
Mammals	44(18.6)	37(15.7)	56(23.7)	42(17.8)	28(11.9)	29(12.
NEMATODA						
Fish	11(15.9)	13(18.8)	18(26.1)	14(20.3)	9(13.0)	4(5.
Amphibia	17(14.8)	18(15.6)	26(22.6)	25(21.7)	22(19.1)	7(6.
Reptiles	35(17.5)	48(24.0)	27(13.5)	24(12.0)	48(24.0)	18(9.
Birds	55(15.4)	66(18.5)	83(23.2)	49(13.7)	64(17.9)	40(11.
Mammals	152(18.6)	124(15.2)	159(19.5)	117(14.3)	171(20.9)	94(11.
TREMATODA						
Fish	12(11.0)	27(24.8)	16(14.7)	30(27.5)	22(20.2)	2(1.
Amphibia	11(12.8)	17(19.8)	22(25.6)	21(24.4)	9(10.5)	6(7.
Reptiles	25(14.3)	35(20.0)	26(14.8)	41(23.4)	40(22.8)	8(4.
Birds	63(11.2)	98(17.5)	166(29.6)	108(19.3)	88(15.7)	37(6
Mammals	46(15.4)	63(21.1)	74(24.7)	63(21.1)	42(14.0)	11(3

*The percentages in each region of the total number of worms in each
class of animals are given in parentheses.

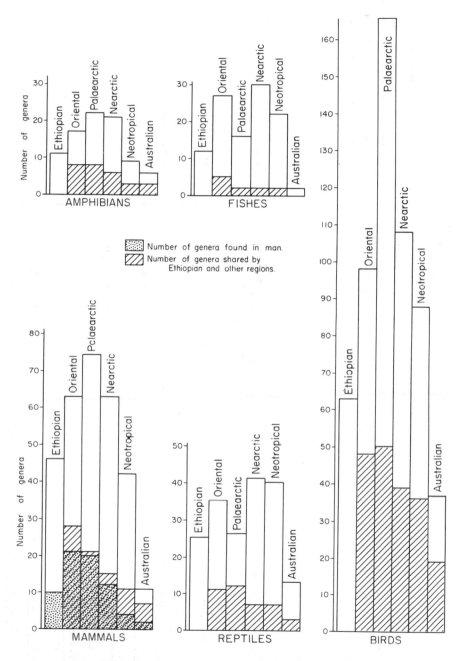

FIGURE 7. The Number of Trematode Genera of Helminth Parasites by Zoogeographical Regions

TABLE 3

SOME PARASITES OF MAN AND DOMESTIC ANIMALS IN AFRICA FOR
WHICH AN AQUATIC ENVIRONMENT IS OBLIGATORY

PARASITES OF MAN

Parasites	Intermediate Host	Method of Infection
VIRUSES:		
About 32 mosquito-borne viruses are associated with human infections [43]	Mosquito	Mosquito bite
PROTOZOA:		
Trypanosoma gambiense Dutton	Glossina palpalis and G. tachinoides (found near water)	Tsetse bite
Plasmodium spp.	Mosquitoes	Mosquito bite
NEMATODA:		
Wuchereira bancrofti (Cobbold)	Mosquitoes	Fly biting man
Setaria equina (Abildgaard)	Simulium, mosquitoes	"
Dipetalonema perstans (Manson)	Mosquitoes, Culicoides, Simulium, tabanids, Pulex, ticks	"
Dipetalonema streptocerca (Macfie & Carson)	Culicoides	"
Mansonella ozzardi (Manson)	Culicoides, Simulium	"
Dirofilaria repens (Railliet & Henry)	Mosquitoes	"

Loa loa (Guyot)	Chrysops	" "
Onchocerca volvulus (Leuckart)	Simulium	" "
Dracunculus medinensis (L.)	Copepods	Drinking water containing infested copepods
TREMATODA:		
Fasciola gigantica Cobbold	Aquatic snail	Infective stage on water plants
Fasciolopsis fuelleborni Rodenwaldt	"	Infective stage on water plants
Heterophyes heterophyes (Siebold)	Aquatic snail, fish	Infective stage in fish
*Stictidora tridactyla Martin & Kintz	" "	" " " "
*Echinostoma revolutum (Froelich)	Aquatic snail	Infective stage in snail or 2nd intermediate host
Echinoparyphium recurvatum (Linstow)	Aquatic snails, frogs	Infective stage in snails or frogs
Paragoninus westermani (Kerbert)	Aquatic snail, crustacean	Infective stage in crustacean
Schistosoma mansoni Sambon	Aquatic snail	Infective larvae enter through skin of man
Schistosoma haematobium (Bilharz)	" "	Infective larvae enter through skin of man
Watsonius watsonsi (Coryngam)	" "	Infective stages on water plants

*Recorded in Africa but in mammalian hosts other than man. However, man is a potential host.

TABLE 3--Continued

PARASITES OF MAN

Parasites	Intermediate Host	Method of Infection
CESTODA:		
Diphyllobothrium sp. larva	Copepod, man	Infective stage in copepod
*Spirometra pretonensis (Baer)	Copepod, reptiles, amphibia, mammals (incl. man)	Infective stage in intermediate host

PARASITES OF DOMESTIC ANIMALS

PROTOZOA:		
Trypanosoma brucei	Glossina palpalis and other Glossina sp. Mechanically by tabanids or mosquitoes	Biting of cattle, sheep, goats, camels, pigs, dogs, etc. by flies
Trypanosoma vivax	Glossina palpalis, etc. Also mechanically by tabanids	" "
TREMATODA:		
Fasciola gigantica Cobbold	Snail	Eating infested vegetation
Paramphistomum cervi (Schrank)	"	"
Paramphistomum microbothrium Fischoeder	"	"
Cotylophoron cotylophorum (Fischoeder)	"	"
Gastrodiscus aegyptiacus Cobbold	"	"
Schistosoma bovis (Sonsino)	"	Infective stages penetrate skin

		Mode of infection	Definitive host
Schistosoma mattheei Veglia and la Roux	Snail	Infective stages penetrate skin	
Schistosoma leiperi (la Roux)	"	"	
Schistosoma margrebowiei (la Roux)	"	"	
Schistosoma curassoni Brumpt	"	"	
NEMATODA:			
Setaria equina (Abildgaard)	Simulium, mosquitoes	Fly biting	horse
Setaria digitata (Linstow)	Mosquitoes	"	sheep, horse
Setaria labiato papillosa (Alesc)	Mosquito	"	cattle, sheep
Dipetalonema ruandae Fain & Herin	Mosquitoes	"	cattle
Brugia patei (Buckley et al.)	Mosquitoes	"	dog
Dirofilaria immitis (Leidy)	Mosquitoes, ticks	"	dog, cat, etc.
Dirofilaria repens (Railliet & Henry)	Mosquito	"	dog
Onchocerca armillata (Railliet & Henry)	?	"	cattle
Onchocerca fasciata Railliet & Henry	?	"	camel
Onchocerca gibsoni (Cleland & Johnston)	Culicoides	"	cattle
Onchocerca gutturosa (Neumann)	Simulium	"	"
Elaeophora poeli (Vryburg)	?	"	ox
Dracunculus medinensis (L.)	Copepods	Cattle, dog, etc. drinking water containing infested copepods	

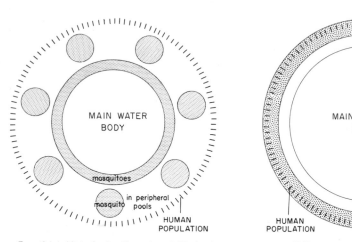

Essential habitats for the life cycles of *Wuchereira,*
Onchocerca, Acanthocheilonema, Loa loa, Dipetalonema, Plasmodium

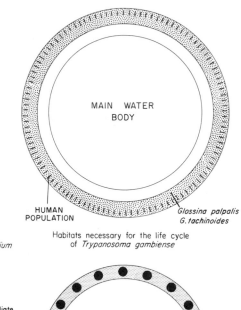

Habitats necessary for the life cycle
of *Trypanosoma gambiense*

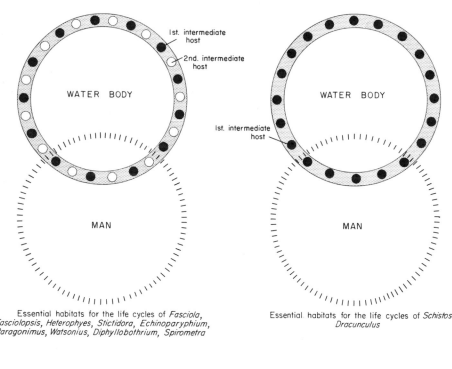

Essential habitats for the life cycles of *Fasciola,*
Fasciolopsis, Heterophyes, Stictidora, Echinoparyphium,
Paragonimus, Watsonius, Diphyllobothrium, Spirometra

Essential habitats for the life cycles of *Schistosoma,*
Dracunculus

FIGURE 8. Essential Habitats of Selected Parasites

probably due to the long, continued association of man with water
in the Ethiopian region. There is good evidence that man first
evolved from prehuman forms in the savanna area of this region in
the early Pleistocene. In the savanna, during the dry seasons,
water tends to become localized in distribution, and, since the
prehumans and early man lacked water carrying utensils, it would
be necessary for them to remain in close proximity to aquatic habitats, which were also utilized by a great variety of other mammals.
It was probably under conditions such as these that the prehumans
and early man acquired the parasitic fauna which are associated
with water. A number of these parasites of man are shared with
the lower mammals, which serve as sources or reservoirs of human
infections and infestations. Such infections are known as zoonoses. In the less developed parts of Africa, even today man and
the reservoir hosts have retained their close association with
water, and the same aquatic habitat may be used for a variety of
purposes, including drinking, washing, bathing, and fishing. The
phenomenon of zoonoses has probably contributed significantly to
the evolution and survival of human parasites. The migration of
man to other parts of the world has helped to break the bondage
between man and parasite, and it is to be hoped that, with improved sanitation, water supplies, and education, it will be possible to break this bond in Africa, by preventing close contact
between man and the vectors. It is probable that from the long-
term viewpoint, such an approach will be more effective and economical than the use of insecticides and molluscicides in controlling the vectors. Complete eradication of the vectors is extremely
difficult, and F. S. McCullough recently claimed that a very small
population of snails, occurring in a habitat frequently used by
the local population, can maintain a high prevalence of infestation in the human population.[44]

ACKNOWLEDGEMENTS

The work carried out on Nungua reservoir would not have
been possible without a great deal of cooperation from numerous
people. Particular mention must be given to Mr. Peter Hill, the
farm manager at Nungua during the time of the investigation. His
encouragement and assistance made the work possible. The writer
is also indebted to Mr. Robert Adjei and to Mr. E. R. N. Amegbe
for assistance in the field, to Drs. K. N. Mann, G. Mandahl Barth,
H. Stenholt Clausen, Professor R. A. Poisson, Mr. D. E. Kimmins,
Dr. E. Pinhey, Mr. D. J. Lewis, Mr. J. Balfour-Browne, Drs. G.
Marlier, D. Bryce, Willis W. Wirth, and Professor T. Harris for
assistance with identifications, to Mr. D. Agyei-Henaku and Mrs.
E. Reid for completing the text figures, and to Mrs. Patricia Jones
for completing the typescript.

THE ECOLOGY OF A SMALL MAN-MADE LAKE IN TROPICAL AFRICA

NOTES

[1] G. E. Hutchinson, A Treatise on Limnology, Vol. I (New York: 1957); J. F. Talling, "Origin of Stratification in an African Rift Lake," Limnology and Oceanography, VIII (1963), pp. 68-78.

[2] E. Trewavas, "The Origin and Evolution of the Cichlid Fishes of the Great African Lakes with Special Reference to Lake Nyasa," Rapp. 13th Congr. Intern. Zool. (Paris: 1948), Sect. 5b, pp. 1-4; R. H. Lowe, "Report on the Tilapia and Other Fish and Fisheries on Lake Nyasa, 1945-47," Fishery Publications - Colonial Office, I (1952), 2; G. Fryer, "The Trophic Interrelationships and Ecology of Some Littoral Communities of Lake Nyasa with Especial Reference to the Fishes and a Discussion of the Evolution of a Group of Rock-Frequenting Cichlidae," Proceedings of the Zoological Society of London, CXXXII (1959), pp. 153-281.

[3] G. S. Carter, The Papyrus Swamps of Uganda (Cambridge: Heffer & Sons, 1955); L. C. Beadle and E. M. Lind, Research on the Swamps of Uganda (Uganda: 1959).

[4] G. Marlier, "Recherches hydrobiologiques dans les rivières du Congo Oriental: La Conductivité électrique," Hydrobiologia, III (1951), pp. 217-27; M. J. Holden and J. Green, "The Hydrology and Plankton of the River Sokoto," Journal of Animal Ecology, XXIX (1960), pp. 65-84.

[5] G. R. Fish, "The Oxygen Content of the Water in Dams in Ankole, Uganda," East African Agricultural Journal, XX (1955), pp. 178-82; A. Maar, "Dams and Drowned-Out Stream Fisheries in Southern Rhodesia," Extract from the Athens Proceedings of the Seventh Technical Meeting of the International Union for the Conservation of Nature (1958), VI, pp. 139-51; M. I. van der Lingen, "Some Observations on the Limnology of Water Storage Reservoirs and Natural Lakes in Central Africa," Proceedings of the First Federal Science Congress (Salisbury: 1960), pp. 1-5; D. Harding, "Limnological Trends in Lake Kariba," Nature, CXCI (1961), p. 119; C. F. Hickling Tropical Inland Fisheries (London and Southampton: Longmans, 1961.

[6] H. O. Walker, "Weather and Climate," in J. B. Wills, ed., Agriculture and Land Use in Ghana (London, Accra: Oxford University Press, 1962).

[7] "Farm Ponds," in D. G. Frey, ed., Limnology in North America (Madison: University of Wisconsin Press, 1963).

[8] A. C. Chandler and C. P. Read, Introduction to Parasitology with Special Reference to the Parasites of Man (New York: Wiley, 1961).

[9] P. H. Nye, "The Relation between Nitrogen Responses, Previous

142

Soil Treatment and Carbon/Nitrogen Ratio in Soils of the Gold Coast Savanna Areas," Transactions of the Fourth International Congress of Soil Scientists (1950), I, pp. 246-49; P. H. Nye and D. J. Greenland, The Soil under Shifting Cultivation (Harpenden: 1960) [Technical Communication No. 51 - Commonwealth Bureau of Soil Science]; H. Bramer, "Soils," in J. B. Wills, ed., Agriculture and Land Use in Ghana (London, Accra: Oxford University Press, 1962).

[10]Holden and Green, op. cit. (see note 4); D. H. Yaalon, "Chemical Changes in Rain-Fed Marsh Waters during the Dry Season," Limnology and Oceanography, IX (1964), pp. 218-23.

[11]Ecology of Inland Waters and Estuaries (New York and London: Reinhold Publishing Corp., 1961).

[12]Op. cit. (see note 5).

[13]"Sulphates in African Inland Waters," Nature, CLXXI (1953), pp. 769-71.

[14]Op. cit. (see note 4).

[15]Fundamentals of Limnology (University of Toronto Press, 1963). Translated by D. G. Frey and F. E. Fry.

[16]W. Einsele, "Über die Beziehungen des Eisenkreislaufs zum Phosphatkreislaufe in eutrophen See," Archiv für Hydrobiologie, XXIX (1938), pp. 664-86; J. A. McCarter, F. R. Hayes, L. H. Jodrey, and M. L. Cameron, "Movement of Materials in the Hypolimnion of Lakes as Studied by Addition of Radioactive Phosphorus," Canadian Journal of Zoology, XXX (1952), pp. 128-33; F. J. Mackereth, "Phosphorus Utilization by Asterionella formosa Hass," Journal of Experimental Botany (Oxford), IV (1953), pp. 296-313.

[17]T. J. Lansbury, "A Review of Some Limiting Factors in the Nutrition of Cattle on the Accra Plains, Ghana," Tropical Agriculture (Trinidad), XXXVII (1960), pp. 185-92; P. H. Nye and D. Stephens, "Soil Fertility," in J. B. Wills, ed., Agriculture and Land Use in Ghana (London, Accra: Oxford University Press, 1962).

[18]Limnology of Santo Amaro Reservoir (Botany Department, University of Santo Paulo, 1939).

[19]Nye and Greenland, op. cit. (see note 9).

[20]Laurie, "The Dissolved Oxygen of an Upland Pond and Its Inflowing Stream at Ystumtuen, North Cardiganshire, Wales," Journal of Ecology, XXX (1942), pp. 357-82; Fish, op. cit. (see note 5).

[21]"Diurnal Changes of Stratification and Photosynthesis in Some

Tropical African Waters," Proceedings of the Royal Society, CXLVII (1957), pp. 57-83.

[22]Worthington, "Observations on the Temperature Hydrogen-Ion Concentration and Other Physical Conditions of the Victoria and Albert Nyanzas," International Review of Hydrobiology, XXIV (1930), pp. 328-57; Gessner, "Die limnologischen Verhaltnisse in den Seen und Flussen von Venezuela," Verh. int. Ver. Limnol., XII (1955), pp. 284-94.

[23]"The Subaerial and Freshwater Algal Flora of the Tropics," Annals of Botany, XXI (1907), pp. 235-75.

[24]Comparative Studies on the Metabolism of Marine Waters (Texas University: Institute of Marine Science, 1958), No. 5, pp. 16-46.

[25]Oxygen Metabolism of Oklahoma Farm Ponds (Texas University: Institute of Marine Science, 1964).

[26]"Interaction of Effects by Environmental Factors on Primary Productivity in Ponds and Microecosystems." Thesis submitted at Oklahoma State University, 1964.

[27]A. G. Fischer, "Latitudinal Variations in Organic Diversity," Evolution, XIV (1960), pp. 64-81; E. Mayr, Animal Species and Evolution (Cambridge: Belknap Press of Harvard University Press, 1963).

[28]K. Berg, Studies on the Bottom Fauna of Esrom Lake [K. danske vidensk Selsk. Sk. 7 (1938)]; J. R. E. Jones, "An Ecological Study of the River Rheidol, North Cardiganshire, Wales," Journal of Animal Ecology, XVIII (1949), pp. 67-88, and "An Ecological Study of the River Towy," Journal of Animal Ecology, XX (1951), pp. 68-86; S. Stankovic, The Balkan Lake Ohrid and Its Living World (Den Haag, Netherlands: Junk, 1960) [Monographie Biologicae IX].

[29]C. Juday, "Quantitative Studies on the Bottom Fauna in the Deep Waters of Lake Mendota," Transactions of the Wisconsin Academy of Science, Arts, and Letters, XX (1922), pp. 461-93; P. R. Needham, "A Quantitative Study of the Fish Food Supply in Selected Areas," in A Biological Survey of the Oswego River System [Supplement to the 17th Annual Report of the State of New York Conservation Department (1928), pp. 192-206]; D. S. Rawson, Bottom Fauna of Lake Simcol and Its Role in the Ecology of the Lake (Ontario Fish Research Laboratory, 1930), No. 34; F. H. Krechner and L. Y. Lancaster, "Bottom Shore Fauna of Western Lake Erie: A Population Study to a Depth of Six Feet," Ecology, XIV (1933), pp. 79-93; Berg, op. cit. (see note 28); M. J. Murray, An Ecological Study of the Invertebrate Fauna of Some Northern Indiana Streams [Investigations of Indiana Lakes No. 8 (1938]; R. M. Badcock, "Studies in Stream Life in Tributaries of the Welsh Dee,"

Journal of Animal Ecology, XVIII (1949), pp. 193-208; D. R. Dunn, "The Bottom Fauna of Llyn Tegid (Lake Bala) Merionethshire," Journal of Animal Ecology, XXX (1961), pp. 267-81.

[30] The Horokiwi Stream: A Study of a Trout Population (Wellington, N.Z.: 1951). [New Zealand Marine Department Fishery Bulletin No. 10.]

[31] R. M. Gambles, "Seasonal Distribution and Longevity in Nigerian Dragonflies," Journal of the West African Science Association, VI (1960), pp. 18-26.

[32] F. S. McCullough, "Further Observations on Bulinus (Bulinus) truncatus rohlfsi (Clessin) in Ghana: Seasonal Population Fluctuations and Biology," Bulletin of the World Health Organization, XXVII (1962), pp. 161-70.

[33] "Observations on the Conservation of Wildlife in Ghanaian Savanna," Ghana Journal of Science, II (1962), pp. 159-75.

[34] E. P. Odum and H. T. Odum, Fundamentals of Ecology (Philadelphia and London: 1959), p. 73.

[35] L. M. Talbot and M. H. Talbot, "The High Biomass of Wild Ungulates on East African Savanna," Transactions of 28th North American Wildlife and Natural Resources Conference, 1963 (Washington, D.C.: Wildlife Management Institute).

[36] "The Swamp Breeding Mosquitoes of Uganda: Records of Larvae and Their Habitats," Bulletin of Entomological Research, LI (1960), pp. 77-94.

[37] "The Productivity of Various Mosquito Breeding Places in the Swamps of Uganda," Bulletin of Entomological Research, XLIX (1958), pp. 437-48.

[38] W. F. J. McClelland, "Studies on Snail Vectors of Schistosomiasis in Kenya," Journal of Tropical Medicine and Hygiene, LIX (1956), pp. 229-42; C. C. Cridland, "Ecological Factors Affecting the Number of Snails in Temporary Bodies of Water," Journal of Tropical Medicine and Hygiene, LX (1957), pp. 287-93; McCullough, op. cit. (see note 32).

[39] C. C. Cridland, "Ecological Factors Affecting the Number of Snails in Permanent Bodies of Water," Journal of Tropical Medicine and Hygiene, LX (1957), pp. 250-56; Cridland, op. cit. (see note 38), and Cridland, "Ecological Factors Affecting the Number of Snails in a Permanent Stream," Journal of Tropical Medicine and Hygiene, LXI (1958), pp. 16-20; F. S. McCullough, "The Seasonal Density of Populations of Bulinus (Physopsis) globosus and B. forskali in Natural Habitats in Ghana," Annals of Tropical Medi-

cine and Parasitology (Liverpool), LI (1957), pp. 235-48, and op. cit. (see note 32).

[40]J. Lietar, "Biologie et écologie des mollusques vecteurs de bilharziose à Jadotville," Annales - Societé belge de médecine tropicale, XXXVI (1956), pp. 919-1036; McCullough, op. cit. (see notes 32 and 39); Cridland, op. cit. - 1958 (see note 39); G. Webbe and A. S. Msangi, "Observations on Three Species of Bulinus on the East Coast of Africa," Annals of Tropical Medicine and Parasitology, LII (1958), pp. 302-14.

[41]Op. cit. (see notes 38 and 39).

[42]Medical Helminthology (London: Bailliere, Tindall & Cox, 1960).

[43]W. C. Reeves, "Mosquitoes and Virus Disease," in C. Maramovosch ed., Biological Transmission of Disease Agents (New York, London: 1962).

[44]Op. cit. (see note 32).

WATER RESOURCES AND ECONOMIC DEVELOPMENT IN NIGERIA

by

Akin L. Mabogunje

In their plans for economic development, most underdeveloped countries put a major emphasis on rapid industrialization. An increase in the number of industrial establishments, however, soon tests at critical points the level of development of the basic infrastructure, notably transportation, electricity, and water supplies, in such countries. The purpose of this paper is to examine how the water resources of Nigeria are being developed to respond to the crisis posed by the increasing tempo of economic development in the country. Emphasis is placed on urban water supplies, since it is their development that has immediate relevance for industrial growth and concentration. The paper is divided into four parts. The first considers the nature of available water resources in Nigeria; the second examines the pattern of its development in urban centers in the recent past during the colonial period; the third indicates the significance of this water resource development for the industrial development which has been taking place in the country during the last decade, and the fourth examines the crisis concerning water supplies in the country and the various ways in which the government is trying to resolve this crisis.

ESTIMATE OF NIGERIA'S WATER RESOURCES

There is an abundance of literature on the nature of the water resources of any country. Basically, these resources are related in a very close way to rainfall. Of the rain that falls in any one year, however, a substantial amount is not readily available for exploitation because of a combination of losses. These include losses by surface runoff, surface retention, and evapotranspiration. Together, these three processes may account for the loss of as much as 70 per cent of the rain that falls in a year.

Not all this water is truly lost to exploitation. This is particularly so in the case of surface runoff, much of which flows into streams, ponds, and lakes, which constitute major reservoirs of surface water. The water resources of a country comprise both this surface water as well as a substantial amount of groundwater. Groundwater is that portion of rain water which eventually percolates through soils and rocks to form a permanent body

of water below the earth surface. It is exploitable naturally
through springs, but more often by direct human intervention
through wells and boreholes.

There is no accurate estimate of the magnitude of the water resource potential in Nigeria. As in many underdeveloped countries, such an estimate is difficult to make because of the appalling lack of the requisite statistical data. R. C. Mitchell-Thome
of the University of Nigeria, Nsukka, however, has offered a preliminary estimate of average annual available groundwater supplies
in Nigeria.[1] According to him, the average annual accumulation of
groundwater in Nigeria is about 2,100 billion gallons. For comparative purposes, he noted that the total average water consumption
in the United States is about 200 billion gallons daily, and pointed out that on this basis the annual accumulation in Nigeria would
suffice the United States for only 10 days! He went on to indicate
that judged by these figures, Nigeria, although occupying 0.7 per
cent of the total world land area, has a groundwater supply above
a depth of 2,500 feet representing only about 0.2 per cent of the
world groundwater total.

There is much to criticize in these figures of Mitchell-
Thome. In the first place, his computations were based on a series
of crude indices and coefficients whose derivations are not indicated in the paper. Indeed, in view of the lack of data of any sort
for surface runoff and surface retention, and the unsatisfactory
results from using Thornthwaite's and Garnier's formulae for pro-
jecting evapotranspiration in Nigeria, his coefficients could not
have been anything but arbitrary. What Mitchell-Thome did was to
measure the area of land bounded by various isohyets of rainfall,
compute for each belt of land what he called "average capital annual volume of rainfall in cubic feet," and from this subtract various proportions based on his arbitrary coefficients. Equally misleading is his statement about daily average consumption in the
United States which, if correct, means that the average American
consumes over 1,000 gallons of water a day! The true figure is
surely less than a fifth of this.

In one important respect, however, Mitchell-Thome's figures
are correct in a general way. They show that Nigeria, although re-
putedly a rainy country, is relatively poor in its reserve of
groundwater. Essentially, this fact derives from the extensive
area covered by rocks of the basement complex. These rocks, which
are archean, crystalline, and on the whole relatively impervious,
cover almost half the area of the country, and contribute relatively little to the groundwater supply. Table 1 gives some idea of
water yields from boreholes drilled in various geological forma-
tions in the country.[2]

None the less, if groundwater is deficient, surface water
is not. Nigeria is a well-drained country with a close network

TABLE 1

RELATION OF ROCK TYPES TO WATER YIELDS FROM BOREHOLES

Rock Type	Typical Borehole	Depth of Borehole	Static Water Level	Yield gal./hr.
Post-Eocene	Asaba I	150'	74'	21,000
Bende-Ameki Group	Imushin	253'	173'	7,800
Upper & Lower Coal Measures	Ifon	265'	206'	2,800
Basement Complex	Ogbona	710'	614'	Small, but water too deep for test pump.

of streams and rivers apart from ponds, pools, small lakes, and
the extensive body of international water known as the Chad. Because of the high seasonality of rainfall distribution, however,
a major problem of surface water in Nigeria is its tendency to dry
up during the dry season. Every year, from November to April,
there is an absence of surface water over a large part of the country. Of the rivers, only the Niger and the Benue, a few of their
large tributaries such as the Kaduna, and a few southern rivers
such as the Cross, the Oshun, and the Ogun continue to flow at all.
Most of the rest simply exhibit their dry sandy beds adorned only
by a scatter of stagnant pools. With the rains starting about
March, rivers and streams begin to flow again, and there is a tendency to high floods annually in August or September.

WATER SUPPLIES IN URBAN CENTERS

The traditional pattern of water exploitation in Nigeria
has been limited to direct collection of rain water with pots and
similar containers and extraction from springs, pools, ponds, lakes,
streams, and wells. In addition to the problems created by the
annual shortage from nearly all of these sources during the dry
season, often necessitating long daily treks in search of water,
a major problem is the liability of water from these sources to
carry organisms parasitic to man. Over a large part of Nigeria,
the guinea worm, for instance, shows a high incidence related
largely to human consumption of surface and untreated water.[3] Dys-
entery also is a constant hazard from drinking water from any of
these sources.

One of the primary objectives of water supply development

during the colonial period was to improve the quality of drinking water and so reduce the debilitating effect of water-borne diseases on the population. In the face of limitations set by available funds, this development was concentrated in those settlements where it would have maximum effect for the growth of the export-oriented economy so vital to colonial exploitation. The settlements which thus profited most from this development were those favorably located along major trade and transportation routes. Thus, out of a total of 28 towns which were provided with modern water supply systems before 1953, 18 were on rail lines and along navigable stretches of the Niger and Benue rivers. These towns were not always the largest nor the most deserving in terms purely of health improvement. Table 2 shows the relation between location on major route and the provision of modern water supplies and reveals that a strong association exists between the two.[*] A chi-square test shows that this association is highly significant at the 0.1 per cent level.[**]

TABLE 2

RELATION BETWEEN LOCATION OF TOWNS AND
MODERN WATER SUPPLY SYSTEMS

Type of Water Supply	Towns on Transportation Route	Towns not on Transportation Route	TOTAL
Modern	18	10	28
Traditional	13	89	102
TOTALS	31	99	130

The earliest modern water supply system in Nigeria was established in 1915 in Lagos, the chief port and capital of the country. Between that date and 1953, eleven other waterworks were built in Western and Midwestern Nigeria, ten in Northern Nigeria, and six in Eastern Nigeria. These 28 waterworks involved a capital expenditure of less than £2 million ($5.6 million). Not all the waterworks were built wholly with colonial government funds. Except for those in Lagos and Akure, all the waterworks in Western Nigeria were built partly with funds from the native authorities. Similarly, in Northern Nigeria, the important native authorities, such as those of Kano, Zaria, and Okene, provided part of the funds

---

[*]Towns included are those with populations of over 10,000.

[**]Chi-square = 31.93.

for their own waterworks. By contrast, in Eastern Nigeria, where all the towns were founded by the British, all the waterworks were financed by the colonial government.

In the remainder of this section, an attempt will be made to analyze the pattern of water consumption in these 28 centers with modern water supplies during the ten-year period from 1944 to 1953. The data concerning consumption during this period come from the annual reports of the Public Works Department which, until the later date, was in general supervision of all waterworks in the country. For the 28 centers, total daily average consumption in gallons rose from 8.8 million in 1944 to 13.8 million in 1953, giving an annual rate of increase of 4.5 per cent. With a total population of over two million for these centers in 1953, this gives per capita daily consumption varying from about four to seven gallons over the period. This degree of consumption is, of course, to be expected, considering the generally low income level, and the tendency for water use among poor people to be limited to drinking, cooking, washing clothes, and occasional bathing.

The average daily consumption per capita, however, varied considerably from town to town. In the circumstances of Nigeria, a number of hypotheses can be put forward to account for this variation. It can be hypothesized, for instance, that consumption patterns among towns would vary, first, on the basis of the level of their involvement in modern economic activities, and second, on the basis of the cost of producing water. The first hypothesis rests on the assumption that the more directly involved in modern economic activities a town is, the more likely it is to have a government-owned waterworks, and the greater its likelihood of having a high proportion of people in the high income class, whose water consumption is known to be prodigious. Towns less directly involved in modern economic activities, on the other hand, would probably have waterworks under native authorities. They would tend to provide water for the generality of the people more for social than for economic reasons, and average daily consumption would generally be low. A comparison of the two different types of urban centers should therefore reveal significant differences. (A few of the government-owned stations, notably Akure, Lokoja, and Makurdi, were excluded from the ensuing analysis because their waterworks provided water only for the government station in the town. As the size of the population of the government station was not known, their figures of per capita consumption, when based on the total population of the towns, turned out to be unrealistically low.) A striking difference does exist between the two types of urban centers. The centers with government-owned waterworks had an average daily consumption of eight gallons per capita, while those with native authority waterworks had an average of only three gallons per capita per day. This difference was found to be highly significant at a level of 0.7 per cent on a student's t-test.

WATER RESOURCES AND ECONOMIC DEVELOPMENT IN NIGERIA

When the analysis was modified to test all centers on rail lines and navigable rivers, irrespective of the ownership of their waterworks, a similarly significant relation was found between relatively high average daily consumption of water per capita and location on a major transportation route. This analysis gave an average daily consumption of 6.4 gallons of water per capita for centers on major transportation routes compared with 2.1 gallons for centers away from such routes. A student's t-test revealed that this difference was significant at the 0.2 per cent level.

The second hypothesis about the relation of the cost of water to average consumption is based on the assumption that the higher the cost of water production the greater the price to consumers and, therefore, the less they will tend to consume. A correlation analysis of the amount of water consumed and the average operating and maintenance cost of the waterworks gave a coefficient of -0.64, which was highly significant at the 0.1 per cent level on the student's t-test. This meant that the cost of water production tended to vary in inverse proportion to the amount consumed. If cost and price were related, it meant that in those centers where a lot of water was consumed, it was also relatively cheap.

In explaining the variance in costs of water production in all the towns, however, the amount consumed was shown to account for less than 50 per cent of the variance. This meant that there were certain other important factors influencing costs in some of these centers. Further analysis to find out whether the type of ownership had any influence showed that it was influential in less than 10 per cent of the cases. None the less, it was found that, where the government operated the waterworks, revenue collection was more efficient than was the case with native authority waterworks. Statistical tests showed a difference of one per cent in efficiency of revenue collection per 1,000 gallons produced.

It is not clear, however, how the cost of production directly affects the degree of consumption, in view of the prevailing system of levying flat water-rates in the towns. The various provincial engineers consulted by the writer on the pricing of water were unanimous in insisting that the minimum economic water rate charged per taxable adult male should be in the neighborhood of 40 shillings ($5.00). Yet, in Northern Nigeria, the government has pegged the rate at 10 shillings ($1.50), and in Western Nigeria it varies between 12/6d. ($2.00) and 20 shillings ($3.00).

The important point to stress about the economics of water production is this--that centers where consumption is already relatively high and cost of production (and therefore price to consumers) relatively low are more likely to attract industrial establishments whose water consumption tends to be metered and charged on the basis of amount consumed. Thus, using data from the 1960 Industrial Directory of Nigeria, it can be seen that, of

675 industrial enterprises employing over ten persons, no less
than 70 per cent were to be found in ten urban centers where per
capita water consumption was in 1953 already well above the national average, and where operating costs per 1,000 gallons were below
the average for the country.[*] These centers, of course, offered
other advantages to industries, such as their being on the major
trade routes and possessing well-organized infrastructures. But
there is no doubt that the availability of piped water in such centers had an important effect on their selection as centers for lo-
cating industries.

INDUSTRIAL USE OF WATER

The examination of the relation between water consumption
patterns before 1953 and industrial concentration by 1960 raises
the issue of the effect of increasing industrialization on the
level of development of water supplies in the country. In order
to assess this, a survey was carried out of the requirements and
uses of water by industrial establishments employing more than 50
persons. Of 235 such establishments to which questionnaires were
sent, 103 sent back replies. Of these, 93 answered the questions
sufficiently well for them to be used in the ensuing analysis.

The questionnaire sought, among other things, to gain some
idea of the major industrial uses of water at the present time, of
the sources from which the industries got their water, and of de-
grees of consumption within each group of industries. For purposes
of analysis, the industries were grouped on the basis of the International Standard Industrial Classification system of the United
Nations. This grouping was not found particularly satisfactory
since it grouped together industries whose products, although derived from similar raw materials, have different demands for water
and are tied to different sources of supply. A good example is
the category "wood, pulp, and paper industries," which embraces
sawmills as well as furniture-making and other urban establishments.
The former, by the very nature of their operations, are large consumers of water, but since they must work in forest areas away from
urban centers, they tend to depend for their supplies on local
streams.

The analysis of the questionnaire returns is shown below.
This table reveals that most industries producing final products
for consumption are concentrated in urban centers. Food and tobacco industries are excellent examples in this respect. Their
consumption of water, however, varies considerably, depending on

---

[*]These centers are Lagos, Abeokuta, Benin, Warri, Kaduna, Kano,
Calabar, Enugu, Onitsha, and Port Harcourt.

the size of the establishment and the type of its product. Among high-water-consuming industries are the breweries, for which water forms an important constituent of their final product. Textile and footwear producers are also urban-centered and require lots of water for generating steam, humidifying the factory, washing, dyeing, and bleaching their products. The two largest textile mills in the country--in Kaduna and Lagos--consume annually over 36 and 46 million gallons of water, respectively.

As noted before, wood and paper industries show two consumption patterns representing different stages in the conversion process. The furniture industries and printing are to be found in urban areas, and their consumption of water is of modest dimensions, usually not more than 250,000 gallons a year. Sawmills, however, even where they are in urban areas, tend to draw their water from nearby streams, since much of the water does not require special treatment before use. The high figure of 74 million gallons was reported by a factory which added plywood manufacturing to its other activities of logging and sawmilling.

The plastics, leather, and rubber industries are similar in their pattern of water consumption to the wood industries. The mainly consumer-oriented industries, manufacturing, for instance, polythene plastics, leather suitcases, and vono mattresses, use relatively small amounts of water. By contrast, the crepe and sheet rubber manufacturing establishments need a lot of water, mainly of an untreated kind, and tend to depend directly on streams and rivers.

Industries producing chemicals, paints, and oils are on the whole minor consumers of water. Where they have to establish in small towns with no developed water supplies systems, they depend on water from local streams or boreholes, which they tend to treat. Clay and cement industries, on the other hand, are raw-material-oriented, and their large water need is often met directly in the field from nearby streams. For instance, the 140 million gallons used by the Nkalagu cement factory came directly from a local stream, while the 136 million gallons used at the Ewekoro cement factory came from boreholes.

Both metal and machinery industries cater directly to consumers and therefore concentrate wholly in cities. They are moderately large users of water, especially where their operations involve the cooling of engines. Generally, their major need for water is for washing their products. The single large user of the 136 million gallons per annum is the Nigerian Ports Authority in Lagos.

The pattern of industrial water consumption has been briefly sketched in order to make possible a discussion on the theoretical level. Most of the industries listed manufacture consumer

TABLE 3

SOURCES AND CONSUMPTION PATTERNS OF WATER BY INDUSTRIAL TYPES

Industrial Type	Total Number of Industries	Main Uses of Water	Urban Sources		Local Rivers or Wells	
			Number of Industries	Range of Consumption in Millions of Gallons	Number of Industries	Range of Consumption in Millions of Gallons
Food & Tobacco	18	A B C D E	17	0.015 – 60	1	–
Textiles & Footwear	7	A D E	7	4 – 45	–	–
Wood, Pulp, & Paper	19	A D E	12	0.020 – 0.24	7	1.8 – 74
Plastics, Leather, & Rubber	13	D E	3	0.375 – 1.2	10	1.5 – 55
Chemicals, Paints, & Oils	12	A B D E	7	0.400 – 2.9	5	0.2 – 9
Clay & Cement	6	A B C D E	–	–	6	2.0 – 140
Metals & Machinery	17	B D E	17	0.120 – 136	–	–

Key to Water Uses: A = Steam raising   D = Washing
B = Cooling   E = Incidental
C = Part of product

goods. In many developing countries, the emphasis on consumer goods industries is related to the rationale of import-substitution which underlies their present efforts at industrialization. For such industries, at least three conditions tend to encourage their location in a few centers. The first concerns transportation costs, which tend to be higher on their finished products than on the raw materials they use. In order, therefore, to minimize the total costs of procurement and distribution, most of these industries have gravitated to their major markets in the urban centers. Second, there is the advantage they derive from linkages with other industries. These linkages increase the attractiveness of those urban centers where conditions were initially favorable for the location of the industries. Third, industries are attracted to these centers because of their higher levels of what are called "urbanization economies."[4] These economies are largely economies of scale and tend to make basic facilities such as electricity, medical facilities, educational institutions, and water supplies readily available at relatively low cost.

As more and more industries seek these advantages by establishing in urban locations, the consumption of water in the next few years is bound to grow phenomenally. Indeed, it was found that when the rate of growth in consumption from 1943 to 1954 for 28 urban centers was extrapolated to 1960, the figure arrived at was only 60 per cent of the level to which the actual consumption of water had risen in these centers at that date. By 1960, the total number of urban centers with modern water supplies system had increased to 67, and total water consumption to over 57 million gallons per day.

TRENDS IN THE DEVELOPMENT OF NIGERIA'S WATER RESOURCES

In spite of increases in water capacity, there is today a crisis in the development of water resources in Nigeria. Part of this crisis stems from certain differences of opinion concerning the objectives of economic development in underdeveloped countries. These differences are reflected in the literature on the subject. On the one hand is the opinion of the school represented, for instance, by G. M. Meier and R. E. Baldwin, which sees the objective of economic development as that of increasing the real national income of a country over a long period of time.[5] According to this school, development planning should concentrate on expanding infrastructural facilities in those centers where their effects on the economy are likely to be greatest. Opposed to this is the view, expressed for instance by J. Viner, that the objective is to raise the general standard of living of the people through an increase in their per capita income over a period of time.[6] Proponents of this view would support the expenditure of large sums of money in constructing waterworks in centers where their immediate effects are likely to be no more than that of eradicating certain endemic diseases.

Policy decisions in Nigeria tend to veer between these two types of development planning, more often towards the latter for reasons of political expediency and national cohesion. The result is that while total water capacity in the country is not necessarily inadequate for present needs, serious strains are placed on supplies in those growing centers where new industries are concentrating. Indeed, in a few such centers, the rate of industrial agglomeration is being checked because no adequate supply of water can be guaranteed throughout the year. Already, of the ten centers mentioned as accounting for over 70 per cent of the industries in the country, eight have had to increase the capacities of their waterworks since 1955. Further substantial increases are projected. Lagos, for instance, which had a capacity of 14 million gallons daily in 1961, is to have this increased to 40 million by 1968. Kaduna, with 2.4 million gallons, is to have a further 5 million; Enugu with 1.5 million has projected another 10 million; Onitsha and Port Harcourt have also planned increases. Similarly, Ibadan, with a present capacity of 4 million gallons, is about to begin on a new scheme to add 16 million gallons.

One factor hindering the increase in water supplies in most growing centers and making the projected increases not easy to realize is that such large amounts of water can no longer be extracted, as in the past, from nearby small streams or springs. To plan for the domestic, commercial, and industrial water needs of the growing cities for the next twenty years means, therefore, choosing as the sources of water large rivers not always close to the cities. To ensure adequate supply from such rivers throughout the year often necessitates heavy expenditure on dams, embankments, and other constructions. The Six-Year Development Plan of Nigeria thus envisages the expenditure of nearly £18 million ($45 million) on expanding water supplies, especially in urban areas. Ibadan, for instance, is to depend for the extra daily output of 16 million gallons on damming the large Oshun river, some 20 miles away, at a cost of nearly £3 million ($8.5 million). Similarly, Kaduna is going to depend on the Kaduna river on a much more impressive scale than was the case in the past.

Increasing governmental awareness of the problems posed by inadequate water supplies is shown in four ways. In the first place, substantial sums of money are being voted both for hydrological investigations of river flows and regimes, and, for prospecting for underground and artesian sources of water. Second, private Israeli companies have been invited, especially in Western and Eastern Nigeria, to undertake exploitation of groundwater resources by means of deep boreholes in places where these are reliable sources of water. Third, to ensure efficient management of water supplies, the various regional governments have set up Regional Water Boards to take over the operation and maintenance of all waterworks in the regions. Such a Water Board was set up in Northern Nigeria in 1961, in Eastern Nigeria in 1962, and is about to be established in Western Nigeria. Finally, draft legislation is under active consideration by all the governments of the Nigerian federation to create Federal and Regional Water Resources Authorities which would be responsible for all matters pertaining to the abstraction of water above a certain quantity anywhere in the country.

One effect of the centralization of management is, of course, to remove the competitive advantage of cheap production costs in the growing industrial centers. In Eastern Nigeria, for instance, the government runs all the water works but charges every local council on the basis of the average annual cost of producing 1,000 gallons all over the region. In this way, the "urbanization economies" accruing to the industrial centers are reduced, and pressure for expansion (to which local councils are more directly subject than is a regional government) is now weakened, since such pressure has to be taken along with pressure from other centers or from other priorities of administration. In a sense, then, the government has tried to resolve the differences in the objectives of their plans for economic development by attempting to combine both economic and welfare goals in the handling of water supplies in the regions.

CONCLUSION

In this paper attention has been specially focussed on urban and industrial water needs. This is not because water for agricultural and irrigational purposes is not considered important (especially in certain areas of Northern Nigeria).[*] Rather, it is because the increasing rate of domestic and industrial consumption in urban centers has been the factor primarily responsible for the greater consciousness about water resources and for many of the developments in water resources now taking place in the country. Over large areas of Nigeria, rainfall is adequate for most agricultural purposes and, apart from the newly introduced rice, there is no crop in the traditional system of agriculture which calls for an extra supply of water. Thus, government interest in the provision of water in the rural areas has been limited to wells and boreholes to ensure wholesome drinking water to the people. It required the crisis in the last few years of industrial growth to highlight the inadequate and unreliable nature of water supplies

---

[*]The high-powered Niger Dam Authority hopes to make large quantities of water available for irrigation in the Niger Valley on completion of its hydroelectric project at Kainji.

in the country, and to force on the governments a greater realization of the need to evaluate the water resources of the country
and to appreciate their singular importance for economic development.

NOTES

[1]"Preliminary Estimates of Average Annual Available Groundwater
Supplies in Nigeria." Paper read at the Conference of the Science
Association of Nigeria, Enugu, December, 1961. [Unpublished.]

[2]Memorandum on the Master Plan for Water Supplies Development
Programme, Western Nigeria, 1960-68 (3 vols., Ibadan: 1962), I,
pp. 4-6. [Prepared by the Chief Water Engineer, Ministry of Works
and Transport.]

[3]K. M. Buchanan and J. C. Pugh, Land and People in Nigeria
(London: 1955), pp. 51-52.

[4]See Walter Isard, Location and Space Economy (New York: 1956),
pp. 182-88.

[5]Economic Development: Theory, History, Policy (New York:
1957), p. 2.

[6]"The Economics of Development," in A. N. Agarwala and S. P.
Singh, eds., The Economics of Underdevelopment (New York: 1963),
pp. 12-14.

OCEAN SCIENCE AND HUMAN PROTEIN MALNUTRITION
PROBLEMS IN MIDDLE AFRICA

by

Wilbert McLeod Chapman

INTRODUCTION

The term <u>kwashiorkor</u> first came into the medical literature from Ghana, where it means "red-headed boy."[1] It describes
a protein malnutrition disease. This is primarily a disease of
preschool children, although lactating and pregnant mothers are
often severely affected. At the level short of the disease stage,
some adverse effects from protein malnutrition may be suffered by
substantially a whole population.

Kwashiorkor is the result, exclusively, of the absence in
the diet of a sufficient quantity of protein containing a balance
of amino acids suitable for maintaining the human body in health.
It can be prevented entirely by the inclusion of an adequate volume of proper protein in the diet; it can be quickly cured by the
addition of such to the diet, although retardation of physical
growth in kwashiorkor is apparently never completely recouped by
subsequent proper diet, and there is mounting evidence that the
same is true with mental retardation associated with this disease
in young children.

Although kwashiorkor, the West African name, is widely used
in the literature for this protein malnutrition disease, it is common the world around where insufficient animal protein enters the
human diet. A conservative estimate has been made that at least
500 million humans suffer from protein deficiency, made up of perhaps four-fifths preschool age children, most of the remainder being pregnant or lactating mothers.[2] In the "carbohydrate belts"
of West, Central, and East Africa, kwashiorkor incidence is very
widespread. There are some areas where substantially every child
passes through a phase of kwashiorkor, and in some areas it is
estimated that the mortality from kwashiorkor for children in
their second and third years may reach 60 to 70 per cent of the
observed cases.[3]

While kwashiorkor has its most dread phase as a killer of
young children, the effect of protein deficiency in the adult diet
also has social effects which are difficult to measure but profound,
as it leads in adults to lack of full physical vigor, lowered resistance to infectious diseases, and sub-optimum mental attitudes.[4]

Kwashiorkor results because vegetable proteins available for the human diet do not contain adequate amounts of certain amino acids (chiefly lysine and those containing sulphur) to provide for the human body's needs. Such of the essential amino acids as methionine and lysine now can be synthesized and added to the diet to remedy these deficiencies. It is expected that the progress of organic chemistry will make such synthesization possible eventually for all or any essential amino acid. However, it does not appear likely that this can be accomplished economically or practically on the volume and cost basis required for the world human diet for a period of some decades, and for some products perhaps never.[5]

Meat proteins contain all of the essential amino acids, but the raising of livestock in the "carbohydrate belt" of Middle Africa is rendered difficult, and in many large areas almost impossible, by endemic animal diseases. The worst of these is the tsetse-fly-borne trypanosomiasis, and the map of occurrence of tsetse flies in Africa almost exactly duplicates the worst areas of occurrence of protein deficiency disease in humans (as well as the even more frightful human disease of sleeping sickness).[6] Tick-borne diseases of animals provide a second major problem, and there are others. Although much research is being done on these animal disease problems by institutions specializing in such work, it is not likely that they will be solved in our generation.

Fish proteins also contain all of the essential amino acids, and in combination well-balanced for the human diet. In addition, fish protein concentrates (and the whole fish) are rich in calcium, phosphorous, and trace elements required by the human body, as well as containing notable amounts of vitamins in the B complex.[7] This is the case with both fresh and saltwater fish, and both kinds can play a major role in solving the human dietary problems of Middle Africa. The questions then become:

(1) Are there sufficient fish resources available to the human populations to fill their present and future dietary needs?

(2) What are the impediments in the way of getting the resources to those who need them in a form they will accept and at a price they can pay?

(3) What actions are currently under way to remove those obstacles?

It is a matter of some embarrassment in preparing a paper of this sort that the factual background for what is to be said is hazy. Much of it comes from personal travels and experiences in Middle Africa, and discussions with other experts having experience in the area. The literature prior to 1960, while copious, suffers from much the same trouble as this paper, and in any event is not very pertinent to present-day problems. The pertinent literature since 1960 is very largely contained in mimeographed background papers prepared for conferences convened by various international and intergovernmental bodies. Much that is going on has not yet been reduced to print, and a good deal of what I shall say arises from international meetings and conversations held very recently. Accordingly a large part of what I shall say is not supportable from the existing literature. To confine my remarks to what could be supported by the existing literature would render the following discussion not very timely, or useful.

AVAILABLE FISH RESOURCES

(1) <u>Present African Fish Production</u>: The most recent source of official fish production statistics for Africa is the Food and Agricultural Organization (FAO) <u>Yearbook of Fishery Statistics, 1961.</u>[8] It indicates the total production of fish for the African continent as 2,470,000 metric tons. This continued the steady rise in fish production by the continent recorded by FAO since it began estimating such production. The FAO estimated fish production for Africa, in selected years, has been:

1938	520,000 metric tons
1948	830,000 " "
1958	1,980,000 " "

Over this period of years the average annual increase has been about six per cent, or a doubling in a little more than every ten years. This has been very close to the world rate of increase in production during the same period of years.

About 20 per cent of the fish in the 1961 estimate for Africa was taken in inland waters. Of the marine fisheries, the west coast accounted for 90-95 per cent of the total, whereas the fisheries of the east coast and the Mediterranean together accounted for only 5-10 per cent of the total continental fish catch.[9]

Tropical Africa, the locus of present particular interest, was estimated by FAO to have produced in 1960 at least one million tons of fish. This was distributed by source of production approximately as follows:

(1) Marine fisheries off the west coast in the Atlantic Ocean-- 500,000 metric tons;

(2) Marine fisheries off the east coast in the Indian Ocean-- less than 20,000 tons;

(3) The inland fisheries in the lakes, swamps, rivers, dams,

and ponds--approximately 500,000 metric tons.

Nobody (including Mr. Gertenback, Chief Statistician for FAO Fisheries Division) has any deep and abiding faith in the accuracy of these statistics. The gathering of fishery statistics, like all other official acts in Middle Africa, presents problems. Nevertheless, these statistics, as crude as they may be, do provide some useful information about fish productivity.

(2) The Freshwater Fisheries: The fresh waters of Middle Africa are extensive and richly productive. FAO estimated the freshwater fish production of the world in 1961 at 4,390,000 metric tons, of which that of Middle Africa was somewhat over 10 per cent.[10] However, these total world figures include somewhat over 2,000,000 tons of freshwater fish production from mainland China. The latter figure is extremely suspect and probably at least double the actuality. If this is so, the freshwater fish production of Middle Africa represents closer to 20 per cent of the freshwater fish production of the world.

Three areas in tropical Africa are especially productive: (1) the "upper delta" of the Niger river in Mali, (2) the Lake Chad area, and (3) the central lake system of Congo (Leopoldville), Uganda, Rwanda, Burundi, and Tanzania. The first two areas in particular provide substantial surpluses of fish over local consumption needs. These have formed the bases of extensive dried fish trades throughout West Africa for a long while. The third provides a substantial portion of the animal protein requirements for the peoples of Central Africa.

The Niger river flows northeasterly from the mountains of Sierra Leone and Guinea across Guinea and the southern highlands of Mali until it reaches the lowlands of the interior Mali Sudan. Here it breaks up into a large number of separate branches, sloughs, swamps, lagoons, and transient bodies of water for a distance of more than 400 miles. This "upper delta" of the Niger is one of the more productive fresh water bodies in the world. Canoe fishermen from as far away as the lower delta of the Niger (over 1200 miles distant) come here for the fishing. The total annual yield from this body of water is reported to be about 70,000 tons per year (A. Meschkat, personal correspondence).*

Much of the drainage from the Cameroun Mountains and the highlands of the Central African Republic flows in the Lagone and Chari rivers which end in Lake Chad (lying at the boundary of Nigeria, Niger, Chad, and Cameroun). To this fishery also come

---

*A. Meschkat is the author of the Directory of Fisheries Institutions in Africa (Accra: 1964).

canoe fishermen up the Benue from the lower delta of the Niger, and from it the product radiates out through the adjacent countries and even further away. The production is estimated to vary between 60,000 and 80,000 metric tons per year.[11]

The catch of fish from the lakes and rivers of Congo (Leopoldville) and Rwanda and Burundi was estimated at 139,000 tons in 1958[12] and 132,500 metric tons in 1960.[13] Statistics since that date have been unavailable.

How much additional fish the natural fresh waters of Middle Africa are capable of producing per year on a sustainable basis is not known closely enough to hazard a guess. Belgian scientists estimated that Lake Tanganyika alone was capable of producing 100,000 tons of fish per year, and under the ministrations of the Belgians production did rise from about 4,000 tons in 1950 to over 33,000 tons in 1958. What has happened since their leaving is not known. Substantial increases in production are expected to be available from Lake Nyasa.[14] On the other hand, the introduction of nylon webbing in many of the inland fisheries has so much increased the efficiency of the traditional fisherman in rivers and swamps that there is growing fear of overfishing and reduced production. In most of the area there is almost complete lack of research capable of indicating overfishing, or of governmental machinery to enforce conservation regulations if they were found to be required. In any event it is likely that major sustainable increases in fish production from natural inland waters of Middle Africa are not to be anticipated.

The enormous production per acre of freshwater fishes that accompany wet rice cultivation in southeast Asia, the substantial carp production in central European and Israeli pond areas, and the abundance of both groundwater and native species of fish suitable for pond cultivation in Middle Africa have given rise to glowing anticipation of great promise for fish production through pond cultivation. For instance, the journal The Belgian Congo Today (quoted in Kimble) says: "In the Belgian Congo . . . [t]here is now a total of more than 100,000 (individually owned) ponds covering a total surface of 10,000 acres, which in 1956 yielded 2,000 tons of fish. . . . There is plenty of room for more ponds and it is expected that, with the natives learning all of the tricks of the modern multiplication of fish, production will rise from 1,000 to 6,000 and even 8,000 pounds per hectare."[15] Shimon Tal also discusses this problem,[16] as have many other expatriate fishery experts who have come into the Middle Africa area for varying periods of time.

The cold facts do not bear out the glowing expectations. The actual production of the 100,000 ponds noted above for the Belgian Congo in 1956 was about 400 lbs. of fish per acre per year (under government supervision). Eight hundred ponds in Western

Nigeria produced about 157 tons totally in 1959, or about 400 lbs. per acre per year.[17]   A competent authority both in respect of carp culture in Germany and in tropical Africa informs me that 400 lbs. per acre per year is a very good average from African fish ponds under good supervision, and that in ponds which are not under governmental supervision in tropical Africa, but are operated by private persons or groups of persons, 100 lbs. of fish per acre per year would be a more realistic average figure (A. Meschkat, personal communication).

The difficulty is not the natural conditions but the lack of trained fish culturists. Fish culture as practiced on a commercial scale both in central Europe and the Far East is a sophisticated form of agriculture requiring a high degree of training and discipline on the part of the operator, regular supplemental feeding of diets suited to the particular species of fish, regular harvesting of the ponds, knowledge of and ability to treat fish diseases, and careful management of the population density in the pond on scientific principles. These skills are practically all absent in Middle Africa. Accordingly one does not anticipate much auxiliary support from pond culture in the near future to attend to the protein dietary requirements of the peoples of Middle Africa. In the longer range this gloomy picture may be capable of alteration.

(3) Marine Fisheries of the East Coast: As noted above the estimate by FAO of marine fish production from tropical East Africa is somewhat less than 20,000 metric tons per year. Furthermore, it seems unlikely that this will be markedly increased in the near future. The reasons are to be found in the oceanic and economic conditions as well as in the primitive nature of the fishing industry.[18]

The tropical east coast of Africa has a very narrow continental shelf incapable of supporting resources substantial enough upon which to base a fishery of large commercial scale. Accordingly recourse must be had to the pelagic fishes--the sardines, mackerels, tunas, etc. These sorts of fishes occur on this coast, but not in great quantities. (There is no upwelling of consequence along this coast even with the change of monsoon. As a matter of fact downwelling is present, if anything. The mixed layer of the ocean [above the thermocline] ranges between 60 and 150 meters.)[19] The situation appears to change to one of greater oceanic fertility both to the north along the Somalia coast and to the south along Mozambique and eastern South Africa, although even there the fertility of the ocean is not high. But along the coast of tropical East Africa the ocean is just not very productive.

In consequence of this relatively low oceanic fertility, commercial fisheries of more than nominal size have not been established in the area. Although tuna are available there and en-

joy a firm world-wide market, they are not so abundant off East
Africa that they will support a fishery capable of producing fish
cheaply enough to compete in the world market against tuna from
areas of higher fertility, such as the eastern Atlantic, the eastern Pacific, the Kuroshiwo current, the Gulf stream, etc. Schooling sardine-like fish are also present, but again in such relatively small quantities that they cannot compete on the world market
with similar products from such fertile areas as Peru, Chile, South
Africa, Angola, Iceland, etc., or for local food with the production from the Central African lakes.

From 1952 through 1961 the East African High Commission
(British Colonial Office) supported a rather substantial research
operation (East African Marine Fisheries Research Organization--
EAMFRO) at Zanzibar. The scientists involved did quite competent
ocean research, considering the harsh circumstances surrounding
the struggle for independence in Tanganyika, Zanzibar, and Kenya.
The fate of fishery research in that area since 1961 has been an
uncertain one.

(4) Marine Fisheries of West Africa: The oceanic fertility
of the West African coastal waters is in direct contrast to that
of the East African waters. This is caused by coastal upwelling
processes resulting from the eastern boundary currents of the area,
and also the shallow thermocline which leaves the mixed layer of
the ocean ordinarily shallower than the "critical depth" governing
phytoplankton production. Accordingly, the nutrient chemicals
that are so abundant in the oceanic depths are brought up within
the range of incoming solar radiation. Under these conditions
phytoplankton (the grass of the ocean) develops in great abundance, upon it vast schools of anchovy and sardine-like fishes
graze and proliferate, and upon them feed the predatory, pelagic
bonitos, mackerels, tunas, etc.[20]

In the early 1950's, the British Colonial Office established a West African Marine Fisheries Research Organization
(WAMFRO) based in Sierra Leone. One of its purposes was to in-
vestigate the marine fisheries resources of the Gulf of Guinea with
a view to assisting the industrial growth of the Gold Coast (subsequently Ghana) and Nigeria. Excellent beginning research work
was done by this organization, but the swift pace of political
events gave it a short life. Ghana achieved independence in early
1957 and established its own fishery organization. Nigeria became independent in late 1960, and had already established a Fishery Service before that time. Thus, the expatriate staff which
had been assembled for WAMFRO in the early 1950's had been dispersed between the three countries before the decade was out, or
dismissed.

The French similarly established ocean research facilities
of excellence in their colonies at Dakar (Senegal), Abidjan (Ivory

Coast), and Pointe-Noire (Congo-Brazzaville). These were established independently in each place by the French government and have fared somewhat better during the period of independence than did the British examples. The stations at Abidjan and Pointe-Noire in particular have continuously thrived from the standpoint of budgetary support and the quality of the ocean research undertaken.

Belgium also undertook substantial offshore fishery research and explorations in the years just prior to the granting of independence to Congo(Leopoldville) in August, 1960. This work terminated suddenly in 1960. Portugal similarly undertook, and still maintains, ocean research and fishery development in Angola, where the fertile waters of the Benguela Current support substantial, if still largely underdeveloped, fisheries. South of this, the Union of South Africa developed and has maintained a fishery research organization, equivalent to any of comparable size in the world, to guide the development of its large, prosperous, and still expanding fisheries in the Benguela Current off South-West Africa as well as South Africa.

Although knowledge of the West African seas and their inhabitants remained fragmentary by 1960, the big year of independence in West Africa, the above noted practical and scientific work had provided a sufficient background of knowledge so that it could be stated with considerable confidence that not only were the West African seas very productive, but that they could easily support fisheries capable of producing more than sufficient animal protein to adequately support not only the whole human population of Middle Africa but also a considerable increase in that population. The problem then became:

> How could these needed protein resources be gotten the short geographic distance from the nearby sea to the stomachs in the adjacent rainforest belt that needed them?

Involved were dietary prohibitions and habits of infinite variety; primitive fishing techniques of great antiquity, often engrained not only into tribal custom, but religion; political division of the area into about twenty sovereign nations; very low purchasing power by those who needed the protein; a primitive but very solidly established local pattern of fish marketing;[21] rampant nationalism; lack of knowledge of the adjacent ocean and its resources as well as their variations in time; some overtones of the cold-war struggle; poor road systems and other transportation means; lack of scientifically trained people in the whole area; little or none of the skills or habits of seafaring people or of managerial skills in the local populations; and an overall shortage of development capital, educational facilities, and governmental organizations with which to meet the problems.

Nevertheless, great developments have taken place in the fisheries of West Africa in the few years since independence, and a solid groundwork has been laid for much further development in the near future. These activities can be conveniently discussed under the headings of practical and scientific developments, although the two have been much mixed together, as is proper in a situation which requires the blending of many talents and much skill in the successful solution of the immense problems that exist.

PRACTICAL APPROACHES

Although Ghana became independent in early 1957 and Guinea in late 1958, the great year of independence in West Africa was 1960, when no fewer than 14 new countries emerged in the area (Cameroun, Togo, Congo-Leopoldville, Dahomey, Niger, Upper Volta, Ivory Coast, Chad, Central African Republic, Congo-Brazzaville, Mali, Senegal, Nigeria, and Mauritania).[22] The effect of this massive splitting of three colonial empires into 16 sovereign national fragments (with Sierra Leone later providing a 17th) has had a profound effect on the development of the marine fisheries of West Africa (as on everything else in the area) that is still going on in ways that are sometimes difficult to trace or whose outcome is difficult to estimate. Some of these developments have been hampering, while the outcome of others appears to be beneficial.

The coming of nationalism in West Africa has been to some extent upsetting to the traditional fish trade in West Africa. Prior to nationalism the inhabitants of the area simply paid little attention to the colonial territorial boundaries. The sea fishermen of Ghana, for instance, customarily went with their families and canoes for great distances along the coast (at least from the mouth of the Congo to Gambia) seasonally. They set up camp on the beach wherever fishing was good, caught fish, and sold them locally. (A census in 1958-59 showed that there were at least 67,000 sea fishermen in Ghana who employed 8,800 or more canoes.)[23] The movement of these traditional fishermen along this great stretch of coast has been considerably hampered by the growth of nationalistic competition in several areas. Similarly, the fishing tribes of the Niger delta traditionally took the long voyages up the Niger to what is now Mali, and up the Benue to the Lake Chad fisheries. Also the very large trade in dried freshwater fish from the upper delta of the Niger and Lake Chad, as well as the dried and smoked ocean fish from the coast up into the interior, flowed up and down traditional pathways most fluidly with no thought for national boundaries. All of this is becoming increasingly hampered and constricted by the new national boundaries and sovereign concepts.

On the other hand, the vigor of the new national governments has given impetus to the modernization of sea fishing that in several places has brought sharp advances. A good deal of this has been stimulated by private enterprises in Europe, Japan, and America, which have been invited, or encouraged, by the new governments to take part in this development. Perhaps the largest stimulant has arisen from the tuna fisheries.

In 1953 Captain L. Bertin, a French national, who had been operating two American-type live-bait tuna clippers out of Panama in the eastern Pacific, moved his vessels to West Africa and began operating them out of Dakar (and subsequently out of Casablanca also). This was the beginning of modern high-seas tuna fishing in the area.[24]

In 1955 small albacore tuna vessels of Basque and Breton origin began coming to Dakar to fish yellowfin and skipjack tuna in the winter season when they could not operate in their home waters of the Bay of Biscay. They were soon followed by their Spanish Basque colleagues. This fishery has grown steadily until in 1964 there were somewhat over 100 of these Bay of Biscay vessels working the tuna fisheries of West Africa.

In 1956 the Japanese began exploratory fishing for tuna off West Africa and elsewhere in the tropical Atlantic. This rapidly expanded into a large commercial fishery, which by 1964 employed about 120 very large and modern tuna clippers producing upwards of 100,000 tons of tuna from the Atlantic as a whole.[25]

In 1957 and 1958 the Van Camp Sea Food Company, after extensive inquiries, sent the large live-bait tuna clippers "Chicken of the Sea" and "White Star" over to explore the tuna fishing possibilities along the whole African coast from Mauritania to Angola. Subsequently, the company established operations in Freetown, Sierra Leone, and, with other partners, in Abidjan, Ivory Coast.

In October, 1959, StarKist Foods, Inc. of California began an exploratory survey for the government of Ghana of the pelagic resources (principally tuna) of the Gulf of Guinea. It has continued to advise and assist the government of Ghana in its fishery developments and does business at Tema, as well as having established itself at Pointe-Noire.

As a result of these several lines of activity, tuna fishing vessels of Japan, Nationalist China, the United States, France, Spain, Portugal, and Italy were fishing along the West African coast from South Africa to Morocco in 1960, landing perhaps 75,000 tons of tuna.[26] Young tuna were found throughout the Gulf of Guinea to Gabon, indicating abundant spawning in the area.[27] Large adults suitable for taking with long-line were found throughout the area and continuously across the Atlantic to South America.[28] A great deal was still to be learned about the seasons of occurrence and availability of tuna in the area, but the commercial fishery was established, and it has continued to grow.

So far Africans themselves have not become much involved in tuna fishery, except as occasional crewmen. The high seas, the complicated machinery of the modern vessels, and the needed team-work at sea are as yet beyond their experience. Original efforts made by the government of Ghana to go directly into the fishery with modern purse seining were a failure, but continuing efforts are being made and will eventually work out.

Aside from the provision of revenue to the governments and shore-side employment for local labor, the tuna fisheries have had another important effect on the growing fisheries of West Africa. At the beginning of the tuna fishing period, there were no facil-ities along the whole West African coast for freezing and storing fish. The tuna fishery required such facilities. Accordingly there now are large, modern, cold storage facilities built and op-erating in Las Palmas, Dakar, Freetown, Abidjan, Tema, Pointe-Noire, Monrovia (under construction), and Fernando Poo (still in planning stage), as well as some such facilities at Lagos.

These fine modern installations are forming the nuclei around which modern fish processing and distributing operations can be built, and these operations are growing slowly but certainly. For instance, at Freetown frozen fish suitably packaged and priced for local consumption are stored in the tuna cold store during the local good fishing season and then distributed, not only locally, but increasingly up-country, during the rainy season when the local fishery comes to a stop, thus levelling out and increasing the sup-ply of fish for local consumption. Recently a small cannery has been established in connection with this facility to can experimen-tal packs of fish for local consumption.

In Abidjan the production of fishery products, both for local and export sale, has gone on equally rapidly. There is quite successful canning as well as freezing, for local as well as export sale. As in Freetown, the establishment of more stable sources of frozen fish of the cheaper varieties on a year-round basis has not only levelled out the seasonal variations in avail-ability, but continuously increased the total supply of fish for local consumption. Aside from sale as a fresh or frozen commodity, it is becoming more common for this fish to be sold as part of the traditional smoked fish trade. The African woman entrepreneur (the local fish trade in West Africa is almost entirely in the hands of women) will buy one or more five kilo packages of frozen fish from the cold store and peddle them by the piece. What is left over at night is smoked in small primitive apparati, and peddled during the next two or three days.

Not only at Takoradi in Ghana, but at the fine new fish

harbor at Tema outside Accra, the Ghanaians are building and operating what will be, in the near future, a fully modern complex of fish catching, processing, and distribution operations that is greatly increasing the flow of fish into the interior, as well as providing some varieties for export. The Ghanaian fisheries currently are a curious combination of highly modern foreign enterprise (Russian, American, and Japanese), local modern private enterprise, local governmental enterprise, and primitive, traditional tribal or family enterprise. But even the family enterprise canoe fishery is becoming motorized with outboard motors. Although fishery developments in Ghana have had considerable ups and downs over recent years, created often by governmental inexperience, the business seems to increase steadily in volume and modernize about as rapidly as can be expected. Among the new governments of West Africa, that of Ghana has been among the most vigorous in pushing the development of its sea fisheries and, despite all of the difficulties experienced, among the most successful. It now has seven modern trawlers being built for it in Norway, of which the first was launched in April, 1964. All seven trawlers will come to Ghana under the command of Norwegian experts who will train Ghanaian fishermen in their use.[29]

In the late 1950's Russia began experimental trawling in the Gulf of Guinea (primarily for <u>Sardinella</u> at first), but now large stern trawlers of the most modern type--of 2,900 metric gross tons, storage capacity of 560 metric tons, crews of 60-70 men, and daily freezing capacities of 30-35 metric tons--are used. They use mid-water trawls that can fish at any depth. They catch principally sardine, mackerel, carangids, and pelagic species.[30] This fishery has developed rapidly to considerable scale and has in the last few years been joined by modern Polish trawlers. The aim of these enterprises has been to provide fish for their home markets. However, the European home markets are selective as to species, whereas the West African market will quite literally take any kind of fish. Accordingly, what has increasingly developed is that the Russian and Polish trawlers working offshore freeze all their catches and sort them into what is suitable for sale in Europe and what is not. The latter are off-loaded in Africa. This trade has so far centered in Ghana, but also operates in Guinea, Togo, and Nigeria--and perhaps elsewhere.

The Japanese have recently begun similar operations. In 1963 thirty-four Japanese trawlers operated off West Africa and produced 92,000 tons of bottom fish. Much of this was shipped home to Japan and to Europe, but 11,500 tons were sold in Ghana, 5,500 tons in Nigeria, and several thousand tons in Liberia and Sierra Leone.[31]

Since April, 1963, about 600 tons of fish is landed per month at Monrovia, Liberia, of which about 40 per cent goes upcountry. Cold stores now under construction in the interior will,

when completed, absorb 60 to 70 per cent of the landings in Monrovia, which it is intended to expand. [32]

In the line of practical developments, mention must be made
of the activity of the FAO Fisheries Division in improving the traditional marketing and catching operations of the local fishing in
several countries of West Africa. Quite strikingly successful has
been the introduction of outboard motors for use on canoes, and
nylon webbing and lines for the fishing. This has been particularly successful in Ghana and also in Senegal, where FAO now has a
naval architect aiding the local government in improving the design of the traditional fishing craft. After material original
difficulties, the marketing of fish in Takoradi, Ghana, was much
improved with the aid of FAO experts. [33] An FAO expert in Ghana
is slowly but surely improving the native ability to catch Sardinella on the open sea. In Nigeria a Special Fund project administered by FAO is, after the normal original period of difficulties,
beginning to improve the local catching, processing, and marketing
of fish from the broad lagoons and delta area of the Niger.

Lastly, there should not be ignored the small European
single or two- or three-boat entrepreneurs who have set up busi-
nesses in several countries in West Africa, ordinarily undercapi-
talized, small in scope, and based upon shallow water trawling
for strictly local consumption. There have been one or more of
these small enterprises in almost all of the West African countries
since independence, and even before. Some have failed, but some
have prospered, and they add their bit to the local fish supply.

Note should be taken also of the bilateral fishery development and assistance projects which are of considerable scope and
variety. Amongst these particularly are the French schemes in
Guinea, Senegal, Mali, Ivory Coast, and Congo-Brazzaville; the
United States schemes in Liberia, Togo, and Ghana; the West German
and East German projects in Guinea; the continued British assistance in Sierra Leone and Nigeria; the Nationalist Chinese scheme
in Cameroun; [34] the Polish schemes in Guinea; the Russian schemes
in Ghana and Nigeria; etc. Some of these have been small; some
have been large. In total they have added considerable impetus
to fishery developments in the area.

SCIENTIFIC APPROACHES

The difficulty with the practical approach to fishery development in a new area is that if the new area is much different
than the area in which the practical fisherman and entrepreneur has
had his training, his training does not apply very well. The practical Europeans who came into the area had not had much previous
experience in the tropical ocean. The Americans had had their
training in the eastern tropical Pacific and, while the eastern

tropical Atlantic resembled it in many respects, it was still different. For instance, purse seining, which was very successful in the tuna fishery of the eastern Pacific, and showed much promise in West Africa, simply has not worked well there as yet. Also the Sardinella, which showed up abundantly occasionally on shore, and could be found in great abundance at depths on the echo sounder offshore, seldom came to the surface offshore where the surface fishery could get at them. While the inshore continental shelf had good catchable quantities of fish on it, the outer deeper portions did not.

By 1960 it was plainly evident that if the full resources of the West African seas were going to be brought to the use of mankind, then a great deal more was going to have to be learned about the oceanic circulation, its variations, and the effect of these upon the variations in abundance and availability of the individual resources. This was the work of scientists and, practically speaking, there were neither the scientists in the area equipped to do the work, the organizations under which the work could be done, nor the funds or ships with which to carry it out. The work was started, nevertheless, and has been carried forward to this point nicely.

The Commission for Technical Cooperation (CCTA--Commission du Coopération Scientifique et Technique en Afrique au sud du Sahara) had been formed by the United Kingdom, France, Belgium, Portugal, and the Union of South Africa in 1950 for the purpose of giving their scientists and technicians a forum in which to conduct cooperative planning on projects of common concern in Middle Africa. In 1953 these nations undertook a considerable improvement and strengthening of this organization. A scientific council (CSA) of nonpolitical orientation was added so that the organization became known as CCTA/CSA. Development funds were added. In 1957, in anticipation of oncoming national independence in the area, the organization was further strengthened and its base broadened so that the new countries could come into membership and full participation in the work of CCTA/CSA, which by now was becoming most important in its joint activities respecting tropical medicine, tropical agriculture, tropical forestry, tropical husbandry, geology, water use planning, etc.

In 1960 Dr. Emile Postel of ORSTOM (Organization du Recherche Scientifique et Technique de Outre-Mere), who had practical experience in fishery oceanography in Senegal, Morocco, and Tunisia, was made Coordinator for Sea Fisheries and Oceanography for CCTA/CSA. Postel organized three regional meetings in 1960 among the available scientists in Africa. One was concerned with the sea fisheries and oceanography of East Africa and was held in Capetown, South Africa. Another was concerned with the same subject for West Africa and was held in Monrovia, Liberia. The third was a symposium on West African tunas held in Dakar, Senegal. From

the latter two meetings came three ideas fully endorsed by the con-
ferees:

(1) A careful scientific survey should be made of the trawl fish
    resources of the continental shelf off West Africa--from
    Senegal to Angola;

(2) An equally competent and thorough study of the oceanography
    of the Gulf of Guinea and the nearby Atlantic should be made
    with a view to its application to the development of the
    pelagic fisheries of the area (particularly Sardinella and
    the tunas); and

(3) A West African Tuna Commission should be established imme-
    diately along the lines of the highly successful Inter-Amer-
    ican Tropical Tuna Commission of the eastern tropical Paci-
    fic.

The parent body (CCTA/CSA) endorsed all three of these
ideas at its meeting in Lagos, Nigeria, in January, 1961. It proposed four substantial undertakings for the fishery exploration of
the Gulf of Guinea:

(1) An oceanographic campaign (for measurement of physicochemi-
    cal conditions, movements of water masses, productivity, etc.),

(2) A trawling campaign on the continental shelf,

(3) An experimental fishing campaign for Clupeidae (Sardinella),
    and

(4) An experimental fishing campaign for Scombridae (tuna and
    tuna-like fishes).[35]

Fortunately these projects were launched at a propitious time politically, and fell on fertile soil.

The action of CCTA/CSA coincided with the incoming of the
Kennedy administration in the United States, and the appointment
of G. Mennen Williams as Assistant Secretary of State for African
Affairs. A group from the California fishing industry who were
interested in West Africa brought the CCTA/CSA proposals to Secretary Williams' attention and pointed out to him the long-range
benefits that might ensue for the new countries of West Africa from
these scientific inquiries. After looking into the situation carefully, he supported the proposals. The U.S. Bureau of Commercial
Fisheries (BCF) sent a team of experts throughout West Africa to
assess the situation. From all this came two important actions:

(1) The United States Agency for International Development
    (USAID) undertook to underwrite substantially all the costs

of the Guinean Trawling Survey (GTS) if CCTA/CSA could provide for its scientific management (The Department of Technical Cooperation, United Kingdom, also aided, as well as the French ORSTOM.), and

(2) The Bureau of Commercial Fisheries brought to Washington, D.C., a top team of three of its experts from Hawaii to lay the groundwork for the oceanographic campaign.

Although the CCTA/CSA plan was intended to work in the opposite way from the standpoint of timing, the oceanographic campaign got off to a flying start first. The reason was that CCTA/CSA experienced delays in attracting a top-notch scientist to direct the Guinean trawling campaign.

The BCF team leading the oceanographic campaign exercised extraordinary skill and diplomacy, and had a good deal of phenomenal luck as well. They first laid out a practical scheme of inquiry to cover the whole tropical Atlantic within the limits of their own budget. Having done this, they circulated their proposals to other public and private oceanographic organizations in the United States to see whether any of them would like to join in some phase of the operation. To everybody's surprise, many did. They included the Wood's Hole Oceanographic Institution, the National Science Foundation, the Office of Naval Research, the U.S. Coast and Geodetic Survey, the U.S. Weather Bureau, the Atomic Energy Commission, USAID, the National Oceanographic Data Center, the Naval Oceanographic Office, New York University, Scripps Institution of Oceanography, Smithsonian Institution, Texas A. & M. University, and the University of Miami. Several of these brought money as well as scientists and ships to the program.

Having now a much broader and better financed program all ready to take to sea (solely on the basis of United States oceanographers, ships, facilities, and money), the team decided to contact other nations to see which among them might like to contribute to the campaign with ships, scientists, and ideas. The reaction was even more gratifying. Joining in at this stage were organizations from Argentina, Brazil, Congo-Brazzaville, Ivory Coast, Nigeria, Spanish Guinea, the United Kingdom, the U.S.S.R., and West Germany.

One final organizational step remained. In 1961 UNESCO had organized the Intergovernmental Oceanographic Commission (IOC). To its second meeting in September, 1962, the team took this now international scheme. It was accepted as an official project of IOC and its director made the International Coordinator of what now became the International Cooperative Investigations of the Tropical Atlantic (ICITA) of the Intergovernmental Oceanographic Commission of UNESCO.[36]

This brilliant organizational work was surpassed by the accomplishments of the program envisioned. What was contemplated was a multi-ship, quasi-synoptic survey program which would include measurements and samples for selected physical, chemical, biological, meteorological, geological, and geophysical properties of the whole tropical Atlantic. This was to be divided into two phases: Equilant I (February - March, 1963) and Equilant II (August, 1963). Most rarely for such multi-nation, multi-ship operations, this entire campaign came off without any major hitch, and approximately within the planned timing. Thirteen ships from six nations completed Equilant I,[37] and the Data Reports have been published in two large volumes. Eleven ships completed Equilant II, and the Data Reports were published in the fall of 1964. For the first time oceanographic and meteorological observations at sea were coordinated with observations made from an earth satellite (Tiros II) and overhead weather observation planes. All of this worked so well that an Equilant III was carried out in the spring of 1964 by six vessels as a bonus.

In the meantime Frank Williams (an English scientist who had spent ten years working at EAMFRO in Zanzibar) was selected as the leader for the Guinean Trawling Survey, and it went ahead operationally, after its slow start, in every bit as fine a fashion as did its bigger brother ICITA--and in close coordination therewith. It also became thoroughly international, with finances from the United Kingdom as well as USAID, and scientists drawn from Europe and West African countries, the U.S.A., and international organizations. As with ICITA it was conducted in two field phases to get observations in two extremes of seasons. Each phase covered the entire continental shelf of West Africa from Cape Roxo to the mouth of the Congo river, a distance of 2,700 miles. Guinean I was completed between September 25 and December 20, 1963. Guinean II was completed between February 15 and June 15, 1964.

The field phases of these two remarkable campaigns having been completed in an extraordinarily efficient manner, the next phase was the scientific analysis of the data and its presentation in a form suitable for application to its prime objective--the development of the sea fisheries of West Africa. This phase also was well planned. The International Coordination Group (ICG) of ICITA met on June 12-13, 1964, in Paris, in conjunction with the third session of IOC, to consider ways and means of organizing and presenting the data gathered. ICG took the following actions:

(1) It was decided that data reports for Equilant III would be combined with the physical, chemical, oceanographic, and meteorological data from the Guinean Trawling Survey. These joint data would be compiled by the U.S. National Oceanographic Data Center, and the combined data reports would be published by the Argentine Navy Hydrographic Office.

(2) An Editorial Committee was established which would direct the preparation and publication of the atlases arising from this extensive research. Instead of drawing this phase out for some years, as had been past practice in such international multi-ship surveys, the atlases were scheduled for completion within 18 months, an unheard-of accomplishment in this field.

(3) A symposium to review the results of both ICITA and the GTS was proposed. It would be held in West Africa (probably at Lagos, Nigeria) in December, 1965, with UNESCO, FAO, and CCTA as joint sponsors, to begin the process of putting the scientific results of these two campaigns into form capable of practical application.

(4) Although the survey aspects of ICITA were completed and it was anticipated that the atlases resulting therefrom would be completed and published promptly, the ICG recommended that it be kept in being as a mechanism for interested member states to collaborate informally on research in the tropical Atlantic region, including continued exchange of information on cruise schedules; inception, progress and results of research and survey programs; consultative services; exchange of personnel and equipment; and other matters of mutual interest.[38]

This series of recommendations was adopted by the IOC on the last day of its third session, June 19, 1964. Accordingly, the first two of the recommendations adopted by CCTA/CSA at its January, 1961, meeting are well on their way to fulfillment.

The third recommendation of CCTA/CSA--the provision for an exploratory campaign respecting Clupeidae--has also been initiated in a modest but reasonably effective way. In 1962 FAO sent Dr. M. Zei to work on Sardinella problems in Ghana under the Expanded Program of Technical Assistance (EPTA). In the ensuing two years Dr. Zei, working in close coordination with ICITA and GTS, as well as with the local fishermen, Ghanaian scientists, and the large Russian trawlers, found out some of the facts governing the irregular occurrence of Sardinella in the local catches, despite their known abundance in the area. Since this is the fish which occurs in such abundance in West Africa as to be able to relieve the human protein malnutrition problems of the area, the first yield of information from this modest program assumes considerable importance. Dr. Zei found that the Sardinella schools always stayed below the thermocline, which in this region of ocean is usually marked by the isotherm of 24°C. His work indicates that Sardinella are not caught often by the local fishery when the surface water is warmer than 25°C., and that temperatures below 23°C. result in the best catches.[39]

The local fishery for Sardinella is entirely a surface fishery with nets operated by canoes. Accordingly it can catch Sardinella only when there is coastal upwelling which brings the deeper, cooler, sub-thermocline water to the surface where the fishery can get at the fish which come up with the cool water. In years of strong upwelling the local fishery is extremely successful (as much as 10,000 tons being caught in a month or so from a small area off the beach of Dahomey). In years when coastal upwelling does not occur, the local fishery is a complete failure.

Echo sounder studies show, however, that the fish are always abundant in the local area, but under the thermocline. ICITA and GTS work shows that the inshore edge of the thermocline, when present off the Gulf of Guinea, ordinarily lies at depths from 20 to 40 meters, shelving outward to a somewhat deeper level. The Soviet exploratory trawling expedition in 1957 reported catching considerable volumes of Sardinella on the bottom in the Gulf of Guinea 20 miles offshore and at depths up to 150 meters. The Guinean Trawling Survey had similar experiences, actually catching considerable volumes of sardines, mackerels, scad, and mackerel scad by trawl in depths of 30 to 100 meters.[40]

The quantity of Sardinella that may be available off the west coast of Africa is indicated by their wide geographic range and the large catches by the primitive local fisheries when there is coastal upwelling. These ordinarily occur off southern Senegal in June, off the Ivory Coast in August, off Ghana in August-September, and off Pointe-Noire (Congo-Brazzaville) in May, June, and December. The quantity of Sardinella caught in these areas varies from 10 to 30 thousand tons per year. But in Angola, where there is reasonably continuous upwelling, the annual catch reaches 300,000 tons.[41]

Germans, Americans, Russians, and Japanese have now developed practical mid-water trawls which can be coupled with echo sounders to fish for pelagic fishes such as Sardinella at any reasonable depth. The echo sounder locates the fish in the water, and another echo sounder on the trawl head rope shows not only the depth of the net, but the number of fish going into the net as well as those going under it. The net can be adjusted to the right depth quickly and accurately. Accordingly, the technology is now available for the harvesting off West Africa of such pelagic fishes as the Sardinella, which do not ordinarily come to the surface.

It is still a long way from the application of this new technology and these new facts to the vast expansion in the production of fish at low cost off West Africa that appears to be possible, but measures are afoot to close this gap. For example, the government of Ghana has applied for a U.N. Special Fund Pre-Development Project to expand and intensify Dr. Zei's work off its coast. FAO's Advisory Committee on Marine Resources Research

(ACMRR) examined a staff proposal from FAO's Fishery Division recommending a very much expanded regional U.N. Special Fund Pre-Development Sardinella Project. It recommended that a working group of specialists be convened by FAO to make a preliminary study of the project.[42] FAO Staff has already conducted a preliminary reconaissance through the affected countries. Accordingly Williams is justified in saying: "[I]t seems likely that a large scale international survey for Clupeidae may be undertaken shortly."[43]

The fourth objective noted by CCTA/CSA in its January, 1961, meeting--experimental tuna fishing--is presently being carried out by the U.S. Bureau of Commercial Fisheries, and with the termination of its heavy part of the field work of ICITA, it is now sharply stepping up this work.

CONCLUSIONS

One can say with some degree of accuracy that (1) the seas off West Africa contain sufficient animal protein resources to bring to a halt (or certainly to affect greatly) the protein malnutrition in the inhabitants of Middle Africa, (2) the harvesting of these resources is increasing and being modernized, (3) the ocean research needed to further enhance this production is continuing, and (4) the practical steps which will lead to the application of the results of this research are being taken at a speed which is reasonably satisfactory considering the circumstances. But the path between knowledge and its application in the developing world is a long, tedious, and exasperating one.

In West Africa the uncertain political situations still resulting from the massive transformation of the whole area from colonial status to sovereign independence is added to the problems normally involved in leading societies that are technically primitive into production methods that are technically sophisticated. CCTA/CSA, for example, which has contributed so much to the developments of which I have spoken, is currently in a weakened state. The colonial powers which started and financed it have been gradually squeezed out, and with them most of their money. A symposium on Crustacea was held under CCTA/CSA auspices in Zanzibar in February, 1964, right at the time when the revolution there was in full swing. Although the symposium was most successful, and might lead to developments as encouraging as the three similar meetings held under CCTA/CSA auspices in 1960, the organization does not have the funds with which to publish the results of the Crustacea symposium.

It is likely that CCTA/CSA will become the scientific arm of the organization of African unity, but this does not ensure the successful continuation of its work. The African states are all short of money. They think that at the present stage of history (and they are perhaps correct) their small available funds should be used for local projects capable of immediate practical returns. Science simply cannot work within these time limits. Anyone asking a scientist to produce useful results in less than five years time is simply making his request of the wrong type of man.

It seems obvious to us who have been working in this field that the best way to accomplish results of a lasting practical value is by having the Africans themselves do the work with only specialized assistance from the outside. CCTA/CSA, on record, seems to be an effective vehicle for this purpose. Purged of the former colonial powers, it is now wholly native African. But, unfortunately, purging the colonial powers has also eliminated most of the organization's working funds.

The outside world is giving much assistance of many sorts to the new countries of Middle Africa. This is through both bilateral programs and through the United Nations family. The difficulty is that these programs encounter complex administrative handicaps in being made regional, and none of the countries or organizations have shown much inclination to give continuing financial support to the native African regional organization--CCTA/CSA. In ocean fisheries problems, there is extreme difficulty in their being handled on a sovereign nation basis. The Gulf of Guinea, both water and contained resources, is a continuous whole, not only along the foreshores of the several small countries facing on it, but with the remainder of the tropical Atlantic Ocean. The acts of sovereign governments cannot affect the regular progression of seasonal and cyclic changes in it which govern the abundance and availability of its resources. These processes must be studied as a whole if sense is to be made of them, whether sovereign nations agree or not.

However, to the present date, progress has been reasonably good. Nationalism has been bothersome and has delayed the work, but not in a vital manner. There is continued evidence that the full tide of political feeling in the area is beginning to recede. Accordingly, one can hope that the work noted above can be carried forward to successful conclusion, and that kwashiorkor will not only be eliminated from Middle Africa, but that the peoples living there can be assured a wholesome diet which will keep them in full health as a result of their own local enterprise.

NOTES

[1]G. H. T. Kimble, Tropical Africa (2 vols., New York: Twentieth Century Fund, 1960), II, p. 44.

[2]"Future Developments in the Production and Utilization of Fish

Meal," Report of International Meeting on Fish Meal, Vol. I (Rome: Food and Agricultural Organization, 1961), pp. 1-36.

[3]Kimble, loc. cit. (see note 1).

[4]Op. cit. (see note 2).

[5]Ibid.

[6]Kimble, op. cit., fig. 35 (see note 1).

[7]Op. cit. (see note 2).

[8]Vol. XVI (Rome: FAO, 1962).

[9]A Note on the Fisheries of Tropical Africa (Rome: Food and Agricultural Organization, 1961) [Fisheries Paper No. 20]; A Note on the Fisheries of Africa (Addis Ababa: 1964), pp. 1-14. [Prepared by FAO for the UN Economic and Social Council.]

[10]Op. cit. (FAO Yearbook of Fishery Statistics, 1961 - see note 8).

[11]A. Staunche and J. Blache, "Preparation and Trade of Fish Products in the Lagone-Chari-Lake Tschad Basin." MS, 1957, pp. 1-8.

[12]Yearbook of Fisheries Statistics for 1958 (Rome: Food and Agricultural Organization, 1959), XII, table A-5.

[13]P. M. de Kimpe, "Summary of Fishing Activities in Lakes and Rivers of the Congo and Ruanda-Urundi," Expanded Technical Assistance Program Report No. 1299 (Rome: Food and Agricultural Organization, 1960), pp. 1-14.

[14]R. H. Santos Monteiro, "Hydrobiological Studies on Lake Nyasa," Expanded Technical Assistance Program Report No. 1299 (Rome: Food and Agricultural Organization, 1960), pp. 49-54.

[15]Op. cit., I, p. 284 (see note 1).

[16]Sea Fisheries, Inland Fisheries and Fish Culture (Ibadan: 1960). [Report to the Government of Western Region, Nigeria.]

[17]Ibid.

[18]J. A. Crutchfield, Report to the Government of Kenya on the Sea Fisheries of Kenya (Rome: Food and Agricultural Organization, 1958) [Expanded Technical Assistance Program Report No. 990] and Report to the Government of Uganda on Fish Marketing in Uganda (Rome: FAO, 1959) [ETAP Report No. 998].

[19]B. S. Newell, A Preliminary Survey of the Hydrography of the British East African Coastal Waters (London: 1957) [Fishery Publication No. 9] and The Hydrography of the British East African Coastal Waters, Part II (London: 1959) [Fishery Publication No. 12].

[20]W. S. Wooster and J. L. Reid, Jr., "Eastern Boundary Currents," in M. N. Hill, ed., The Sea: Ideas and Observations on Progress in the Study of the Seas (3 vols., New York and London: Interscience Publishers, 1963), II, pp. 253-80.

[21]G. R. Allen and J. Chaux, Some Aspects of the Marketing of Dried Fish in Central and West Africa (Rome: Food and Agricultural Organization, 1961).

[22]G. Etzel Pearcy, "Africa: Names and Concepts," Department of State Bulletin for 26 December, 1960, pp. 1-9.

[23]"The Fisheries and Their Development in Ghana," Expanded Technical Assistance Program Report No. 1299 (Rome: Food and Agricultural Organization, 1960), pp. 23-27.

[24]E. Lassarat, "Situation de la Pêche Industrielle en Côte d'Ivoire." [Rep. d. Côte d'Ivoire, 1961 - MS.]

[25]Suisan Tsushin, June 15, 1961, p. 1. Periodical.

[26]Foreign Service Dispatch CERPD-A-1 and 3 FSM, 552.9 (Department of State: November 15, 1960).

[27]Lassarat, op. cit. (see note 24).

[28]Nagai, Kawaguchi, and Nagome, "Operations of Japanese Long-Liners and Tuna Fishing Conditions in the Equatorial Atlantic (Particularly 1960 Trends)," Tuna Fishing Magazine (Misaki), No. 77 (April, 1961), pp. 16-22.

[29]South African Shipping News and Fishing Industry Review, April, 1964.

[30]Fisketsgang (Norway), L, February, 1964, pp. 119-20.

[31]Shin Suisan Shimbun (Tokyo: June 22, 1964), p. 1. Periodical.

[32]A. Freeman, Annual Report for 1963 of the Liberian Bureau of Fisheries (1964), pp. 1-6.

[33]J. L. Dibbs, Report to the Government of Ghana on Fish Marketing in Ghana (Rome: Food and Agricultural Organization, 1961). [Expanded Technical Assistance Program Report No. 1300.]

[34]United States Embassy Dispatch (Yaonde: April 10, 1964).

[35]F. Williams, Guinean Trawling Survey: A Summary to 20 May, 1964 (Lagos: CCTA/CSA, 1964), pp. 1-4.

[36]Report of the Second Session of the Intergovernmental Oceanographic Commission (Paris: UNESCO, 1962), pp. 1-66.

[37]U.S. Coast and Geodetic Survey: Data Report Equilant I, Vol. I (1964).

[38]Report of the Third Meeting of the Coordinating Group of the International Cooperative Investigations of the Tropical Atlantic [June 12-13, 1964] (UNESCO, 1964).

[39]M. Zei, Some Facts on Sardinella in Relation to Temperature. Annex to Food and Agricultural Organization's Advisory Committee on Marine Resources Research Working Paper 10 (January, 1964).

[40]Williams, op. cit. (see note 35).

[41]Zei, op. cit. (see note 39).

[42]Report of Advisory Committee on Marine Resources Research, May 20, 1964, Rec. 13. [Food and Agricultural Organization: Intergovernmental Oceanographic Commission Working Paper 26.]

[43]Op. cit. (see note 35).

THE EVOLUTION OF THE CULTIVATED KAPOK TREE:
A PROBABLE WEST AFRICAN PRODUCT

by

Herbert G. Baker

INTRODUCTION

For about ten years I have been carrying out ecological
and evolutionary studies of the tropical plant family Bombacaceae. [1]
In the Bombacaceae at least two species are of great economic and
ethnobotanic interest. These are the baobab tree of Africa, Adansonia digitata L., and the more widespread and variable kapok tree,
Ceiba pentandra (L.) Gaertn. When evidence came to light of the
kapok tree being cultivated first in West Africa, its study took
on a special significance in view of suggestions that there was
an important center of plant domestication in the nuclear Mande
area around the headwaters of the Niger river in the extreme western part of the Sudan. [2] To interpret the ethnobotanical, phyto-
geographical, and ecological pictures which kapok presents now, it
is necessary to unravel the history of the genus Ceiba and of C.
pentandra in particular. (This species may also be encountered
in the literature under the name Eriodendron anfractuosum DC.)

The tree with which we are concerned is known by many non-
botanical names even to extra-tropical peoples. The commonest
name--kapok--is of Javanese origin. In British West Africa it has
long been called the silk cotton tree, and it is le fromager or
le faux-cotonnier (and only rarely le kapokier) in French Africa.
In Latin America it is simply çeyba or ceiba. Nowhere does it escape having a well-known local vernacular name. [3] This alone is
indicative of its importance to man in all areas where it grows.
There is also no doubt that man has played a significant role in
the history and distribution of the various forms of the species.
As I have pointed out previously, it may be one of the relatively
few agricultural domesticates from upper Guinea. [4] It is the purpose of this paper to indicate the basis for this view.

It was fortunate that, while I was a member of the faculty
of the University College of Ghana, I was able to make field studies in the African range of the species and to cultivate material
derived from Asia, tropical America, and Africa. I also had opportunities for cytological work and investigations into the genetics
of various characters which differentiate the forms. Subsequently,
I have been able to make field observations on tropical American
material and grow a limited number of plants in Berkeley, Califor-

nia. It appears that this is the first time that such a range of experience has been available to a single investigator. The advantage which it has given me in working out the history of the cultivated kapok tree has been enormous.

BOTANICAL NATURE AND USES OF KAPOK TREES AND KAPOK

Kapok trees are large and fast growing, with digitate compound leaves. The trees are deciduous, and when flowers and fruits are produced, they are borne during the leafless phase. The species is strictly tropical, the trees being susceptible to cold-damage and unable to reproduce by seed in places where night temperatures at the time of flowering fall much below 20°C (68°F.).[5] For the same reason, the trees are not productive above 1500 feet elevation, although they can grow up to 4000 feet above sea level.

The flowers of <u>Ceiba pentandra</u> are borne in fascicles, and each is potentially capable of producing a single fruit (although many potential fruits are "voluntarily" shed by a tree after flowering). Botanically the fruit is a capsule, up to a foot long and two to three inches in diameter. A mature tree may produce from 600 to 4,000 fruits at a time.

Kapok itself is the floss which surrounds the brownish-black seeds inside the fruit, but unlike cotton, which it otherwise resembles, it is not joined to the seeds. The individual "fibers" which make up the floss are attached to the inside wall of the fruit and, in the mature state, are dry and air-filled. As a consequence, they serve admirably to assist the distribution by wind of the several hundred seeds which are entangled in them after each capsule splits open (usually into five longitudinally running valves).

The hairs (or "fibers") of kapok are 0.6 to 1.2 inches in length and have a beautiful silken sheen, due to a waxy covering, but they are too short, too smooth, and too lacking in twist to be spun, except in combination with other fibers such as cotton, or after chemical roughening. Consequently, in commerce, as well as locally in the areas of production, kapok is almost exclusively employed for stuffing purposes. It has very good sound and heat insulating properties, and it is so light and resilient that it requires a smaller quantity to stuff a mattress, a pillow, or a marine life-preserver than would be needed with any other material. Its superiority as a filling for life-preservers is further evidenced by its tendency to repel water and by the fact that, even after prolonged immersion, its buoyancy is soon restored by drying. This is a feature which should be borne in mind when considering the occurrence of the species on both sides of the Atlantic Ocean. Kapok is used by natives of all areas in which it occurs for the stuffing of cushions, mattresses, and saddles, and, being inflammable when dry, it is also used as tinder.

The seeds of kapok trees are easily beaten out from among the fibers and have valuable properties themselves, most notably their content of about 20 per cent oil which is edible and has lubricatory and manufacturing uses. Kapok-seed cake, the residue left after the extraction of the oil, is a moderately rich protein source, or it may be used for manurial purposes. In many areas of West Africa the seeds are crushed and roasted or used in soups. The young, unripe fruits may even be eaten, while the fiber-hairs are still succulent.

Kapok-tree wood is soft and absorbent, very light, and easy to work with crude tools. However, it is not durable and becomes brittle when dry. Consequently, Ceiba pentandra has not been exploited as a timber tree, although its softness combined with the straightness of the trunk in some varieties has led to its utilization for dugout canoe manufacture on both sides of the Atlantic Ocean, and for the manufacture of coffins, stools, carvings, etc. (The term ceiba is the native word for canoe in parts of ancient Spanish America.)[6]

In some varieties large plank buttresses are developed at the bases of the trunks, and these have been utilized for the manufacture of doors, tables, and platters. Wood ash from kapok trees is widely used in tropical lands as salt and in soap-making. Additionally, various parts of the trees have been used in medical fashion and, almost universally, some sacred significance is attached to kapok trees. Here, then, is a species for which man may be expected to have shown a regard through the ages and a desire to propagate any unusually advantageous variety when it made its appearance.

However, not all varieties are equally suitable for man's purposes. For example, the trunks of most forms of Ceiba pentandra are heavily armed with stout and very sharply pointed conical prickles or spines. Any spineless mutant which appeared might be expected to be selected. Similarly, the irregular fruiting of many trees (intervals of up to ten years have been recorded) is a disadvantage, and any tree which showed regular annual fruiting would be viewed with favor. Most important of all, the dehiscence of the fruit, with the resultant drifting of the kapok over the landscape, is a serious disadvantage, and the appearance of a tree with an indehiscent, easily harvested fruit must have seemed a godsend to those living in the nearby area. It will be shown later that all of these characters have been selected in the production of the kind of kapok tree which is now most widely cultivated in the world.

SOURCES OF KAPOK

Some kapok is produced in tropical countries from other

members of the Bombacaceae, most notably red-flowered species of
the genus Bombax. Bombax malabaricum DC. in Asia and Australia
and B. buonopozense P. Beauv. in West Africa are such other sources.
In Mexico, Ceiba acuminata (S. Wats.) Rose and C. aesculifolia
(H.B. & K.) Britten and E.G. Baker (known locally as "pochote")
are other sources. However, none of these species is cultivated
to any extent comparable to that of Ceiba pentandra, which provides the vast bulk of the world's supply of kapok, particularly
from Southeast Asia, where the export from Java alone exceeded
12,000 tons annually immediately before World War II.[7] After the
war Thailand took over as the largest exporter, with Indonesia,
Cambodia, Kenya and Tanganyika, India, and French West Africa following in that order.[8]

    A single tree of C. pentandra may produce 6-10 lbs. of ka-
pok each year, derived from several thousand fruits.[9] Trees come
into bearing after only two to six years of growth from seed or
the rooting of a cutting,[10] and may continue to yield indefinitely.
The age to which trees may live has never been established with any
certainty, but it is noteworthy that individuals which become established as pioneers in secondary succession when a forest farm
is abandoned in West Africa survive to become enormous emergent
trees in the forest which develops.

PHYTOGEOGRAPHY OF CEIBA PENTANDRA

    Ceiba pentandra is most unusual among tropical tree species
in possessing a triply disjunct distribution range. The species
is to be found in tropical America, in West Africa, and in Southeast Asia, coinciding with the distribution of the major areas of
tropical rain forest. In the American tropics, C. pentandra ranges
from southern Mexico to the southern boundary of the Amazon basin
and Peru, and it is also well represented in the islands of the
Caribbean Sea as far north as Cuba. In West Africa it is found
from the Cape Verde peninsula in Senegal southwards to Angola (and
in the islands of the Gulf of Guinea); eastwards it extends almost
as far as the Great Rift valley. In Southeast Asia its distribution is less well-defined, ranging from western India through Ma-
laysia, Indonesia, and Indochina to the Philippines, and as far as
Samoa and Tahiti (see map).

    It is not at all unusual for both families, or even genera,
to show such a wide, disjunct distribution, but for a single species it is virtually without parallel. It is this circumstance
more than any other which has led most botanists who have considered the matter to doubt that Ceiba pentandra can be native in all
these areas. The suspicion is aroused that the distribution has
been produced by human transportation of seeds between the areas.

    In 1753 the great Swedish systematist Linnaeus first

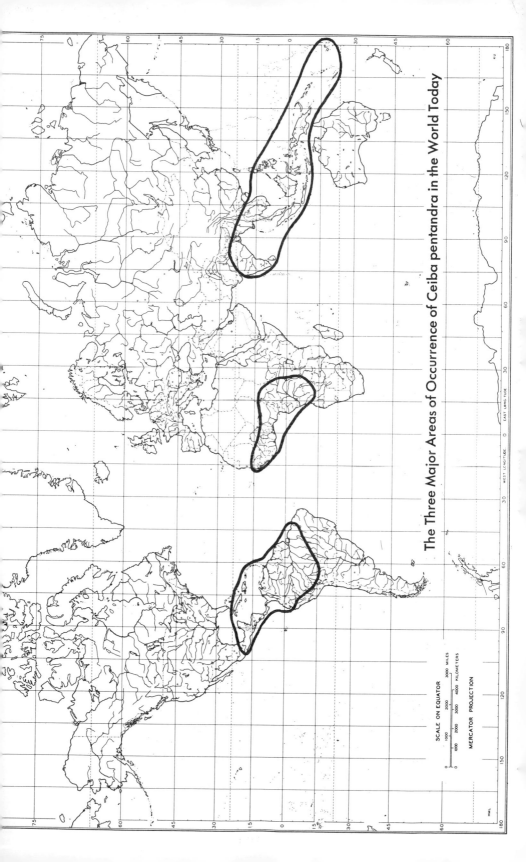

The Three Major Areas of Occurrence of Ceiba pentandra in the World Today

gave the kapok tree an acceptable botanical binomial--Bombax pentandrum--basing it on trees with spineless trunks growing in "India."[11] This may have given a cachet of respectability to Ceiba pentandra in the flora of Southeast Asia, but, unfortunately, it is just in this area that the tree is least likely to be native.

Virtually every possible explanation of the prevailing situation has been propounded. One botanist or another has suggested that C. pentandra is native in each of the three areas and has been carried naturally or with man's aid to each of the others. In most cases the attitude adopted appears to have resulted from the author in question having been acquainted with the species only in one area and guessing about its status in the other areas. The situation has been further complicated by the extensive creation of botanical synonyms all of which refer to members of the Ceiba pentandra complex of forms, and by a lack of consistency in choosing from among them.

(1) The American Tropics: Almost all interested botanists concur in the belief that Ceiba pentandra is native in the American tropics. The compelling reason for this is a taxonomic one. There are nine other well-defined species in the genus Ceiba, and they occur without exception in the American tropics or sub-tropics. Schumann divided the genus Ceiba into three sections; the one containing C. pentandra is the section Campylanthera Endl.[12] It contains four species, and the other three are all endemic to the American tropics. By contrast, there are no species of Ceiba except C. pentandra in Asia or Africa. In these circumstances it is simply an application of the principle put forward by A.L.P.P. de Candolle in 1883[13] to conclude that the center of origin of the genus Ceiba, and of C. pentandra in particular, lies somewhere in the American tropics.

Even so, one reads, on occasion, the suggestion that seed of Ceiba pentandra was carried from West Africa to the New World with African slaves! Such an explanation of the distribution-picture, which never could have been likely to be true, is in any case rendered unnecessary by the clear historical record. Dr. Chanca, physician to the fleet of Christopher Columbus on his second voyage, described trees which he saw in 1494 on the island of Española (Santo Domingo) in the following terms:

> We have met with trees bearing wool, of a sufficiently high quality (according to the opinion of those who are acquainted with the art) to be woven into good cloth; there are so many of these trees that we might load the caravels with wool, although it is troublesome to collect, for the trees are very thorny, but some means may be easily found of overcoming this difficulty.[14]

In 1535, El Capitan Gonzalo Fernandez de Oviedo y Valdes

wrote a whole chapter in his Historia general y natural de las Indias on the tree called çeyba.[15] He pointed out that he had seen many enormous trees of this kind and gave measurements for some of them. He wrote:

> The wood of these çeybas is soft and easy to cut and of little weight and the tree is not held in esteem for building or for more than two purposes. One is its wool and the other the shade. . . . The fruit of these trees is a pod, shaped like the largest finger of the hand, but as thick as two fingers, rounded and full of delicate wool; after ripening, these pods dry and open through the heat of the sun, and then the wind carries away the wool, in which are certain little grains which are its seed, as is the case with the cotton. . . . This wool is short and it seems to me that it could not be spun into thread; but for bed-pillows and cushions of the drawing-room (free from wet) it is a wool unique in its softness and without any ill-effects to the head. . . .[16]

There are other early accounts of trees which are most reasonably identified as Ceiba pentandra and these are summarized by Howe[17] and listed by H. C. Bakhuizen van den Brink.[18] Consequently, there can be no doubt that this species is native in the American tropics.

(2) Africa: By contrast, there are many botanists who maintain that the kapok tree was introduced into West Africa by man. The majority of these reckon that Portuguese navigators brought it from the New World in the early sixteenth century--as they did cassava, the papaya, the peanut, and many other economically important plants--or that it came in on returning slave-ships. There is no historical evidence for either of these views, however.

A more extreme view of the same sort was held by the great French botanist and Africanist, August Chevalier, who patriotically thought it possible that Norman sailors from Dieppe might have brought Ceiba pentandra from Brazil at an even earlier date.[19] There is no historical evidence for this idea, which stemmed from Chevalier's recognition that, if the C. pentandra species had been introduced into Africa as recently as during the sixteenth century, it had become remarkably widespread, common, and variable in the course of only five hundred years.

Nevertheless, the French school of African botanists (A. Aubréville, J. Trochain, etc.)[20] and others such as E. G. López[21] have tended to follow Chevalier's lead in accepting the idea that Ceiba pentandra was introduced from the New World at an early date, although Aubréville had once included this species in a list of trees which he believed made up the ancient littoral forest of

Dahomey.

Later in this paper, I shall consider various lines of evidence which seem to demonstrate quite conclusively that Ceiba pentandra reached West Africa in times which are ancient in the geological rather than merely the historical sense. Even Chevalier considered it possible that unopened fruits might have drifted naturally across the Atlantic Ocean (they are perfect "life-preservers," stuffed with kapok) or that seeds might even have blown across the ocean entangled in kapok in the teeth of a cyclone.[22] (Bakhuizen van den Brink [cited from L. Pynaert][23] had previously put forward the flotation theory.) If unopened but nearly ripe pods of C. pentandra should fall into the waters of a river from a nearby tree (and the species is often to be found in such a habitat), they could subsequently float out to sea and across the ocean. Even if only a single viable seed germinated at the end of such an ocean voyage, it could be the founder of a new colony. Trees of this species are fully self-fertile, as my own experiments have shown.[24] My experiments with floating fruits in seawater have shown that there is some penetration by salt water after a few weeks, but this need not be destructive of all the seeds by any means.

Should this hypothesis of a natural connection between populations of Ceiba pentandra on both sides of the Atlantic Ocean fail of acceptance, it may be necessary to fall back upon an hypothesis put forward by H. J. Toxopeus to explain their present disjunction. In this theory it is postulated that the African and American populations were in much closer--even complete--contact at some time in the past, perhaps in the Eocene Period, about 60 to 70 million years ago. At such a time, according to the upholders of the theory of continental drift, there were contacts between Europe and America. Tropical climates certainly extended farther toward the poles than at present (reaching the latitude of southern England in Europe and a roughly similar latitude in North America). Then, when climatic conditions changed, Ceiba pentandra was cut off in the more southern latitudes on both sides of the ocean.[25] (There is a little--admittedly not very convincing--fossil evidence in favor of this interpretation.)

Whatever the means by which the present distribution of the species was attained, it does not seem necessary to invoke man's aid in its achievement. Further evidence will be presented later, when the various African forms of kapok tree are considered separately, that each form must be considered an African native.

Nevertheless, one piece of indirect evidence may be cited at this point, for it is of general application. It concerns the discovery that many trees of Ceiba pentandra growing in West Africa are infected with various strains of the virus which causes swollen shoot disease in cacao.[26] The cacao tree, Theobroma cacao, was unquestionably introduced into West Africa from the American tropics in the nineteenth century. In the Americas it had never encountered the virus and, consequently, there had been no opportunity for the development of resistance to it. When cacao trees came into contact with the virus in Africa (conveyed to them from African trees of several species in the families Sterculiaceae, Bombacaceae, and Tiliaceae by mealy bug vectors), they reacted violently. Epidemics of swollen shoot disease now threaten to wipe out cacao growing in some parts of West Africa, so strong and rapid is the lethal effect of the virus on the trees. By contrast, those trees of Ceiba pentandra which are known to be infected show only the mildest of symptoms and no suggestion whatever of being affected lethally. It is hard to imagine the development of resistance to the extent which is to be seen if the tree were introduced as recently as the sixteenth century, for the behavior of the tree is much like that shown by the unquestionably indigenous baobab tree (Adansonia digitata).

(3) Southeast Asia: The situation in Southeast Asia is quite different from that in the Americas or in Africa, for there is virtual unanimity of opinion that Ceiba pentandra is not native in Asia and was brought there by man. Only in a few encyclopaedic works is it suggested that the species is native in the Malaysian region,[27] and this unquestionably stems from the extent and length of time of its known cultivation there and the acquisition of information about it simply from those concerned with it as a plantation tree. It is unknown in any habitat which approaches being natural, and grows only as a roadside, plantation, and orchard shade tree.[28]

C. Pickering thought (without evidence) that the Asian material had been carried directly across the Pacific Ocean by Europeans (presumably Spanish and from the American tropics),[29] but this seems out of the question, as the varieties present in the two areas do not agree morphologically. The same evidence appears to dispose of Chevalier's view that it was carried by the same route in more ancient times.[30] There can be no doubt that the introduction of C. pentandra into Asia predates European influence in the area (for it was already there when the first botanically interested explorers arrived), and there is some historical evidence, to be quoted later, which suggests that it was introduced into Java by the tenth century A.D., but the route was not from the Americas.

Overall, then, Ceiba pentandra is unquestionably native in the American tropics, almost certainly native in Africa, and not native in Southeast Asia. It is now necessary to consider the varieties or forms which may be distinguished within the species. From this consideration will emerge not only confirmation of the theory of the distribution of the species presented here but also a demonstration of the origin of the cultivated form now mostly associated with Southeast Asia. The latter is the result of the hybridization of two African forms at a time before European influence was felt in either sub-Saharan Africa or Southeast Asia.

THE FORMS OF CEIBA PENTANDRA

(1) The American Tropics: In the American tropics, Ceiba pentandra has not yet received careful study over its very extensive range from northern Central America to the South American tropics and the Antilles. Most attention has been given to the trees which grow in the various islands of the Antilles. Consequently, there is probably greater variability in the American material than has yet been recorded. Nevertheless, the most frequently encountered kind of tree has well-marked characteristics. (Illustrations may be found in Howe, Record and Hess, and many other references.)[31]

The tree possesses a stout, unforked trunk from which whorls of horizontally disposed branches stand out almost at right angles. It may reach as much as 150 feet in height. Both trunk and branches are heavily armed with conical spines, and large plank buttresses are developed at the base of the trunk. (These are strikingly illustrated by Howe.)

The flower buds form while the tree is leafy, and their maturation is the signal for leaf-fall to begin so that flowering (and the subsequent fruiting) takes place in a leafless phase. The flowers are generally rose-colored; their relationships with pollenators have yet to be worked out. The fruits, which are produced in clusters hanging from short, strong stalks, have a rather stout cylindrical shape, tending to be narrowed at the base but obtuse at the apex. (See Fig. 1, p. 202.) They open by the separation of valves while still hanging on the tree, and the white or greyish-white kapok containing the seeds is released to blow away in the wind.

Trees of this kind are to be found in forests and forest margins and along riversides, and are sometimes planted in the vicinity of villages. They are restricted to lowland sites, not usually being found above 1,500 feet in altitude. Chevalier has suggested that there may be some differences between the trees most frequently seen in the Antilles and those of the Amazonian forests,[32] but, in essence, these consist only of the possession by the latter of cream-colored rather than rose-colored flowers (making them resemble West African forest trees even more closely than the Antillean trees do).

The kapok trees of the New World have been variously named by taxonomists, and the following are the most frequently encountered binomials and trinomials. The first appears to be the legit-

imate name, but a full range may be seen in Bakhuizen van den Brink and in Chevalier.[33]
  (1) CEIBA PENTANDRA (L.) Gaertn. VAR. CARIBAEA (DC.) Bakh.
  (2) C. caribaea (DC.) A. Chev.
  (3) C. occidentalis (Spreng.) Burkill
  (4) Eriodendron anfractuosum DC. var. caribaeum DC.
  (5) E. caribaeum DC.
For the purposes of this discussion we may refer to this kind of tree as the American spiny form. (See Table I, p. 200.)

(2A) West Africa - Forests: The American spiny form of kapok tree is the sort which some authors have suggested was introduced by man into West Africa. Indeed it does have a very close counterpart in the West African forests. As a result of this, Bakhuizen van den Brink included West African trees in his variety caribaea.[34] In general, however, those botanists who divide Ceiba pentandra into varieties (or even a number of species) give separate names to the American and African forest trees. There are slight morphological differences to add to the geographical separation (including a small difference in fruit-shape), but the nomenclatural distinction is really defensible only on a basis of convenience.

In West Africa, Ceiba pentandra is a rather rare constituent of the evergreen rain forest, but is very common in moist semideciduous forests. In addition to its occurrence as an emergent tree (sometimes exceeding 200 feet in height) in the forest generally, it occurs especially frequently along the banks of rivers which flow through the forest. Also, it is a common constituent of the gallery forests which line the river banks as these lead out from the true forest areas into the savanna woodlands and the true savannas. The trees have very thin bark (through which the chlorophyll-containing cortex may show), and to this must be attributed their susceptibility to fire and termite damage, both of which are hazards particularly associated with savannas but less serious in the forests. The primary requisites for their successful growth appear to be sufficient available soil-moisture (without actual waterlogging) and some protection from the ravages of bush-fires. This is shown by the frequent occurrence of the trees in groves in the savanna regions where the topography is such as to provide a local accumulation of drainage water.

These are enormous trees. When they grow to maturity in the forest, they may have columnar trunks which rise unbranched for a hundred feet or more, producing persistent limbs only in and above the canopy of the forest. On the other hand, young trees (and trees grown outside the forest) show persistent branches at a lower level, and these, then, may be seen to have a generally horizontal alignment. (See Plate I, p. 201.)

THE EVOLUTION OF THE CULTIVATED KAPOK TREE

In all cases the trees develop large plank buttresses from the persistent asymmetric growth of roots which run near the surface of the ground at right angles to the base of the trunk. In the region of the buttresses the trunk itself may taper downwards so that at the point of entry into the ground it is quite narrow. The trees are very shallow rooting and are, as a consequence, virtually "standing on their buttresses." An investigation has shown that the extent and disposition of the buttress-development is under both genetic and environmental control. (Details of this will be published elsewhere.)

The buttresses, trunk, and branches of these trees are covered with spines which are continuously developed throughout the life of the tree (although they may become rather sparse on the buttresses in very large trees). The ecological function of the spines is rather obscure (although protection of the thin-barked tree from rubbing by forest animals may be one advantage to their presence), but they are a memorable feature of this kind of tree.

The trees are deciduous, leaf fall being irregular in occurrence (during the months October to March) in the moister forest regions, but becoming more closely associated with the onset of the dry season, for example, as one gets farther away from the Gulf of Guinea towards the interior of Africa. Flowering, which occurs during a leafless phase, shows a corresponding geographical progression from irregularity to regularity; whereas adjacent trees (or even branches of the same tree) may be completely out of phase with each other in coastal forest regions, the flowering phases are more regular inland. However, an important characteristic of the forest trees is that they do not flower every year. At least one flowerless leaf-fall takes place between each one that signals flowering, and in some cases lapses of as many as ten years between successive flowering episodes have been recorded.[35]

The flowers of the African trees are creamy-white in color, strongly (and rather unpleasantly) scented, and open in the evening, persisting till the following morning. Seeds may be set by self-pollination when the stigmas and stamens of adjacent flowers come into contact; the flowers are also pollinated when visited by bees in the early morning for such nectar as may be left in them. However, the bulk of their nectar and some of their pollen and petals are taken by bats which visit the trees at dusk and during the night; the bats are unquestionably the major agents of cross-pollination.[36]

The fruits of these forest trees are rather short and broad and rather abruptly narrowed at each end. (See Fig. 1, p. 202.) It takes about 80 to 100 days from flowering for them to become fully mature. They open by five valves (which are shed) to release the kapok and the seeds entangled in it. The kapok varies in color from tree to tree, but it is often quite white.

These spiny trunked, strongly buttressed forest trees are to be found from Senegal to Angola in all of the major forest areas, and reach eastwards across the continent to Ubangi-Chari in the Central African Republic. This is a very complete and wide distribution, entirely compatible with a native status for this African spiny form. (See Plate I, p. 201, and Table I, p. 200.)

Even disregarding the inevitably dubious references to African kapok trees claimed for second century writers (e.g., Pollux and Philostratus) by Bakhuizen van den Brink,[37] there is historical evidence of the presence of this kind of kapok tree in Africa from early times. Thus, W. L. Smyser notes that the Portuguese navigators who discovered São Tomé in 1470 observed trees which can be identified as Ceiba pentandra growing on that island.[38] In 1594, another Portuguese, Alvares de Almeida, saw giant trees of this sort on the banks of the River Barbaeim, in what is now Portuguese Guinea.[39]

Just before 1700, W. Bosman, travelling along the Guinea Coast, made some notes about very large trees which were being used for the manufacture of canoes:

I have seen some of these trees so high that their tops and branches growing out of them were scarcely to be reached by a common musquet-shot. They are here called Capot-trees, because on them grows a certain sort of cotton here called Capot; which is very proper for filling of beds, especially in this country, where feather-beds are much too hot.
The wood of this tree is light and porous, and scarcely fit for any other use than the making of canoes.
The tree which our countrymen, at the latter end of the fifteenth century, found on Ilha de Principe, or Prince Island, which was four and twenty fathom in compass, was, I doubt not in the least, this Capot-tree. There is also one at Axim, which ten men would have much ado to grasp; not that the body of the tree is so bulky, but that it is so vastly extended by its prodigious sprouts, which closely surround it.
If we had any Romish priests in this country, we could give them some of these branches to build them small oratories, and then the thorny prickles with which this tree is abundantly stored, would serve to correct and chastise their unruly flesh and save them the charge of buying whips.[40]

Further, later references to kapok trees in Africa may be

found, including accounts of the spiny forest trees by M. Adanson (1757),[41] P. Thonning (1803),[42] and J-A. Guillemin and S. Perrotet (1831).[43]

Suspicion that <u>Ceiba pentandra</u> might not be native in West Africa seems to have stemmed from two kinds of observation--that trees of this species are often seen in and near towns and villages (where they have obviously been planted), and that the trees are more commonly found in secondary forest rather than in any which appears to be primary. Nevertheless, the implication of human introduction is not valid from either observation.

In the first place, the planted trees seldom belong to the spiny forest form. Consequently, they are irrelevant to any consideration of this form. Secondly, while there is no doubt that the spiny forest tree has benefited from human disturbance of the forest, this is no reason for doubting its indigenous status. (One may recall the very similar status of the African oil palm, <u>Elaeis guineensis</u> Jacq., an unquestionable native.)

<u>Ceiba pentandra</u> tends to be left when other forest trees are cut down because it makes poor lumber and it is no easy matter to fell an enormous, buttressed giant. In addition, it is, in many areas, regarded as a sacred tree.[44] A third reason for allowing trees of this form to remain in forest clearings is that they are useful as standing trees, producing kapok, seeds, leaves, buttresses, and thorns which all have their value to the local inhabitants.

Being allowed to remain in this manner, they shed a vast quantity of seeds which, in the full light available in the forest clearing, produce innumerable fast-growing seedlings within a couple of weeks. According to T. F. Chipp, a tree may grow to 40 feet in height in only three years.[45] Only slightly less sensational, C. J. Taylor reports that saplings will grow six feet or more in a single year.[46] They are remarkably indifferent to soil conditions and can grow in soil too exhausted for crop plants. Even if no parent tree be left in the clearing in question, the kapok-tangled seeds may blow in from some distance. Consequently, the spiny forest form of the kapok tree is a very common pioneer in secondary succession, and with its capacity for rapid growth to a great height, it keeps pace with the regrowth of the forest, maintaining its own place in the canopy or developing even as an emergent. Because man has vastly increased the opportunities for such successions, there is no mystery about the abundance of the spiny forest form of <u>Ceiba pentandra</u> or its frequent association with human occupation of the forest.

The following names are most frequently encountered in reference to the African spiny forest trees:

(1) CEIBA PENTANDRA (L.) Gaertn. VAR. CARIBAEA (DC.) Bakh.
(2) C. thonningii A. Chev.
(3) Eriodendron anfractuosum DC. var. africanum DC.
(4) Bombax pentandrum Schum. et Thonn.
(5) B. africanum R.Br.

(It should be remembered that the name var. caribaea is also applied to material from the American tropics. A fuller consideration will be found in Bakhuizen van den Brink.[47] Chevalier lists several rather confusing names which he has proposed at one time or another.)[48]

(2B) West Africa - Savanna Woodlands: There is a considerable degree of variability in West African Ceiba pentandra, in itself evidence that the species is not recently introduced by way of a small quantity of seed. There are at least two other forms of this species worthy of separate description. They are quite unlike anything which has been described from the American tropics. Unfortunately, the literature is extremely confused, because some writers have not realized that extra forms exist and, as far as I know, no one before me has commented upon the differences between the two extra forms to be described here.

The more strikingly different form of C. pentandra is known to me particularly from the lightly-wooded Accra plains area of Ghana, although it may also be seen north of the forest belt in Ghana, in the savanna woodland. It must have a much wider distribution than this, because an examination of herbarium specimens in the Royal Botanic Gardens in Kew, England, the British Museum (Natural History), and the Muséum National in Paris has indicated its presence in savanna areas of Togo and Dahomey as well as in coastal areas in the Ivory Coast. Thus, its habitat comprises Guinea zone savannas as well as coastal savannas, but it appears to be completely restricted to West Africa.

Differences between this form and the forest form extend through all parts of the tree. The tree itself is only of moderate height, its maximum of about 50 feet contrasting with the forest form which may reach four times that height. Another striking difference is the complete absence of buttresses at the base of the trunk. The bark is thicker and, possibly for this reason, does not need the extra protection of spines. At any rate, these are entirely missing. (See Table I, p. 200.)

The trunk is often forked, and the branches (which are numerous and rather narrow) leave the trunk at a markedly ascending angle--again contrasting strongly with the almost horizontal disposition of the major branches in the spiny forest form. The leaflets of the deciduous leaves of the spineless savanna form are somewhat broader and less attenuate at the apex than those of the forest trees. (See Plate I, p. 201.)

THE EVOLUTION OF THE CULTIVATED KAPOK TREE

TABLE I

FORMS OF KAPOK TREES

American and African spiny forms	African cultivated form	South-East Asian cultivated form	African spineless form
Spiny trunk	Usually spineless	Usually spineless	Spineless
Big buttresses	Small buttresses	Small or none	None
Horizontal branches	Ascending to various degrees	Partially ("pagode") or strongly ("lanang") ascending	Strongly ascending branches
Unforked trunk	Unforked	Unforked	Often forked
Flowers irregularly	Flowers annually	Flowers annually	Flowers annually
Narrow leaves	Broader leaves	Broader leaves	Broadest leave
Fruits rather short and broad	Fruits short and narrowed at both ends or long and banana-shaped (with ridges)	Fruits short or long; narrowed at both ends	Fruits elongated and narrowed at both ends
Fruits dehiscent	Fruits indehiscent	Fruits indehicent	Fruits dehiscent
Kapok grey to white	Kapok usually white	Kapok usually white	Kapok grey
2n = 80, 88 chromosomes	2n = 72 - 80	2n = 72, 80, 84 ("88")	2n = 72

Artificial hybrids between spiny African and spineless African gave 2n = c. 80.

PLATE I

PPER LEFT: Spiny forest form of kapok tree, standing as an emergent in secondary forest, southeastern Ghana.
WER LEFT: Trees of the spiny forest form left
standing after cutting of the forest around them.
The tree in the foreground is shedding kapok from
dehiscent fruits. Near Aburi, Ghana.

UPPER RIGHT: Tree of spiny forest form showing
persistence of lower branches when grown just
outside the forest. Note the strong buttress-
development. Near Kintampo, Ghana.
LOWER RIGHT: Spineless savanna form of kapok tree,
with forked trunk and ascending branches.
Dodowa road, Accra Plains, Ghana.

PLATE II

LEFT: Avenue of trees of African cultivated form. Slight buttress-development and horizontal or somewhat ascending branches. Lawra, Ghana.

RIGHT: Trees of African cultivated form showing "pagode" habit (foreground) and "lanang" habit (left rear). Plantation near Tamale, Ghana.

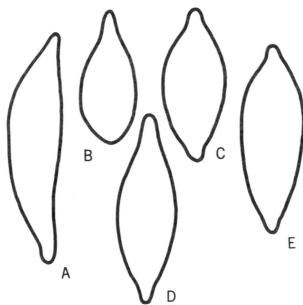

FIGURE 1. SILHOUETTES OF FRUITS OF VARIOUS FORMS OF CEIBA PENTANDRA

A - African cultivated tree (extreme form from Yendi)
B - American spiny tree (from British Guiana)
C - African spiny forest tree (from Senchi, Ghana)

D - African spineless savanna tree (from the Accra Plains, Ghana)
E - African cultivated tree (from near Lawra, Ghana)

Unlike the spiny forest form, the spineless savanna tree flowers regularly every year. The flowers are creamy-white and attractive to bats. The fruits which develop from them are elongated and are narrowed at both ends (see Fig. 1). They are dehiscent on the tree, and the seeds are released to blow away in the usually rather greyish kapok.

This African spineless form appears to be a thoroughly distinguishable variety of C. pentandra (see Plate I and Table I). In some areas, as for example on the Accra plains, it does not occur far from human habitations, but in such a heavily farmed and burned area this cannot be surprising and carries no implication of a non-native status. Irvine refers to a tree which appears to be this form growing in semi-cultivated fashion on the Accra plains and gives Twi, Ga, and Ewe names for it, but he is in error in stating that it differs from the forest tree in having five rather than fifteen stamens in each flower (all Ceibas have five stamens) and that its kapok is whiter than usual.[49]

This spineless savanna tree, with dehiscent fruits, has been named botanically, but the nomenclatural situation in the literature is unclear because of the confusion with a cultivated form (with indehiscent fruits) which will be described later. E. Ulbrich[50] and Chevalier[51] have been responsible for much of this confusion. Chevalier called all spineless kapok trees Ceiba guineensis. He was under the impression that all spineless trees with dehiscent fruits were forest giants with large buttresses (and he called them Ceiba guineensis var. ampla), but it seems most likely that these trees are rather uncommon segregants from hybridization between the spiny forest form and the spineless savanna tree whose name we are seeking. Ulbrich based his taxonomy exclusively on whether the fruits are dehiscent or not and took no account of any vegetative features. Consequently, his Ceiba pentandra var. dehiscens can include both the spiny forest form (which is presumably what he had in mind) and the spineless savanna form.

Bombax Guineense Thonn. appears to be the sole valid name which has yet been given to this form. It is based on material observed and collected by the Danish doctor and explorer Peter Thonning, who was sent by his government to explore "Danish Guinea" from 1799 to 1803. He collected particularly in the Accra and Akwapim areas of present-day Ghana. His own set of specimens was burnt when Copenhagen was subjected to naval bombardment in 1807, but he had previously distributed many duplicates. F. C. Schumacher formally published his botanical results from him.[52]

Thonning's description of Bombax Guineense as an entity separate from trees which he identified as Bombax pentandrum includes the spineless nature of the trunk, the difference in branching (described very accurately), and the absence of buttresses.

He describes the fruits as being dehiscent by five valves. His
Latin diagnosis is perfect for the African spineless form, and his
material came from the area where the tree is most easily found
today--the general area of the Accra plains.

Natural hybrids between the spiny forest tree and the
spineless savanna tree may be seen, usually growing around villages
on the forest margin in Ghana. I have also made them artificially
by pollinating a spineless savanna tree with pollen from a spiny
tree on the campus of the (then) University College of Ghana in
1955, imitating the crepuscular activities of the bats who are
usually responsible for such pollen-transfer. Both the natural
and artificial hybrids appear to be highly fertile, indicating that
the forms should be placed in the same rather than separate species,
as was suggested by Thonning. Consequently, it is necessary to
reduce Thonning's species to varietal status within Ceiba pentandra,
whereupon the name becomes CEIBA PENTANDRA (L.) Gaertn. VAR.
GUINEENSIS (Thonn.) H.G.Baker comb.nov.

(2C) West Africa - Cultivated Trees: Whereas the two
forms of Ceiba pentandra described previously are sometimes found
growing in unnatural situations, the third African form is always
found in circumstances which suggest that the trees have been
planted. We may refer to it as the African cultivated form. (See
Plate II and Table I.)

This is the kapok tree which is to be found at the en-
trances to villages, lining roads, in groves and, occasionally,
laid out in row form in plantations, mostly in the savanna zones
north of the West African forests. In most of the literature
references to African spineless trees, it is this form to which
attention is being directed, even though there may be a measure
of confusion with the previously described spineless form. In
most characteristics the cultivated form partakes of the characters
of one or the other of the previously described African forms or
is intermediate between them. An exception is the indehiscence of
the fruit.

The cultivated tree is moderate in height, has easily
climbable branches standing out from the trunk, bears no deterrent
spines, and forms fruits regularly every year. These fruits remain
closed so that the kapok will not escape, and they may be hand-
picked or knocked to the ground with poles, making it an ideal tree
for the production and collection of kapok. The fibers from these
cultivated trees are usually white in color.

In addition to the economically important characteristics
just described, the cultivated form is intermediate between the
forest and savanna forms in the degree to which buttresses are
developed at the base of the trunk and in the breadth and shape of
the leaflets. Ecologically, the trees show a wide range of toler-

ance, so that although they are usually grown in savanna regions, they can, and occasionally do, grow in forest areas (as for example in Suhum, Ghana).

The habits of the tree are rather variable: clearly many genes are involved. The branches are neither horizontal nor strongly ascending (as in the two putative parents), but show all manner of intermediate conditions. (See Plate II.) The greatest variability is in fruit shape and, because this is a character beloved by taxonomists, this variability has given rise to a good deal of confusion. The fruits may be short and narrowed at both ends, in which case they are clearly intermediate between the fruits of the putative parents, or they may be long and banana-shaped with a longitudinally ridged surface. (See Figure 1.) A full spectrum of shapes between these extremes may be found, but fruit shape may be relatively uniform in one geographical area. For example, the cucumber shape is particularly common in Togo, the adjacent Volta region of Ghana, Chad Ubangi-Chari, and the Cameroons.[53] In other areas (e.g., north Cameroun, according to Aubréville, and in parts of Ghana), fruits are very variable in shape. Nevertheless, in all cases the indehiscent nature of the fruit is maintained.

The indehiscent fruits of this cultivated kapok tree have one very important ecological consequence. They remove from the tree any possibility of seed dispersal by natural means, and in this respect there is a parallel with the development of corn solidly attached to a "cob" in maize.[54] In kapok, as in maize, the greater ease of harvesting is diametrically opposed to efficiency of seed-dispersal, and the cultivated kapok tree is no more able to propagate itself in the wild than is cultivated maize.

Indehiscent fruits are produced by some other members of the Bombacaceae, such as the baobab (<u>Adansonia</u> <u>digitata</u>), but in the baobab the fruits contain a sweet though acid pulp surrounding the seeds. This makes the fruits attractive to animals with powerful jaws (baboons and elephants, especially), which crunch open the fruits, eat the contents, and eventually disperse the often unchewed seeds, which pass through their guts and are left in a viable condition in their feces.[54A] On the other hand, any animal which bit open a mature fruit of the kapok tree would get only a mouthful of floss and would be most unlikely to repeat the experiment. Consequently, we may be confident that anywhere the African cultivated form of kapok tree is found, it will have been carried there by man.

The African cultivated form stands in a strikingly intermediate position between the spiny forest form and the spineless savanna form in the sum of all its characteristics, with the solitary exception of the indehiscent fruit. It matches the natural and artificial hybrids between these extreme forms so completely that I have no doubt whatsoever that it was derived from them by one or more acts of hybridization. The persons who took the hybrid into cultivation later had the good fortune to find a tree in which, by genetic mutation, the fruits stay closed while they hang on the tree. So advantageous was this characteristic for the harvesting of the kapok that these people deliberately propagated and distributed this form.

It was this particular kind of spineless kapok tree to which Ulbrich[55] and Chevalier[56] were referring when they remarked on its propagation by some indigenous peoples exclusively by cuttings. By this means any genetical segregation of characters would be prevented. The occasional trees of this form with spiny trunks to be seen in present-day plantations presumably have resulted from further hybridization involving pollen from forest trees growing near to their seed-parents (for spiny trunks are genetically dominant to spineless ones--See Table III, p. 210). Similar "back-crossing" to the spiny forest parent would account for the range of intermediate forms commented upon by Aubréville.[57]

As early as 1831, Guillemin and Perrotet had recorded the deliberate planting of kapok trees (possibly of this form) in avenues near riversides in the French territory of Senegal,[58] and this had probably been practised for a long time before. However, it was not until the first decade of the twentieth century that the German colonial administrators of Togo and Kamerun and the French in Dahomey realized that kapok of a quality equal to that of the product being exported from Java existed in their own territories, and could provide an export industry for those colonies. Kapok was particularly suitable because, in the absence of railroads, it could be head-carried to the coast and loaded onto ships with the aid of surf-boats and without needing specially constructed harbors.

In 1911, a conference was called at the botanic garden in Berlin-Dahlem, and reports were sent in subsequently by local administrative officers in the various German territories telling what kinds of kapok trees occurred in their areas. The overall report on the findings was then published by Ulbrich, the German expert on the subject.[59] Ulbrich recommended that the form which we have referred to here as the cultivated form (and which he points out that the natives were already growing) should be made the basis of a plantation industry. He gave as detailed an account of the ecology of this kind of tree as was possible at that time.

The outbreak of World War I followed soon after the implementation of these recommendations began. Togo and Kamerun were occupied by British and French forces, and it was particularly the French authorities who took up the idea and spread the plantings widely through West Africa, into Tchad, and farther east.[60] Most plantings were made along roadsides in or just outside villages, but some "orchard-type" plantations were set out in Haute-Volta, the Ivory Coast, and the French Sudan.

With the onset of world-wide economic depression in the late 1920's, however, the kapok-plantation experiment seems largely to have died, and most of the French plantations were abandoned, except for local use, by the 1930's.[61] A 40-acre plantation near Tamale, in Ghana, is still in active production, however, and others must exist. Much growing for local use still takes place.

There is little difficulty in ascribing a valid botanical name to this particular form of kapok tree. The African cultivated form is CEIBA PENTANDRA (L.) Gaertn. VAR. PENTANDRA. The reason for the bestowal of this name--the type variety of the species--to this cultivated form will be given after the consideration of cultivated Southeast Asian material (which was the first to receive the name pentandra). The implication, however, is obvious--that the cultivated material in both of these areas is taxonomically identical.

Synonyms commonly encountered in the literature which particularly refer to the African cultivated material are the following:
(1) C. pentandra var. clausa Ulbrich (including formae albolana and grisea--names which refer simply to kapok color)
(2) C. guineensis A. Chev. var. clausa (Ulbr.) A. Chev.
(Synonyms used only for Asian material are not cited here.)

(3) Southeast Asia: The great majority of the world's supply of kapok is produced in Thailand and Indonesia, the area from which the kapok tree was first described botanically, but to which there is little likelihood that it is native. The trees which occur there show a rather small amount of variability compared with African material and may, therefore, be placed in a single variety or form. (See Table I.) Nevertheless, there is some difference between individual trees in the branching habit which varies from what Toxopeus has called the "pagode" form to the "lanang" form.[62] The "pagode" trees have branches which run more or less horizontally, while in the "lanang" form the lower branches are more persistent and all are obviously ascending. This range in habit can, however, be perfectly matched in the African cultivated form. (See Plate II.) Occasional spiny trunked trees appear as a result of mutation or of contamination.

Cultivated trees from Southeast Asia have been carefully described by Toxopeus.[63] His descriptions, supplemented by my own observations on Indonesian material growing in experimental plots, show that these trees match the African cultivated form and the artificial hybrids between the African spiny forest and spineless savanna forms. Because I had all of these trees growing together in uniform conditions in Ghana, I am completely convinced of the identity of the African and Asian cultivated forms. They must have had a common origin in West Africa, the only region where both parental forms occur.

Cultivation requirements for this form are given in some detail by Kirby;[64] they appear to be based chiefly on Southeast Asian material.

Although the correct botanical name for the Southeast Asian material (under the universally accepted International Rules of Botanical Nomenclature) must be CEIBA PENTANDRA (L.) Gaertn. VAR. PENTANDRA, the following synonyms have been used quite frequently:

(1) Ceiba pentandra var. indica (DC.) Bakh.
(2) Eriodendron anfractuosum DC. var. indicum DC.
(3) E. pentandrum (L.) Kurz var. indicum (DC.) Backer
(4) E. orientale Kurz
(5) Bombax pentandrum L.
(6) B. orientale Spreng.

CYTOLOGY AND GENETICS

The description of the various forms given in the previous sections of this paper have been based on field observations, specimens in herbaria, and trees raised from seeds or cuttings together in uniform conditions in the botanical garden of the University (College) of Ghana at Legon and, more recently, at the University of California, Berkeley. Seed from each of the major areas in which Ceiba pentandra occurs was assembled during the years 1954-57 to provide the cultures in Ghana. The trees grew rapidly after germination of the seed, and many were flowering at an age of less than three years. In addition, the artificial hybrids already alluded to were raised along with seedlings derived from the self-pollination of their parents. In all, 209 trees, representing 15 difference collections of seed, were grown.

(1) Cytology: Cytological studies were, of necessity, restricted to the examination of root-tip cells by sectioning and staining with Heidenhein's haematoxylin and also by the acetocarmine staining of squashes. The results (summarized in Table II) provide a complete validation of the putative parentage of the cultivated form of Ceiba pentandra (both in its African and its Asian populations).

Spiny African and American trees possessed various chromosome numbers between 2n=80 and 88. This agrees with determinations by A. N. J. Heyn, who counted 88 chromosomes in plants raised in Java from seed collected in Surinam and the Congo.[65]

For the spineless African form, two determinations are available, both with 2n=72, the commonest number to be found in the Bombacaceae.[66] Consequently, we might expect the artificial hybrid between the spiny tree (which had 2n=88) and spineless

TABLE II

CYTOLOGY OF KAPOK TREE FORMS

Form	Chromosome counts on individual trees
Spiny forest	African 80, 80, 88, 88 (and 88 by Heyn)
	American 88 (and 88 by Heyn)
Spineless savanna	72, 72
Cultivated	African 72, 72, 72, 72, 72, 74, 74, 75, 76, 80
	Indonesian 72, 80 (and 72, 72, 72, 80, 84 by Heyn)
	("88" by Tjio)
Hybrid, Spiny x Spineless	c.80
Progeny from natural hybrid, Spiny x Spineless	75, 83

tree (with 2n=72) to have an intermediate number. It does, showing 2n=c.80.

The various trees of the African cultivated form have chromosome numbers between 72 and 80, and two samples of Indonesian cultivated material gave counts of 72 and 80. Heyn, who found the chromosomes difficult to count accurately in his material, also reported a range of numbers between 72 and 84 for Indonesian trees of the cultivated form. The persistent nucleolus which caused his difficulty is, in fact, characteristic of the whole family Bombacaceae.[67] J. H. Tjio found 2n=88 in several trees which by implication were of the cultivated form, but, as he cites no voucher specimens and gives no indication of where in the world they came from, these counts can be accepted only with reserve.[68]

(2) Genetics: Measurements made on the sapling trees growing in the uniform conditions of the experimental plots provided extra information on inheritance of the characters which differentiate the forms. These can be added to the results already accumulated by Toxopeus.[69] As a result of our combined studies, the following tabulation of relative dominance and recessiveness is possible:

TABLE III

DOMINANT AND RECESSIVE CHARACTERS IN KAPOK TREES

Dominant character	Recessive character
"Pagode" habit	"Lanang" habit
Spiny trunk	Spineless trunk
Green trunk	Yellow-green trunk
Red flush of new leaves	Green flush
Late and irregular flowering	Early and regular
Dehiscent fruits	Indehiscent fruits
Long fruits	Very short fruits
Colored kapok (various)	White kapok
Narrower leaves	Broader leaves

Toxopeus pointed out that in the genetic makeup of the cultivated form there is an accumulation of recessive characters.[70] It is not necessary, as he does, to claim this as an example of one of Vavilov's principles, viz., that a greater proportion of recessives will be found near the periphery of the distributional area of a species than at the center.[71] On the other hand, it is entirely consonant with the view that characters of value to plants in a state of nature will tend to become genetically dominant and that the mutations (such as the indehiscent capsule) which are valuable only in a cultivated derivative will therefore be genetically recessive.

HISTORY

There is no possibility that there was once a more continuous distribution of Ceiba pentandra between its presently disjunct areas of occurrence in West Africa and Southeast Asia. Any natural link between the areas at a time of more favorable climate in the intermediate regions would have involved either the spiny forest tree or the spineless savanna tree, which are unknown in Asia. Human transportation must have been involved.

There are no records of Ceiba pentandra growing in apparently native conditions anywhere in East Africa, Asia Minor, or western India. Plantations of kapok trees are to be seen in Uganda, Kenya, Tanzania (including Zanzibar), Mozambique, Zambia, and even on the Comoro Islands, but these plantations, according to local floras, were started by Europeans at and since the turn of the twentieth century.[72]

In 1905, W. Busse suggested that Arabs brought kapok trees to West Africa from "the East,"[73] but this was nothing more than a guess. However, there are two records of African plantations being started under European influence with material brought from Southeast Asia. E. de Wildeman provides such a record for Madagascar[74] and J. Gossweiler for Angola,[75] but it is notable that these are two African areas in which the cultivated form has not been recorded as being grown by the natives. Neither putative parent of the cultivated form occurs in Madagascar, and only the spiny forest tree is found in parts of Angola. These must be looked upon as examples of a "feed-back" from Asia of a form originally taken there from Africa, where it originated.

What might have been the method of transfer of cultivated kapok from West Africa to Southeast Asia? The likeliest travellers to have picked it up in West Africa and carried it across the continent are Arab traders. They would have had easy access to it growing in the savanna areas north of the forest belt. The first object of trade may have been the kapok itself, but, as this is seldom shaken clean of all seeds in native preparation, some seeds would inevitably have been transported in addition. Later, a deliberate traffic in seeds may have developed.

Presumably, the direction of Arab transportation of kapok in Africa would have been to the east or northeast. There is a possible reference to kapok grown and utilized in the Axum area of northern Ethiopia in observations made prior to 1522 by Brother Raphael of the Franciscan Order.[76] From northeast Africa kapok could have been carried to Asia by either a land or a sea route. According to Toxopeus, the armies of Alexander the Great, at the time of their expeditions to India, were familiar with kapok as a stuffing material for pillows, etc.[77] This would suggest that kapok was being carried by a land route from Africa. However, it must be borne in mind that Alexander's kapok might have been cotton or could have been derived from a species of Bombax (e.g., B. malabaricum) growing in western India. Climatic conditions are unsuitable for the cultivation of Ceiba trees in Asia Minor and northwestern India, but once the seeds had been carried beyond these areas, trees could be grown successfully from them.

The oldest indication of the presence of Ceiba pentandra in Asia is provided by a stone carving on a fountain in Java. This is at the seaside resort of Djolotoendo, in the Djamboeng district of the city of Surabaya, and has been dated as being made in 967 A.D. According to A. Steinmann, the habit of the tree in this stylized representation is distinguishably different from that in other stone-carvings in Java which are held to represent the wild "Randoe alas" (Bombax malabaricum),[78] but the photographic representation which he gives in his paper suggests that it would be desirable if further evidence of identity could be obtained.

If, however, this dating in the tenth century is correct for Ceiba pentandra, it coincides with a period of intense land traffic between the Sudan and India by way of Asia Minor, and also brings within the bounds of possibility transportation directly across the Indian Ocean by Arab sailors. Unfortunately, there is a gap in the pictorial record until the first printed drawing of a kapok fruit in Dodonaeus' Cruydt-Boeck in 1608 (see Bakhuizen van den Brink),[79] which clearly represents the cultivated form. Perhaps experts on early Afro-Asian relations can take it from here. In any case, they have a clear instance of a cultivated tree which originated in West Africa and was carried to Southeast Asia, where it has become a commercial success.

NOTES

[1]H. G. Baker and B. J. Harris, "Bat Pollination of the Kapok Tree, Ceiba pentandra (L.) Gaertn. (Bombacaceae)," Journal of the West African Science Association, V (1959), pp. 1-9; H. G. Baker, "Opportunities for Evolutionary Research in the Tropics," Taxon, XIII (1964), pp. 121-26.

[2]G. P. Murdock, Africa: Its Peoples and Their Culture History (New York: 1959). Cf. H. G. Baker, "Comments on the Thesis that There Was a Major Center of Plant Domestication Near the Headwaters of the River Niger," Journal of African History, III (1962), pp. 229-33.

[3]For West African lists, see E. Ulbrich, "Die Kapok liefernden Baumwollbäume der deutschen Kolonien in tropischen Afrika," Notizblatt des Königlich botanischen Gartens und Museums zu Dahlem bei Steglitz (Berlin), VI, 51 (1913), pp. 1-37; J. M. Dalziel, The Useful Plants of West Tropical Africa (London: 1937); F. R. Irvine, Woody Plants of Ghana (London: 1961). For Southeast Asia, see I. H. Burkill, Dictionary of the Economic Products of the Malay Peninsula, Vol. I (London: 1935), pp. 501-5; H. J. Toxopeus, "Kapok," in C. J. J. van Hall and C. van de Koppel, eds., De Landbouw in de Indische Archipel, Vol. III ('s Gravenhage: 1950), pp. 53-102.

[4]Op. cit. (see note 2).

[5]Toxopeus, op. cit. (see note 3).

[6]M. A. Howe, "Some Photographs of the Silk-cotton Tree (Ceiba

pentandra), with Remarks on the Early Records of Its Occurrence in America," Torreya, VI (1906), pp. 217-31.

[7]The Economic Development of Ceylon (Baltimore: 1953). Report for the International Bank for Reconstruction and Development - Anonymous.

[8]R. H. Kirby, Vegetable Fibres (London: 1963).

[9]Op. cit. (see note 7).

[10]E. de Wildeman, Notices sur des plants utiles ou intéressantes de la flore du Congo (Brussels: 1903); S. J. Record and R. W. Hess, Timbers of the New World (New Haven: 1943); op. cit. (see note 7); H. G. Baker, unpublished.

[11]C. Linnaeus, Species plantarum (Stockholm: 1753), Vol. I, p. 511.

[12]K. Schumann, "Bombacaceae," in C. P. F. Martius, Flora Brasiliensis, Vol. XII, 3(Monaco: 1886) and "Bombacaceae," in Engler and Prantl, Die Naturlichen Pflanzenfamilien, Vol. III, 6(Leipzig: 1895).

[13]A. L. P. P. Candolle, Origines des plantes cultivées (Paris: 1883).

[14]Quoted in Howe, op. cit., pp. 225-26 (see note 6).

[15]Historia general y natural de las Indias, islas y tierrafirme del mar Oceano (Madrid: 1535). Primera parte, lib. IX, cap. XI.

[16]Quoted in Howe, op. cit., pp. 228-29 (see note 6).

[17]Op. cit. (see note 6).

[18]"Revisio Bombacearum," Bull. Jard. Bot. (Buitenzorg: 1924), sér. 3, VI, pp. 161-241.

[19]"Arbres à kapok et fromagers," Révue de Botanique Appliquée et d'Agriculture Tropicale, Bulletin No. 188, p. 257.

[20]A. Aubréville, Flore forestiere Soudano-Guinéene (Paris: 1950); J. Trochain, Contribution a l'etude de le végétation du Sénégal (Dakar: 1940). [Memoire Institut Français d'Afrique Noire, No. 2.]

[21]Ensayo geobotánico de la Guinea continental Española (Madrid: 1946).

[22]Op. cit., pp. 257-58 (see note 19).

[23] L. Pynaert, "Le Faux-Cotonnier," _Zooleo_ (1953), No. 18, pp. 453-56.

[24] "Self-Compatibility and Establishment after 'Long-Distance' Dispersal," _Evolution_, IX (1955), pp. 347-49.

[25] H. J. Toxopeus, "On the Origin of the Kapok Tree, _Ceiba pentandra_," Meded. Alg. Proefst. v. d. Landbouw, LVI (1948), pp. 1-19.

[26] See D. H. Urquhart, _Cocoa_ (2nd ed., London: 1961).

[27] "Forest Tree Species Suggested for Trial under Humid Conditions in the Tropics and Subtropics," in _Tree Seed Notes_ (Rome: 1955) [United Nations Food and Agricultural Organization Forestry Development Paper No. 5, Part 2] - Anonymous; R. J. Streets, _Exotic Forest Trees in the British Commonwealth_ (Oxford: 1962); Kirby, _op. cit._ (see note 8).

[28] Toxopeus, _op. cit._ (see notes 3 and 25).

[29] _The Chronological History of Plants_ (Boston: 1879), p. 783.

[30] _Op. cit._ (see note 19).

[31] _Op. cit._ (see notes 6 and 10).

[32] _Op. cit._ (see note 19).

[33] _Op. cit._ (see notes 18 and 19).

[34] _Op. cit._ (see note 18).

[35] Chevalier, _op. cit._ (see note 19).

[36] Baker and Harris, _op. cit._ (see note 1).

[37] _Op. cit._ (see note 18).

[38] "São Tomé, the Chocolate Island," _National Geographic Magazine_, LXXXIX (1946), pp. 657-80.

[39] Cited in C. de Ficalho, _Plantas uteis de Africa portugueza_ (Lisbon: 1884).

[40] "A New and Accurate Account of the Coast of Guinea," in J. Pinkerton, ed., _A General Collection of the Best and Most Interesting Voyages and Travels in All Parts of the World_, Vol. XVI (London: 1814). [Originally written and published in Dutch, 1705.]

[41] _Voyage au Sénégal_ (Paris: 1757), p. 93.

[42] In F. C. Schumacher, Beskrivelse af Guineiske Planter (Copenhagen: 1827).

[43] "Bombacaceae," in J-A. Guillemin, S. Perrotet, and A. Richard, Florae Senegambia tentamen, Tom. 1, fasc. 2 (Paris: 1831).

[44] Chevalier, op. cit. (see note 19); R. Schnell, La forêt dense (Paris: 1950); Irvine, op. cit. (see note 3).

[45] The Gold Coast Forest: A Study in Synecology (Oxford: 1927). [Oxford Forestry Memoirs No. 7.]

[46] Synecology and Silviculture in Ghana (Edinburgh: 1960).

[47] Op. cit. (see note 18).

[48] Op. cit. (see note 19).

[49] Op. cit. (see note 3).

[50] Op. cit. (see note 3).

[51] Op. cit. (see note 19) and "Le role de l'homme dans la dispersion des plantes tropicales: échanges d'espèces entre l'Afrique tropicale et l'Amerique du Sud," Révue de Botanique Appliquée et d'Agriculture Tropicale, XI (1931), pp. 633-50.

[52] Op. cit. (see note 42).

[53] Toxopeus, op. cit. (see note 25); Aubréville, op. cit. (see note 20).

[54] P. C. Mangelsdorf, "Reconstructing the Ancestor of Corn," Report of the Smithsonian Institution, 1959, pp. 495-507. Reprinted.

[54A] H. G. Baker, unpublished observations made in Ghana.

[55] E. Ulbrich, "Die Kapokbaume von Togo," Notizblatt des Königlich botanischen Gartens und Museums zu Dahlem bei Steglitz (Berlin), VI, 52, pp. 39-65.

[56] Op. cit. (see note 19).

[57] Op. cit. (see note 20).

[58] Op. cit. (see note 43).

[59] Op. cit. (see note 55).

[60] See Chevalier, op. cit. (see note 19).

[61] Ibid.

[62]Op. cit. (see notes 3 and 25).

[63]Ibid.

[64]Op. cit. (see note 8).

[65]"Du nombre de chromosomes chez quelques végétaux en culture aux Indes néerlandaises (Coffea, Ceiba, Oryza, Derris et Palaquium), Ann. du Jard. Bot. de Buitenzorg, XLVIII (1938), pp. 103-120.

[66]Baker, op. cit. (see note 1).

[67]Ibid.

[68]"Notes on Nucleolar Conditions in Ceiba pentandra," Hereditas, XXXIV (1948), pp. 204-8.

[69]Op. cit. (see notes 3 and 25).

[70]Op. cit. (see note 25).

[71]N. I. Vavilov, Studies on the Origin of Cultivated Plants (Leningrad: 1926).

[72]Chevalier, op. cit. (see note 19); Streets, op. cit. (see note 27).

[73]Vegetationsbilder, IV (1905). Reihe, Heft 5 (Jena). [Periodical founded by G. Karsten and H. Schenk.]

[74]Op. cit. (see note 10).

[75]Flora exotica de Angola (Luanda: 1922).

[76]G. E. Nicholson, "The Production, History, Uses and Relationships of Cotton (Gossypium spp.) in Ethiopia," Economic Botany, XIV (1960), pp. 3-36.

[77]Op. cit. (see note 25).

[78]A. Steinmann, "De ondste afbeeldingen van den kapokboom op Java," Tropische Natuur, XXIII (1934), pp. 110-13.

[79]Op. cit. (see note 18).

LAND RESOURCES OF THE HAYA

by

Priscilla Copeland Reining

In this paper I examine the land resources of the Haya--
the inhabitants of the northwestern corner of Tanganyika (now Tanzania)--as they can be characterized physically, as they appear to
be manipulated by cropping techniques, and as they are utilized by
groups and by individuals in ways which are significant to the nature of Haya society.[*] The Haya act about their land resources as
if they were immutably allocated into different categories: village land, grassland, forest, and swamp, and I propose to review
the available data on their physical environment in this light.

The extreme northwestern corner of Tanganyika lies west of
Lake Victoria. The area is further defined by the course of the
Kagera river, which arises some distance inland from the lake and
flows north and then east to empty into the lake. These natural
boundaries, river and lake, demarcate a block of land indigenously
inhabited by a Bantu-speaking people known as the Haya.[**] The area
can be divided into three differing regions: the coastal region,
an interior basin, and the Karagwe escarpment. The coastal region,
where most Haya are concentrated, has distinctive topographical
features and coincides with a zone of relatively high rainfall.
This region (approximately 1000 square miles in extent) and the
land resources found within provide the focus for this paper.

The Haya are closely related culturally and in the general
form of their political system and means of social stratification
to the neighboring Lacustrine peoples such as the Ganda, Nyoro,
and Soga of Uganda. The Haya are sedentary, with very stable vil-

---

[*]The field data were obtained while I was a Fellow of the East
African Institute of Social Research, 1951-53, 1954-55. The present tense used throughout refers to the years indicated. I wish to
acknowledge the assistance of Mr. Hesloa Kibira, who was in my employ, the information and advice received from Mr. Reakes-Williams
of the Maruku Coffee Station and from Mr. Boos of Kawalinda, and
the helpful criticism of my husband, Conrad C. Reining.

[**]Haya country is divided into two administrative districts, Bukoba and Karagwe. Bukoba includes an area north of the Kagera
river and south of the Uganda-Tanganyika border.

217

lages occupied under conditions of high population density, and
they practice a type of mixed husbandry involving tree crops and
the keeping of cattle. Formerly they were organized into a small
number of petty kingdoms which have since been incorporated into
the colonial administrations (German and British) and into the new
national administration. In addition to the territorial groups
which form the constituent units of the indigenous and recent administrations, there are also descent groups in the form of clans
and shallow lineages.

The general interest of the Haya data derives from the Haya
having accommodated to the problems inherent in land scarcity,
dense population, and sedentary residence over a long period of
time. They have formed a society based on descent groups and territorial groups. While the details of Haya social history differ
from those of any other society, so that the Haya are in this sense
unique, a social structure based on some combination of descent
groups and territorial groups is very common in African societies.

The allocation of land resources by the Haya appears
to have had the effect of making certain types of land scarce.
The long-term land scarcity has resulted not only in an intensive
scrutiny of the physical environment but has had a profound effect
on the social structure as well. The earliest succinct statement
of the relationship between natural factors and their cultural consequences in Haya country is found in G. Milne:

> It would seem then that this Lake-coast strip,
> well watered, densely populated and modestly prosperous,
> must have a soil of fairly high fertility, or at least
> that it is cultivated by enlightened and intensive agri-
> cultural methods that are well worth study. The first of
> these inferences is true of those parts of the ground
> that are actually the seat of the bulk of production, but
> this in turn is so only because of a measure of truth in
> the second. The fertility of the soil in eastern Bukoba
> as determined by natural factors is actually low, but it
> appears to have been concentrated in blocks of initially
> more eligible land which form only a fraction--perhaps
> one fifth or less--of the total area. Outside these
> blocks (the banana gardens) expansion is deterred by an
> unusual degree of infertility which for some crops amounts
> to complete barrenness.[1]

PHYSICAL ENVIRONMENT

Geology: The general outline of the geological history of
the Bukoba coastal area is established. In Eozoic times, a formation now identified as Muva-Ankolean in Karagwe was being laid
down in the form of sediments.[2] At some period during the Paleo-

zoic these sedimentary rocks provided the basic material for the formation of the Bukoban system of sedimentary rocks. The geographic distribution of the Bukoban system coincides with and partially serves to define what we are designating as the coastal region. The system does not occur elsewhere in Bukoba District, although a related formation extends for many miles south into other districts in Tanganyika.

Intruded into the Bukoban system are sills of dolerite, a few of which provide distinctive landmarks. The three parent materials are unevenly distributed. Says Milne:

> [A] mantle of irregularly-mixed detritus had accumulated, derived here mainly from the sandstone, there mainly from the shaley rock, locally from the delerita, most often from some proportion of all three. . . . [W]herever mature forms of the topography favoured the convergence of subsoil seepages . . . sheets of concretionary ironstone ('murram') tended to form.[3]

Neither the Muva-Ankolean formation nor even that of the much younger Bukoban system contains fossils. Recently (in geological terms), the surface has been subject to a series of faults paralleling the lake.[4]

Topography: The dominant features of the landscape in Bukoba are the stony scarp faces and the long slopes between them. Except where it is broken by drainage systems, the easternmost escarpment parallels the lake shore--indeed provides the major definition of the lake shore, although there is commonly a slope below it, fronting on the water. Where configuration and drainage system allow, beaches have been formed. The top of the escarpment forms a virtually level plateau which slopes very gradually to a valley bottom, approximately five miles distant. The lower slope and face of the next escarpment lie beyond. (The level of Lake Victoria is 3700+ feet; the highest scarp is 5000 feet.) At frequent intervals, following the gradient of the sloping plateau, there are many minor all-season streams. The many small streams are bordered by quite dense, natural, in the sense of uncultivated, vegetation. The main inland stream, draining the western side of the escarpments, has some swamp area adjoining it.*

Climate: Haya country lies well within the equatorial belt having a double rainy season. The prevailing winds associated with both the northeast and southeast trades move westward across Lake Victoria according to the season. The resulting rainfall in the

---

*True forest (in Haya vocabulary) occurs only in one area ten miles or so inland.

coastal area averages as much as 80 inches a year, with a range between 64 and 105 inches. The pattern of rainfall distribution is as important as the totals. Some rain falls every week in the year, but following the pattern of the double rainy - double dry season, there are two maximum rainy seasons and two minimum. The maxima center on April, the rainiest month of the year, and on November. The minima center on July, the driest month of the year, and on January. The months August through February are actually characterized by a relatively consistent rainfall. However, the rainiest months of April and May are abruptly followed by the driest-- June and July--resulting, of course, in a marked discontinuity in rainfall at that time of year. There is some time lag before the effect is apparent in the vegetation.

The excellent map compiled by Dr. David N. McMaster summarizes the rainfall data for Haya country (Map 1).[5] These data provide one more criterion for demarcating the coastal region: the zone of relatively high annual rainfall, 45-80 inches, is confined to a strip along the coast. The outline of this zone conforms to the pattern of the escarpments.

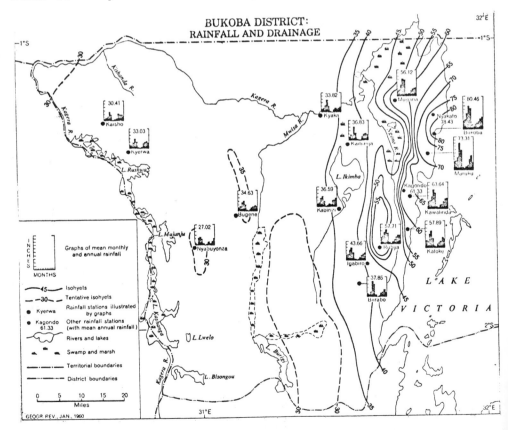

MAP 1

During the rainy months of March, April, and May, there
are many stormy days with heavy downpours. At other times during
the year, there are often cool days with a light rain falling most
of the day. The moderate temperature represented by a monthly
mean of 68°F. ± 1 degree reported by Milne[6] is supported by the
meteorological information published by the East African Statistical Department.[7]

Soils: The soils are red in appearance whenever they are
exposed through cultivation or road cuts, and feel friable when
they have been worked. Milne describes them as having a "range in
texture from pure sand to fine-sandy-clay, according to the degree
to which their products of weathering and denudation have been
mixed."[8] From the numerous places in which rocks are exposed in
the vicinity of the escarpments (on top, as well as below) and from
the experience of the grassland cultivators, it would seem that in
many areas the soils are shallow.

Milne's analysis of the geological history of Bukoba is
followed by one of his principal conclusions: "[T]he total effect
of all denudation processes to date is expressed in the present
patchwork distribution of the raw materials of soil. . . ."[9] Where
the patchwork distribution has resulted in greater fertility, there
are now villages; where it has resulted in lesser fertility, there
is now grassland. It was with Milne's thesis in mind that soil
samples from villages north of Bukoba town and from the intervening
grassland were taken for analysis in the government laboratories.
The intent was to determine whether chemical analysis of samples
from village land and from grassland would reflect the apparent
vegetational differences. A table giving the results as they were
obtained from the laboratory is appended (Appendix I).

The results were interpreted by the government chemist in
these terms:

Phosphorus status throughout is quite good, poor
soils in this respect usually containing less than 10 ppm.
This may be due to hut refuse or old boma sites or to local parent material of a volcanic type. Exch Ca figures
are variable. This element which is of major significance
nutritionally will in a first class soil amount to 10 me%
or more. Below 1 me% is very low. Adequate Ca levels so
far as crop growth is concerned usually means that other
nutrients are adequate. Organic matter contents are moderate to high as in No. 36 top soil (Personal communication, 1953).

An explanatory review of the technique of analysis was made available by the Regional Director of Agriculture and transmitted with
a covering letter containing this statement: "Calcium is badly
deficient in the grassland soils of Bukoba, and coffee and bananas

221

will not grow on these soils" (Personal communication, 1955).

    To clarify the interpretation of the results concerning village land and grassland, a review of them was made by Mr. William Holton of the Department of Geography, Howard University, at my request. His opinion is that "there is no inherent difference in the two soils. Any difference must reside in management. The indications are that these soils should be good for agriculture" (Personal communication, 1964). The consultants both caution against looking to the chemical analysis for a definitive statement of soil fertility or infertility. Productivity was suggested by Mr. Holton as a more useful criterion for agricultural purposes than relative fertility. There appears to be a striking difference in the productive capacity of the soils for different crops. For example, the 1953 Annual Report of the Maruku Coffee Station indicates that tree crop cultivation is difficult to establish in the grassland even with the many modern techniques available to the trained agronomist.[10]

    The Siting of Villages: If variability in the inherent capacity of the soils to support certain types of vegetation results from the regular operation of long-term processes (following Milne's analysis), and if this is matched by a finding of differences in productivity for different crops, then we should look for a regular pattern in the siting of villages. Upon inspection, we find villages in three locations: on the level plateau tops of escarpments, in the middle reaches of slopes with a moderate gradient, and on the slopes below an escarpment, but not at the ultimate base. Villages are never sited along valley bottoms nor along streams following a pronounced gradient, nor in the in-between reaches of the sloping plateau.

    Comparative historical data on the extent and stability of village land among the Haya are available through the map published as a result of Hans Meyer's expedition of 1911.[11] On a contour map outlines are shown of "banana groves," many of which are named. Since no recent comparable map for the entire district existed, I mapped one sub-chiefdom in outline fashion. Villages show a notable consistency between the 1911 map and my 1953 map. All of the named "banana groves" of 1911 were extant in 1953 and in the same position. A number of smaller, undesignated outlines which occur on the 1911 map were also present in 1953. (These data are useful for comparative purposes because they show the distribution of villages before coffee was expanded as a cash crop and before population increases had occurred.)[*]

---

[*]To study the stability of tree crop cultivation in the entire coastal region by comparing the 1911 Hans Meyer map with one derived from aerial photographs would be an interesting research

To arrive at a more thorough understanding of a village, I mapped one by using a compass and pacing the boundaries shown me by each villager (Map 2). The particular village represented in the map is close to average size--some 100 acres. It lies two miles due south of Kawalinda, where the mean annual rainfall is 65 inches. It is two miles inland from the lake, lying above the first major escarpment. A prominent sill, locally named Madzibu, is a mile and a half to the southeast between the first major escarpment and the lake. (Milne had suggested the intruded sills as a likely source of enriched parent material, but in their present relative positions, the sill cannot have contributed to the village.) The village appears with the same name, in this location and approximately this size, on the Hans Meyer map of 1911. Subsequent work in five other villages showed this one to be similar to them in its main characteristics.

Each numbered area on the map outlines a single small farm, called a kibanja (plural bibanja) which provides much of the wherewithal to make its occupants self-sufficient. Residence at the end of a cleared forecourt, quarters for animals, the major portion of subsistence foods, and a coffee crop from which a modest income is derived are what Haya commonly expect to have in a kibanja. A group of bibanja is called a kyaro (plural byaro), which is translated as "village." Although each kibanja is demarcated with boundary plants, the vegetation of one kibanja is continuous with that of its neighbors, so that the entire village has similar, consistent cover. In addition to the main tree types--banana and coffee--there are a number of large trees of other types in each village. Common ones are the wild fig, used for barkcloth, and Chlorophora excelsa, locally called mvule.

The totality of vegetation which we are calling a village appears to adjust to the fluctuations in the seasons, so that the general character of the village is much the same throughout the year. The vegetation never has a dry season; the small variation in temperature and the fact that it rains at least once every week undoubtedly are influential in obtaining this result. The floor of a kibanja is always moist. A house fire, which scorches the vegetation in the immediate vicinity, never spreads to the rest of the kibanja. There are no reports, nor any evidence, of a kibanja or a village fire.

CROPS AND CROPPING TECHNIQUES: VILLAGE LAND

The Haya use a distinctive set of crops and cropping tech-

---

project. As yet only small portions of the region have been photographed, since this area has not been included in the systematic aerial photographing of Tanganyika.

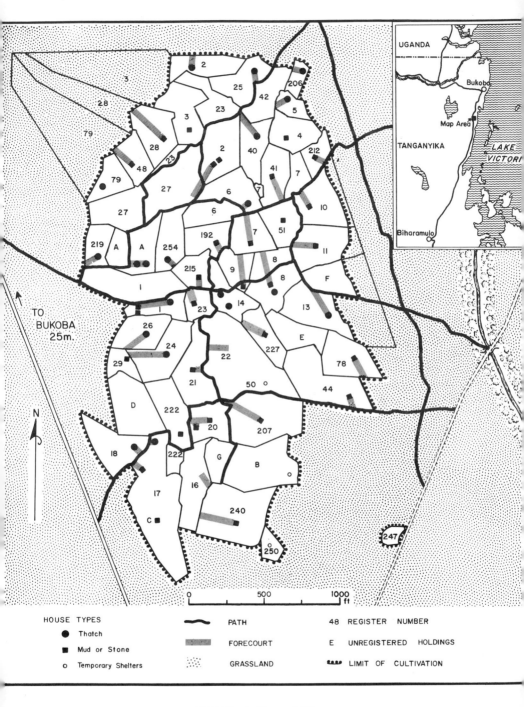

MAP 2. A Haya Village

niques for each main type of land. From the way they designate
different types of land and from my observations of cropping techniques, it is my opinion that all of the land in the coastal region is under some form of human management. One must distinguish,
of course, between the known domesticates and those naturally occurring plants whose status is observed or controlled in some fashion. Because of the pervasive character of human management, it
is very difficult to speak of vegetation apart from the way it is
used culturally. The two principal sets of crops--bananas and
coffee--and the ways in which they are grown tend to accentuate
the differences between village land and grassland.

Bananas: The Haya grow different varieties of bananas,
but the kind whose fruit (bito-ke) must be cooked to be edible is
much the most important. The entire plant is called ngemu. They
also grow a banana for roasting (nkonjwa), a banana for making beer
(mbi-li), and a small, sweet banana (bi-isi) for children, among
others. The manner of cultivation is the same for all varieties
of bananas.

The Haya have a large vocabulary devoted to the banana to
distinguish the different parts of the plant, the stages in the
growth cycle (which they liken to the phases of human life), the
various phases of cultivation, and the several locally-fashioned
tools used in cultivation. Depending on where and when the cultivator desires a new plant (in an established kibanja), he will dig
a small hole close to the root base of a parent stem to encourage
the parent to put out a shoot. The Haya expect this shoot to be
a narrow-leafed "sword sucker," which they believe to be the most
appropriate for bearing fruit. Unwanted additional shoots are
systematically removed, except for a single small one which they
refer to by a term meaning "useless." When the fruit on the parent
stem is ripe and has been cut, the leaves are cut and spread on
the ground, but the stem is left upright to nourish the growing
shoot. Only when the stem has dried will it be cut down and allowed to rot on the floor. Later still the old root mass is cut
out at about the time the new shoot reaches full size, but before
it has fruited. After it has fruited and as it approaches maturity,
its progress will be observed. When the angle formed by a single
bito-ke fruit and the shoot is wide, the bito-ke will be considered
ripe, and it will be cut. The Haya say that if it is left, it will
turn yellow and rot in a few days. If it is cut while immature,
it will wither and dry and be inedible. After cutting, the fruit
may be cooked any time within a week. The stem from which the
fruit has just been cut is allowed to stand until it dries, and
so forth. The process takes from 18 to 30 months, the variation
depending on the area and the skill of the cultivator.

The Haya see the maintenance of the kibanja to be accomplished through the return of all parts of the plant--stem, leaves,
root mass, peelings--to the immediate environs in which it grew.

(Insofar as the human occupants eat the bito-ke and also use the kibanja for latrine purposes, there is a further indirect contribution from this source.) With a main subsistence product as perishable as the banana, the general management of the kibanja in such a way that different plants will be fruiting at different times is seen as important and as a man's job. It is his prerogative to cut the bananas. Haya say that bananas ripen well during the drier months and grow well during the rainier months. When a kibanja is under proper management, it will have bananas in all different stages of growth.

Production of bananas eludes quantification. A very small portion of those grown are marketed at local weekly markets. Bananas are ubiquitous and are commonly regarded as a staple.

Coffee: The Haya grow two kinds of coffee. A variety of Robusta named bukobensis, which is indigenous to the area, was formerly held as a monopoly by the ruling dynasty, and was used as a masticatory. It was also an item of trade. The Haya still grow Robusta. Each household keeps coffee for use as a masticatory, a usage which presumably requires a minimal portion of the crop, the remainder of which is marketed under the auspices of a coffee board. Arabica coffee, introduced by Europeans, forms 20 per cent of the crop. [12]

The coffee is planted in among the bananas in varying proportions. Where Arabica is cultivated, an attempt is made to devote a separate area to it, without bananas. Robusta is intermixed and shaded by bananas. The coffee culture is started with Robusta seedlings distributed by Coffee Board nurseries. [13] While trees in varying stages of growth can be observed, many a kibanja has relatively large, mature-looking trees only. Some of these trees are said to be 30 years old. The coffee flowers and ripens throughout much of the year. The predominant style for a kibanja is an apparently random fashion planting of bananas and Robusta coffee, the bananas taking perhaps 75 per cent of the space. When the planting is intermixed in this fashion, the banana litter protects and fertilizes the coffee. For additional protection cut grass is brought in from the open land and laid down as neatly as the carpet grass is in the house.

Coffee production data are available in the form of sales to the local cooperative, recorded by quantity, type (Arabica or Robusta), quality, date, and price paid, for each member of the cooperative. (About half of the men living in this village belong to the cooperative. Two of the men who belong are small-scale traders who are marketing coffee through the cooperative which they purchase rather than grow.) From these data and from cumulative data for the sub-chiefdom in which the cooperative is located, one gets an overall picture of coffee production, together with the particulars for all those households belonging to the cooperative.

226

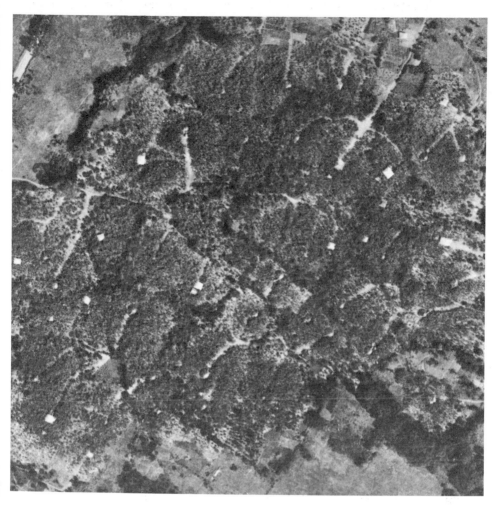

Aerial View of Haya Village

LAND RESOURCES OF THE HAYA

(The household by household coffee production varies wildly from 7 to 256 kilos when calculated on a unit per acre basis--see Appendix III.) Some coffee is marketed every month in the year. The higher grade Robusta peaks in March and again in July. Somewhat less than half the crop is marketed in the drier months of June-September. The poorer grade Robusta follows a similar pattern but peaks again in November. Some small amount of Arabica is sold in every month from March through December. The pattern of sales to the cooperative is the same for the single village and for the sub-chiefdom in which it is located.

Beans and Corn: The floor of the kibanja is planted with beans on a seasonal basis. They are planted in October, and by mid-December the normal litter is obscured by the annual plants. When ripe, some are used as fresh vegetables, and the remainder are dried and stored. Some few stalks of corn are interplanted with the beans. At certain times of the year a layering of crops-- beans, corn, coffee, bananas, and shade trees--are all growing on an intermixed basis on the same piece of ground. Single plants of corn are sometimes spaced at intervals along the forecourt in an ornamental fashion. Only households with able-bodied adult women have beans and corn.

Sweet Potato, Sorghum, Peanut Succession: The only significant part of a kibanja without permanent tree cover is that area some twenty by twenty feet where sweet potatoes, sorghum, and peanuts are planted in a succession pattern as follows:

Crop	Planted	Harvested
Sweet potatoes	September	September
Peanuts	September	February
Sorghum	February	July
Fallow	July	September
Sweet potatoes	September	September
Sorghum	September	February-March
Fallow	March	September
Sorghum	September	February-March
Peanuts	March	July
Sweet potatoes	September	September

The sorghum is used in the making of beer.

A wide variety of other plants are often cultivated in the kibanja environment. The appended list (Appendix II) was intended to be as exhaustive as possible, although no one kibanja is likely to contain every single plant listed. The large trees, the bananas, and the coffee appear to provide a basic framework within which other plants or trees may be cultivated in a manner which is minor but contributive to the overall pattern both in terms of the kibanja as a cropping unit and in terms of Haya economy. Gourds, reeds for fencing, special spinaches used for relish, tree tomatoes, chili peppers, and pineapples come to mind especially.

As these data indicate, cropping in the village is a year-round activity. Many of the phases occur continuously throughout the year: mulching, weeding, harvesting, banana cultivating, coffee drying, and hulling are not seasonally ordered but are recurrent. The demands on labor are moderate but consistent. Weeds are a problem. Haya cope with this problem through active mulching, especially with the normal refuse from banana but also with grass. They are compulsive weeders, and the condition of a kibanja is determined by the degree to which the banana flourish and the mulch is uniform and weed free. No data are available to me on the identification of the weeds, however.

CROPS AND CROPPING TECHNIQUES: GRASSLAND

The terms grassland, open land, and rueya are used synonomously to refer to treeless expanses of grass. Unlike the village land, the open land reflects the seasonal changes associated with rainfall fluctuation. During the drier months the grasses become tough and dry out, while during the rainier months, especially where patches have been burned, the grasses are green and tender.

Only two crops are cultivated on the grassland: Bambara nuts and peanuts. A similar cropping technique is used for both. The open land plot having been selected, the ground is worked into low mounds about a yard wide and ten yards long, in which Bambara nuts are planted. (The ridges or mounds create a very distinctive patterning which is discernible when one walks over ground previously cultivated.) A group of women prepare their open land cultivations side by side, resulting in a patch varying in size according to the number of women and the number of plots each has chosen to do. Occasionally peanuts will be planted after Bambara nuts, but otherwise the plot reverts to grassland after a single cropping.

The grass of the coastal region is classified as Hyparrhenia rufa.[14] Following cultivation, the reestablishment of grasses is as follows: 0-11 months--Eragrostis milbraedii, Paespalum spp. and Brachiaria spp.; 12-15 months--Hyparrhenia filipindula; 15 months or more, Eragrostis blepheroglumis, and finally, Hyparrhenia spp.[*] When the latter becomes dominant, the Haya will recultivate for Bambara nuts. The lapse of time is seven to eight years, but the condition and type of grass rather than time, as such, are the

---

[*]The botanical identification of these grasses is that of Mr. Reakes-Williams.

determining factors.

The grassland is also the site of cattle grazing. The grassland is deliberately burned by the Haya to improve pasturage for the cattle. The herds are small. All the cattle belonging to the people living in the village are pastured as a herd, the herdsmen being selected from the men and boys on a rotation basis. The task is considered a menial one, although the cattle are valued for their products. About 40 animals constituted the village herd-- many villagers had no animals and only one man had more than two. No tsetse flies are found in the coastal area, because the bush cover which provides the tsetse habitat elsewhere in the district does not occur here. (McMaster discusses the role of the cattle in maintaining the open character of the grass.)[15]

Certain grasses are selected for mulching in the village, and other grass is used for thatching. Yet another kind is used first as a kind of carpet several inches deep inside the house, and then, when it has become soiled with household refuse, as mulch on the kibanja. Whenever material suitable for domestic cooking fires can be gleaned from the grassland, it is taken. These various techniques serve to perpetuate the open quality of the grassland on the one hand, and enrich the manure and grass of the kibanja on the other.

To summarize, one may distinguish between the village land cultivation and the grassland cultivation in terms of productivity. The grassland has very low yields per cropping unit (one crop in eight years) and per person, by the standards of mechanized agriculture. In the village land, the yields appear to be relatively high per cropping unit, although low per person.

SOCIAL AND DOMESTIC GROUPS AND FAMILY DEVELOPMENT PHASES

The Haya have distinctive sets of social arrangements with respect to their land resources. In examining the social arrangements we will be considering the relationship between the plant life and the social community.

The fixed character of its main resources has its effect on all major aspects of Haya society. The village provides the locus for a Haya territorial group in the true sense of the term. The village is the permanent constituent unit in the territorial system, the larger units of which change with changing political conditions. The superstructure of the political system has been rebuilt a number of times in the last 100 years, but with the same village blocks. The village is also a permanent unit in the sense that it is independent of the life cycles of its residents. Using the map of the village as a reflection of a long series of social decisions, we will see a connection between particular domestic

groups in the various phases of their development cycle and the
bibanja in which they live.

(The set of social arrangements for the open land is distinctive, but can be discussed here only very briefly. The annual
cultivation in the grassland is done by women who arrange among
themselves, each year, who shall cultivate together and where.
These small groups are composed of congenial friends, neighbors,
or relatives, who may live in any of several different villages.
While the women as individuals are subject to no more than a minimal rule of tenure and to no explicit social guide, the groups
they form undoubtedly reflect local preference and consensus.)

Bibanja in the Village: The irregularity of bibanja boundaries represent numerous minor adjustments of the cultivated land
among its occupants. A few intruding features must be accommodated,
for example, the trunks of large trees. Villages below an escarpment occasionally have large boulders and often have minor streams.
The villages have paths forming boundaries which are less likely
to be changed than the invisible ones between bibanja. The paths
frequently are at a level lower than the bibanja they separate.

Haya negotiate for quite small pieces of bibanja land. The
one small piece belonging to 7 (see Map 2) is calculated at a tenth
of an acre, and the long sliver belonging to 23 is calculated at
three-tenths of an acre. The partners to negotiations over such
pieces believe that they are making an adjustment in their holdings: with pieces of this size neither believes the transaction
to be a transfer of a kibanja. Such transactions--only two of
which are visible--multiplied over the years have contributed to
the irregularity of outline of each kibanja. These pieces, not
contiguous with the home kibanja, became evident in the course of
mapping. Except for these two small pieces, all of the outlined
holdings with name or number are called bibanja and are seen by
the Haya as being viable.

Bibanja-Families: Meyer Fortes[16] has proposed a method of
analysis of domestic groups based on the cyclical character of family development starting with the marriage and ending with the
death of the partners to the marriage. The phases are: (I) expansion as children are born, (II) dispersion as children marry,
and (III) replacement as the heir's family replaces that of his
parents.   The developmental approach is a useful way of ordering
household data, although certain modifications in detail were found
appropriate for the Haya village. Haya distinguish between the
people of the household and a family. A young man with a family
generally lives on his father's kibanja, and does not become head
of his family until his father dies. In the discussion which follows a man with a wife and children will be considered the head of
a family whether in Haya terms he is or is not a family head.

Phase 0 - Pre-Marriage: (I have added this phase to those
of Fortes, to allow for certain "potential" families.) During the
mapping of the village a number of unoccupied bibanja were located.
Since there were no houses on them, they were indistinguishable
from the surrounding bibanja to the uneducated eye, although, of
course, they were known to the villagers. The occupants of neighboring bibanja went round the boundaries of the unoccupied ones.
With one exception, these unoccupied bibanja were owned by boys who
had inherited them and were still minors. It is the general ex-
pectation of the Haya that these young men will marry in due course.
They do not, in any proper sense of the term, form families as yet,
but they are considered potential family members, as the allocation
of resources for the future sustenance of themselves and their families indicates. In one sense this pre-marriage phase might be considered "replacement," but Fortes specifically regards the phase
of replacement as ending with the death of the original partners of
a marriage. (The Bushmen, Konkomba, and Zande come to mind as societies in which bride service may be seen as a similar pre-marriage
phase.)

If we take the potential family as being in the earliest
phase of development of a domestic group, the unoccupied but not un-
owned bibanja of E, G, D, and 42 are in this phase and are so
marked. The bibanja are without houses and have no crops of beans,
corn, or sweet potatoes. They are under banana cultivation, and
some have coffee trees. Relatives, or friends, or even the young
man himself, do caretaker cultivation. In the two other potential
family bibanja, A and 51, the actual owners and potential family
heads are also immature, but the bibanja are not left unoccupied,
relatives caring for the children and the bibanja jointly as the
children grow. The relatives are acting as surrogate parents but
they are not construed by themselves or by others as being the
principal family heads, but rather are seen as caretakers for the
children and their heritage.

Phase I - Early Marriage and Expansion: Among the Haya,
a bride leads a life of seclusion for a period of months. If she
becomes pregnant, her seclusion will not terminate until her baby
is a month or more old. During this period, she is responsible
only for certain fine handwork in the way of domestic tasks, and
she and her groom do not maintain a household. The recently married couples in the village, then, have no houses on their bibanja,
or have only a preliminary shelter in which they are not really re-
siding. Their sustenance comes from some other family in the village, usually the groom's parental one. (The kibanja of a bride
is small and is not sown to beans or sweet potatoes, although the
new husband will be cultivating the stand of bananas.) F's fami-
ly--himself and his bride--are in this phase, and 250 and 231 have
but recently changed from it. 247 was in this phase, but his
young wife has left him.

The families with one or more growing children are in the expansion phase of development, and many of the bibanja are occupied by families of this type. The number of children varies-- several families have four or five. These families are making maximum demands on the bibanja, which are fully cultivated, varying in size from one to more than four acres. (By and large these families are not marketing their coffee through the cooperative.) The prevailing pattern is one wife to a kibanja. Only if a man has two separate bibanja is he likely to maintain a successful polygynous marriage. 23's first wife and their children live in his northern kibanja, while he has provided his second wife with his central kibanja. Many men have tried to keep two wives in a single holding, but it very rarely works.

Phase II - Dispersion: Some of the most favorably established older families of the village are in this phase of development, including the family of the territorial chief. They are not many in number, for the phase includes only that portion of the development cycle from the time when the first child marries until the time when the youngest only remains. With one exception, all have married sons living in the village. Their bibanja are relatively large and are fully cultivated, and the coffee grown on them is marketed through the cooperative. The relationships among the men on these bibanja are:

Father	Son
1	27 and 227 and F
14	222
17	231 on 17's kibanja
240	226 on 240's kibanja

Some significant dispersion of the sons of the family heads has occurred, but within the confines of the village.

Phase III - Replacement: In this phase the heads of families have only one or no children who are still minors. Almost by definition they are older men and are relatively few in number. They market their coffee in the cooperative and still have fully cultivated bibanja. The relationships among the men on these bibanja are:

Father	Son
22	45 (away)
10	205 on 10's kibanja (unmarried)
20	P on 20's kibanja
206	208 and 259 on 206's kibanja (unmarried)

Exceptions: A number of bibanja provide residence and sustenance for people whose households do not form families: non-Haya tenants who are unmarried, and adult women who are heads of their own households.

THE OWNERSHIP AND TRANSMISSION OF LAND

The Haya village presents the general appearance of a developed social community. Most of the families are in the middle phases of development, with growing or married children. Thus, the purchase of small slivers of bibanja land side by side with unoccupied bibanja leads one to the conclusion that there must be compelling social reasons for valuable land being left unoccupied for long periods. The kibanja is not only a cropping unit—it is also the locus for a social unit. The kibanja has the character of being fixed or stable in Haya social usage. The Haya treat bibanja as if they are identifiable units which have continuity as property. The occupant of a kibanja must also be identifiable. Haya today have ways of identifying owners, meaning specifically those persons who have rights in land. In the indigenous society one could be an owner-occupier, or a landholder (in the political sense), or a tenant. Today one may be an owner-occupier, a landholder (in the political or in the new economic sense--significantly the term in Luhaya is the same for both senses), or a tenant (either in the political sense or in the economic sense).

The most fitting way, in Haya eyes, for a man to become an owner of a kibanja is to have inherited it from his father. In the normal course of events, a land-owning Haya father with a growing son will assume (as will his son) that the son will inherit the land from the father. However, such a direct succession is not always automatically assured, as in the case of polygynous marriages. While the Haya consider polygynous marriages to be desirable, and certainly proper, relatively few men outside of the ruling dynasty do in fact have more than one wife in stable marriages. In the village under study only four men have more than one wife: the territorial chief, who is also a member of the indigenous ruling dynasty, and three other men whose bibanja holdings are large enough to accommodate two wives, each wife being domiciled on a separate kibanja. But few men own two bibanja. One practical effect of these social circumstances is that men do not commonly have large numbers of sons to accommodate.

Within the general social considerations just sketched, there are two means which serve in a complementary fashion to assure the succession from father to son. The first is the designation of one son as the heir (musika). If there are several sons, only one can be the primary heir, and his father's kibanja will be transferred to him as a unit. If a man is able to provide his other sons with bibanja, he will gladly do so, but if only one is available, it is handed down as a unit.

On the other hand, in the past, if a man did not have a son, he was in the position of being heirless, the Haya thought, and his property reverted to the Mukama (top level political authority). In fact, few instances of this have occurred in the histories of particular bibanja (I have discussed this elsewhere,)[17] for the Mukama has other ways of controlling village land. The mechanism whereby a man can acquire a son is referred to by the term bisisi. A man can obtain the rights of pater in a child whose genitor was someone else, the rights of pater taking precedence over the rights of genitor. (I have also discussed this elsewhere.)[18] One instance from the village points up the relationship presumed to exist between donor and recipient in such a situation. One young man, whose father lives in the village with another son who is the father's heir, was given a kibanja by his father's brother, who also "gave him a wife," by providing him with the bridewealth and performing the negotiations. The father's brother had already provided for his own sons. The young man changed the acknowledgment of father from his true pater-genitor to his father's brother and considered himself a son, in the strict sense, of his father's brother.

In the normal course of events, then, a kibanja is transferred from father to single son, the definition of heirship confining it to one son and the mechanism of bisisi providing a son if none is available. The emphasis on the transfer of property as a unit from father to son leads to the settlement of other sons in other places. The pattern of dispersion of clans is entirely consistent with the social displacement of sons other than heirs.

The Haya have a strong sense of time depth. A man in describing the acquisition of his kibanja will say, with a rising inflection, that it came to him from his father, from his father's father, from his father's father's father, and so on back into eternity. Haya, then, are very conscious of the line of inheritance. What they lack is a sense of collaterality: the line does not spread to include agnates.

LINEAGE AND LAND TENURE

As noted earlier, the bibanja have a continuity transcending the development cycle of a single family. They are negotiable only as units. Their state of cultivation is somewhat independent of occupancy, but detailed examination, kibanja by kibanja, reveals a close relationship between phase of development of the occupying family and condition of cultivation.

A number of observations can be made about the Haya social arrangements with respect to land. The first such observation is that Haya regard a kibanja as a specific piece of ground. This piece, this unit, is available for occupancy by a family. It is a single, independent cropping unit, although it stands with other like units in a group. The second such observation is that a kibanja is transferred from one individual to another individual. When there is genetic relationship between the individuals across generations, the result is a line. When there is a contract between individuals of a semi-permanent nature, the result is a landholder-tenant relationship. The third observation is that the Haya pieces of property are fixed in their location. Because they have a fixed locale they can form permanent territorial units.

Insofar as the Haya view bibanja as specific pieces of ground, they are approaching land in a manner quite different from the Tiv, who envisage all plots under annual cultivation as shares in the total land resources. The plots may change, but the shares do not.[19] (Among the Haya, the plot has continuity; the share is by no means certain.) Marshall D. Sahlins suggests, specifically with regard to the Tiv, that "lineality is a product of repetitive, long-term use of restricted resources. If this ecological factor is absent it seems unlikely that a segmentary lineage system will appear."[20] As it stands, this statement could apply as well to the Haya, who have, however, a system of territorial groups. Clearly, the terms "restricted" with reference to resources and "lineality" with reference to a principle upon which groups may be formed may be used in two quite different ways.

The phrase "restricted resources" can be used to refer to productivity or to locale or to both. From the vantage point of the Haya, Nuer herds and Tiv crops appear to have the significant quality of flexibility of locale, even if the total productivity of the groups is restricted. Among the Tiv and the Nuer, the relationship of the plant and animal communities with the human community is such that in any one season or year, a new adjustment between a group and its land and animal resources is almost inevitable. The individual shares are subject to redefinition depending on the particular needs of the group.

"Restricted resources" may thus refer to overall productivity, as in the cases of the Tiv, the Nuer, and the Haya. When, however, there is restriction to locale as well, a system of territorial groups is likely to result. When there is flexibility of locale, a system of segmentary lineages is more likely.

The principle of lineality as the basis for the formation of groups among people who share common descent finds its most extreme expression in a line of individuals which has great generational depth but is no more than one person wide. The lines are projected with no merging, and there is no extension to include contemporaries. An example of minimal collaterality associated with lineality is seen among the Haya, where the collateral line of kin is restricted and the relationship of other kin is specified with respect to the line of descent.

On the other hand, the lineages occurring in segmentary societies vary in size. Although some may be quite small, the largest of them encompass groups of substantial size. Descent groups of large size can only result from some ready means of extending the "line" to include contemporaries, thus combining lineality with collaterality. When agnates only are selected from among kin (to follow the distinction commonly used), the combination is expressed in a system of lineages. The groups of agnates are ordered lineally; any one group can be related to any other group only through reference to some lineally antecedent group. Lineality then may refer to a line of individuals to which groups are attached--as among the Haya--or it may refer to groups which are ordered lineally, as among societies with a system of segmentary lineages.

APPENDIX I

RESULTS OF SOIL ANALYSES

Village land

Sample No.	Level in inches	pH	Conductivity	Exch Ca me%	Available P ppm	Organic C %
61	T 0-6	6.4	236	10.6	215	2.1
	M 6-12	6.5	100	1.2	40	1.8
	B 12-18	6.2	95	1.1	10	0.6
5	T 0-6	6.4	500	18.9	705	3.6
	M 6-12	6.2	400	11.7	585	2.9
	B 12-18	6.6	300	5.3	342	2.8
129	T 0-6	6.0	102	6.7	158	2.2
	M 6-12	6.2	95	5.2	171	1.9
	B 12-18	6.2	90	4.7	73	1.5
149	*T 0-6	5.8	380	2.0	133	0.4
	M 6-12	6.0	205	1.6	133	1.8
	B 12-18	6.0	288	1.5	171	0.8
33	T 0-6	6.8	90	0.8	69	1.1
	M 6-12	6.2	150	0.9	70	1.4
	B 12-18	5.5	135	0.6	20	0.8
43	T 0-6	6.1	320	3.9	84	1.7
	M 6-12	6.2	100	1.7	58	1.4
	B 12-18	6.3	115	1.0	16	0.7
6	T 0-6	6.6	142	1.9	57	2.0
	M 6-12	6.6	92	1.1	58	1.8
	B 12-18	6.2	152	1.4	43	0.3
36	T 0-6	6.2	135	6.1	562	6.1
	M 6-12	6.4	102	2.7	262	2.6
	B 12-18	6.0	125	2.2	166	2.2
42	M 6-12	6.2	450	2.3	70	2.3
2	T 0-6	6.4	170	2.9	109	2.8

Grassland

West of	6-12	5.5	130	2.1	65	2.3
Buhembe	?	5.5	110	1.4	41	1.9
	12-18	6.4	100	1.5	18	1.3
Between	T 0-6	6.5	60	1.8	87	1.8
Buhembe	M 6-12	6.5	135	2.3	57	1.7
& Kyasha	B 12-18	6.5	55	2.3	52	0.7
East of	T 0-6	6.0	245	2.0	70	2.0
Kyasha	M 6-12	6.5	140	2.5	53	2.5
	B rock	-	-	-	-	-

*M is probably T and T is probably B, according to the laboratory.

APPENDIX II

PLANTS GROWN OR USED FOR FOOD BY THE HAYA

	Luhaya	English	Botanical
1.	Bito-ke	Banana-plantain	Musa sapientum
2.	Biise	Banana-sweet	*Musa paradisiaca
3.	Mbi-le	Banana-beer	Musa spp.
4.	Nshoro	Bambara nut	Voandzeia subterranea
5.	Binyobwa	Ground nut	Arachia hypogea
6.	Mperege	Beans	Phaseolus lunatus
7.	Obukiga	Cow peas	Vigna sinensis
8.	Nku-ku	Hyacinth bean	Dolichoo lablab
9.	Njegere, Mashaza	Peas	Pisum spp.
10.	Kigando	Cassava	Manihot utilissima
11.	Mugusha	Sorghum	Andropogon sorghum
12.	Bicholi	Maize	Zea mays
13.	Birai	Yams	Dioscorea spp.
14.	Kigusha	Sugar cane	Saccharum officinarum
15.	Kijungu mwani	Coffee Arabica	Coffea arabica
16.	Mwani	Coffee Robusta	Coffea robusta
17.	Ndimu	Lemon	Citrus medica
18.	Machunkwa	Oranges	Citrus aurantium
19.	Madalena	Tangerine	Citrus nobilis
20.	Limao	Lime	Citrus limetta
21.	Inembe	Mango	Mangifera indica
22.	Fenesi	Jack fruit	Artocarpus communis
23.	Mulili	Wild spinach	
24.	Mfuma	Sweet potatoes	Ipomea batatas
25.	Manumbu, Bilazi-ulaiya	White potatoes	Solanum tuberosum
26.	Na-nazi	Pineapple	Ananas sativus

*The difference between species does not coincide with the sweet-plantain distinction.

	Luhaya	English	Botanical
27.	Pap-li	Pawpaw	Carica papaya
28.	Mape-ra	Guava	?Psidium
29.	Buroi	Eleusine	Eleusine corocana
30.	Bituzi	Mushrooms	
31.	Ntongo	Tree tomatoes	?Cyphomandra
32.	Entura	Tree tomatoes	
33.	Nyanya	Tomatoes	Lycopersicum esculentum
34.	Matunda	Passion fruit	Passiflora
35.	Nkereri	Wild berries	?Rubus
36.	Nziru	Tree fruit--looks like cherry	
37.	Mashasha	Fruit	
38.	Nsharazi	Husks of tree fruit	
39.	Nkaraito	Husks of tree fruit (different kind)	
40.	Maso-ma	Yams (different kind)	Dioscorea spp.
41.	Kikwa-la	Taro	
42.	Mwongu	Gourd	
43.	Nkonjwa	Banana-roast	Musa spp.
44.	Emoi	Tree fruit	
45.	Ekikungu	Fruit, similar to pineapple but a tree	?Pandanus utilis
46.	Oluguluma	Pepper	
47.	Ntuntunu	Ground cherries	?Physalis
48.	Nshenya	Wild underground yam	
49.	Mutontozi	Leaves of gourd	
50.	Muboligo	Cassava leaves	Manihot utilisima

APPENDIX III

SOME CHARACTERISTICS RELATING TO THE VILLAGE OF MAP 2

Register Number	Estimated Acreage	*Kilo per Acre of Coffee	Phase of Family Development	Name of Family Line (Enda)**
1	3.8	52.3	II	Rugomora
2 North House	1.0 2.1	100.8	III	Ngabona
3	1.8		I	Not given
4	1.5	120	II	Byabasaija
5	.7		I	Banenwa
6	2.8	13.6	II	Kikondo
7 East Piece House	.8 .1 1.4		I	Mukunzire
8	2.2	53.1	Other	Not given
9	1.3	107.7	I	Not given
10	1.8		III	Banenwa
11	1.9		I	Kitama
13	2.1		Other	Not given
14	1.6	99.4	II	Ntegwa
16	2.0	15.	II	Lwamo
17	1.3	113.	II	Ntaraga
18	2.0	93.5	I	Ntaraga
20	1.5	201.	III	Muiza

*An additional 1403 kilos of coffee were marketed by the two traders.

**Enda, which is commonly translated as "lineage" in the Lacustrine Bantu literature, does not refer to lineage among the Haya, but to a very small group--sometimes no more than a set of brothers, not including their father. The enda is specifically unlike the lineage in a segmentary social system in that the enda does not have any control over the use of the land and its resources. As noted, a series of individuals exercise this control. At the same time, families occupy the land and utilize it. Hence, I use the term enda for "family line" to carry the meaning of a line of succession to which families are attached.

Register Number	Estimated Acreage	Kilo per Acre of Coffee	Phase of Family Development	Name of Family Line (Enda)
21	2.0	7.5	I	Kyamajamba
22	3.5		I	Byombalirwa
23 North Piece House	1.5 .3 .7	11.5	I	Kasigwa
24	2.0		I	Not given
25	1.7		I	Isize
26	1.5	84.6	I	Nshunta
27	4.8	61.7	I	Buberwa
28	2.0	16.5	I	Butonya
29	.8	155.	I	Nshunta
40	1.6	40.6	I	Muiza
41	1.7		I	Buberwa
42	1.5		0	Wamara
44	2.9		I	Not given
48	1.4		I	Wamara
50	1.0 (estimated)		Other	Kaiguru
51	1.4		0	Not given
78	2.0		Other	Not given
79	1.1		I	Shuka
192	1.3		I	Rubuli
206	.5		III	Mweru
207	3.0		I	Kinyonyi
212	.8		I	Kifumbe
215	1.0	20	I	Nzeye (Burundi)
219	.9		I	Not given (Burundi)
222	2.2	13.6	I	Mutegwa

APPENDIX III--Continued

Register Number	Estimated Acreage	Kilo per Acre of Coffee	Phase of Family Development	Name of Family Line (Enda)
227	1.3		I	Buberwa
240	3.3	43.	II	Buberwa
247	.3		I	Not given
250	.5		I	Lwenduru
254	1.4		I	Mbanda
A	2.1		0	Isize
B	2.7	31.1	0	Kapalala (Bi-haramulo)
C	3.2		I	Barakana
D	2.2		0	Karumuna
E	1.2		0	Not given
F	1.3		I	Rugomora
G	.9		0	Not given

NOTES

[1] "Bukoba: High and Low Fertility on a Laterised Soil," East African Agricultural Research Station Report, XIV (1938-Amani), pp. 14-15.

[2] J. F. R. Hill and J. P. Moffett, Tanganyika: A Review of Its Resources and Their Development (Government of Tanganyika: 1955), pp. 675, 677.

[3] Op. cit., p. 17 (see note 1).

[4] W. W. Bishop, "The Later Tertiary and Pleistocene in Eastern Equatorial Africa," in F. C. Howell and F. Bourliere, eds., African Ecology and Human Evolution [Viking Fund Publications in Anthropology, 36 (1963)], p. 270.

[5] "Change of Regional Balance in the Bukoba District of Tanganyika," Geographical Review, L, 1, fig. 5. Dr. McMaster's map is reproduced with permission from the author.

[6]Op. cit., p. 16 (see note 1).

[7]Quarterly Economic and Statistical Bulletin (Government Printer, 1954), p. 112.

[8]Op. cit., p. 17 (see note 1).

[9]Ibid., p. 18.

[10]Annual Report for the Year 1953: The Bukoba Native Coffee Board (Moshi: KNCU Printing Press, 1953), Appendix I.

[11]Hans Meyer's Ostafrika-Expedition 1911 Blatt 1. Ihángiro und der Burigi-See. Mitteilungen aus den deutschen Schutzgebieten (1913).

[12]Annual Report, op. cit., p. 11 (see note 10).

[13]Ibid., p. 9.

[14]Harold F. Heady, Range Management in East Africa (Nairobi: Kenya Department of Agriculture and East African Agricultural and Forestry Research Organization, 1960), p. 24.

[15]Op. cit., p. 83 (see note 5).

[16]"Introduction" in Jack Goody, ed., The Developmental Cycle in Domestic Groups (Cambridge: Cambridge University Press, 1962), pp. 1-4.

[17]"Haya Land Tenure: Landholding and Tenancy," Anthropological Quarterly, XXXV (1962), pp. 58-72.

[18]A. I. Richards and P. C. Reining, "Report on Fertility Surveys in Buganda and Buhaya, 1952," in Frank Lorimer, ed., Culture and Human Fertility (Paris: UNESCO, 1954), pp. 374-78.

[19]Paul Bohannan, "'Land,' 'Tenure,' and Land-tenure," in Daniel Biebuyck, ed., African Agrarian Systems (London: Oxford University Press, 1963), pp. 105-6.

[20]"The Segmentary Lineage: An Organization of Predatory Expansion," American Anthropologist, LXIII (1961), p. 342.

NUTRITION IN ITS SOCIOCULTURAL MATRIX: FOOD GETTING AND USING ALONG THE EAST AFRICAN COAST

by

Luther P. Gerlach

As he invited me to share with him a substantial evening meal of fresh mangoes and maize meal porridge flavored with a sauce of cooked beef, Sulymani Mwarongo, a Digo schoolteacher from the Kenya coastal village of Waa, proudly praised the food getting system of the Digo. "We aren't like other Africans," he affirmed as he poured water from a coconut shell ladle over his right hand to wash it in the Islamic fashion. "We have no time of hunger. We always have some food available." Then, after showing me how to scoop up a chunk of thick ugali porridge in the fingers of my right hand and dip it into the meat sauce, he explained how the Digo grow a variety of different crops which ripen at different times, so that some vegetable or fruit is always ready for harvest.

While the Digo food production system was not as good as Sulymani would have it, it certainly was better than many government officials believed. Sulymani might also have commented on the trading and marketing and ritual systems which help to distribute food throughout the coastal area, or he might have discussed other aspects of the food preservation and utilization practices of the Digo and their coastal African neighbors. But, after taking the unusual step of praising the diversity of Digo agriculture, Sulymani remained true to Digo norms and bemoaned the "poverty" and backwardness of his people. A Digo characteristically—and with some justification—believes that everyone else will be envious of any success he may have, and attempt to make him share his wealth. Thus, to protect his interests and also save him from higher taxes, a typical Digo will pretend to be poor, and Sulymani was scarcely an exception to this pattern.

It is partly because of such patterns of dissimulation that the government of Kenya believed that the Digo food economy was much poorer than was actually the case. This belief was reinforced by the fact that medical officers attempting to assess the nutritional status of the Digo and other coastal Africans were unable to examine a representative sample of the entire population. The Kenya Digo feared that medical examinations were somehow designed to injure them through a type of witchcraft. It appears that most examinations were conducted on hospital patients or on frequently ill up-country Africans, such as Nandi and Kamba, living rather unhappily in the government-sponsored Shimba Hills

Settlement some 30 miles from Mombasa, in Kenya. Such groups probably had a much higher incidence of malnutrition than is normal
throughout the coastal population.

Because of the paucity of exact information, I am unable
to comment on the nutritional status and physical condition of the
Digo, Duruma, and other coastal peoples, except to state that a
capable medical doctor at the district hospital, Msambweni, Kenya,
confided to me that the coastal Africans were probably quite a bit
better fed "than they admitted." I am also unable to give precise
information about amounts of food produced and consumed throughout
this coastal area or about the nutritive value of typical daily
diets. It is clear that, just as anthropologists can contribute
much to the work of nutritionists,[1] so must anthropologists interested in nutritional studies work with nutritionists, biochemists,
geographers, agriculturalists, veterinarians, and other specialists
concerned with nutrition and food if they are to get the precise
data required for a complete study of diet. (In her pioneering
work on Bemba diet, Audrey Richards comments both on the difficulty of obtaining information about diet among an African people
and the advantage of working jointly with medical and nutritional
experts.)[2]

I unfortunately did not participate in such joint research,
and no government or research office had adequate information on
diet and nutrition among the coastal peoples. I did, however, obtain considerable information on the food economies of the Digo
and Duruma tribes of the Kenya and Tanzania coast during my anthropological field research on Digo and Duruma society and culture
from 1958 to 1960. My own researches were supplemented by information from coastal agricultural and veterinary officials. Continuing correspondence with Digo informants has kept me somewhat
abreast of the current situation in this area.

The Islamized Digo, with a population of some 110,000,
and the mostly pagan Duruma, about 75,000 strong, are members of
the Nyika group of northeast coastal Bantu tribes and occupy the
coastal belt from Mombasa in Kenya to Tanga in Tanzania.[3] Other
members of this Nyika group include the Giriama, Jibana, Kauma,
Chonyi, and Kamba--all living more or less to the north of the
Digo and Duruma, and south of the Pokomo tribe, another closely
related northeast coastal Bantu people living along the Tana river
in northern Kenya.

During my research I was unable to do more than briefly
survey the cultures of these other Nyika, coastal Arabs, and Afro-
Arabs, and there is very little published material on them. George
P. Murdock[4] and A. H. J. Prins[5] have written useful surveys of
these peoples, but present little data on their present food economies. There also exist some quite dated works of only limited
value in assessing contemporary food economy.[6] In this paper,

therefore, I shall concern myself chiefly with a study of food getting and using among the Digo and Duruma, with some consideration also of Digo and Duruma economic relationships with their Arab, Afro-Arab, and Indian neighbors. I shall discuss Digo and Duruma patterns of and capabilities in food production, distribution, preservation, preparation, and consumption, showing how these patterns and capabilities are in turn dependent upon related sociocultural and environmental factors. Finally, I shall indicate how failure to understand these patterns and the factors which affect them prevented authorities from improving Digo and Duruma diet. In short, I shall examine food economics and nutrition in its sociocultural context among peoples whom I consider to be quite representative of the ecosystem of the East African coast.

FOOD PRODUCTION

The Digo, like many Giriama, some Duruma, and other Nyika and Afro-Arabs, are essentially agriculturalists, although a number of the Digo graze some livestock, notably goats and sheep. The Digo are unable to herd cattle over most of their domain because of the prevalence of tsetse-borne sleeping sickness, but many older Digo are the absentee owners of cattle and other livestock which they give to the neighboring Duruma to herd for them in the more tsetse-free Duruma country. Chickens are common among all of the Nyika, with ownership vested chiefly in women. While the Digo will eat the milk, meat, and eggs of their domestic animals, they do not own enough stock to subsist on such produce. They regard their livestock chiefly as a form of savings to be used in time of real need, such as to help pay for bridewealth, to be sacrificed and eaten during ritual, to be sold to meet pressing debts or pay taxes, or to be eaten during a time of real famine.

The staple crops of the Digo are maize and cassava. Important subsidiary food crops are bananas, beans, sweet potatoes, coconuts, and rice. Much of Digo country also abounds in roots and wild grasses of various types which the Digo collect to supplement their diet. They will sell or barter a portion of such staple or subsidiary produce partly because they frequently grow a surplus, partly because they do not have the capacity to store produce for long periods without spoilage, and partly because they sometimes need cash to pay taxes, debts, and the costs of bridewealth, ritual, and the like. In addition to such food crops, the Digo produce various items chiefly for barter or sale, including copra, sesame, cotton, kapok, cashews, red peppers, and palm wine.

The agricultural technology of the Digo and other Nyika peoples is not as inefficient as many government officials at least officially maintain. The Digo, like other Nyika, practice slash-and-burn agriculture and shifting cultivation, with rotation and interplanting of crops. After their gardens are exhausted by several years of cultivation, they allow them to lie fallow and move on to develop new fields, usually within a few hundred yards of their former sites and often on land which had been cultivated and returned to fallow long ago but at least within living memory.

The Digo clear a new field of trees and other thick growth by cutting, girdling, and by fire. Firing, unfortunately, often burns larger areas than will be cultivated, destroys valuable forest, and may, through excessive heat, damage the soil. The Digo do not ordinarily climb and pollard trees in the Bemba manner,[7] although they may lop off low-hanging branches of large trees which they can reach from the ground. Dead trees are left standing or lying as they have fallen to bleach and whiten in the hot sun. Indeed, a Digo field ready for cultivation often looks like a battle-field--ash strewn and dotted with the skeletons of lifeless trees frequently interspersed with blackened ant hills. The Digo, like other Nyika, attempt to clear an area for cultivation immediately before the rains fall,* but on occasion the rains are late or fail entirely, and the burned fields may become a wasteland of baked mud or dust. If the rains are sufficient, however, crops grow well in the newly-prepared soil, fertilized by the ashes of the burnt growth. Furthermore, a district officer claimed, the fire clears the area of harmful insects, rodents, and diseases, such as rusts harbored in the soil.

The favorite agricultural implement of the Digo and other Nyika is the all-purpose short handled iron hoe, which they often make themselves, using scrap metal. If a field is covered only by grass and other light growth the Digo will often not burn it, but rather chop it off at the roots with this hoe. Then, instead of raking off this grass as American or European farmers usually do, they allow it to remain on the ground, where it protects the soil, seeds, and plants, eventually rots, and becomes a good fertilizer. Like the Bemba,[9] the Digo hoe and weed out of necessity, not for the sake of appearance. The Digo and other Nyika weed their fields only once or twice during the growing season, and again do not rake the weeds from the field, but rather allow them to cover the soil. They do not plant their crops in neat and order-ly rows, but, because they do not use machines in their gardening, they have no need for such order. Furthermore, they do not pull weaker seedlings and plants from the ground, partly because they do not believe that this will actually help the stronger crops to grow and partly since this appears to be both wasteful and too much work. On the other hand, whereas the Bemba tend to sow broadcast

---

*There are two rainy seasons along the coast--a heavy rain in about April or May and a lighter rain in about October or November. It should be added that rainfall in this area is quite irregular, as indeed it is for most of Africa.[8]

their primary seed crops, the Digo and other Nyika generally hoe them into the soil, placing several seeds in a small hole scooped out of the ground which will be covered again with dirt and cut weeds.

The Digo whom we observed in the location known as Lunga-lunga obtained good harvests using these methods. The Digo teacher in the local government primary school had his students grow crops using methods learned in a government teachers' college. His students used long handled hoes in the European manner, although most found these to be awkward to handle. They raked the land clear of weeds and grass, and the hot sun baked the exposed soil, killing most of the maize and other seeds. It is worth noting that, using traditional methods, the teacher's wife grew maize in an adjoining field, and obtained a good harvest.

The government had a large experimental agricultural station near Mombasa and often invited Nyika peoples to see demonstrations of new and improved methods and crops. The Nyika are not as slow to accept innovations as some of the government officials believed, but they were frequently not certain that the government station adequately demonstrated that European and American techniques were superior to those of the Nyika, at least given Nyika resources. The government also supports in the attractive Shimba Hills region of the Kenya coast a settlement scheme and erstwhile model peasant farm community of migrant Nandi and Kamba farmers. This community has not been too successful, even though it has employed various kinds of modern agricultural equipment. The Nyika could have joined the settlement if they wished, but they were not willing to give up their independence from government control simply to obtain the benefits of government assistance and agricultural machinery. Instead, they shrug off the settlement as a failure, commenting that the Shimba Hills area is haunted by evil spirits. In any event, as L. Dudley Stamp, the social geographer notes, hoe agriculture is frequently more suitable in Africa than mechanized cultivation.[10] He points out how agricultural machinery consolidates the surface of African soils rather than cultivating it, while frequent plowing, even with animal-drawn plows, exposes vital organic matter, causing rapid oxidation. Stamp also suggests that Nyika methods of clearing and weeding the land are typical of African methods and, like Audry Richards,[11] shows that these may be quite adaptive in their environmental context.

Slash-and-burn shifting agriculture of this kind does, however, require a rather extensive land area, with considerable land held in reserve for future cultivation. While land is adequate in much of the interior region of Digo country, there is some land hunger around Mombasa, Tanga, Vanga, and along the coastline, from the Indian Ocean inland for a distance of from three to four miles. Traditional milpa (slash-and-burn) agriculture is not efficient within this area. In any event, most of the land is densely covered with coconut palms, or cashew and kapok trees. Furthermore, there is considerable controversy over land tenure, and insecurity of rights militates against effective land use. The area does not produce enough food to feed its population, and food is imported from other coastal areas and the cities. Those who live in this area often cultivate gardens a good many miles from their homes, using temporary dwellings during the main agricultural seasons. In time they may establish permanent residences in these locations. Others often turn to commercial or subsistence fishing, to trading, or to wage-labor in urban centers or on plantations in order to earn money for food, other essentials, and luxuries.

The coastal peoples manifest both wet and dry rice raising technologies. Some groups irrigate their rice from local rivers which flood annually. For example, the Arabs, Digo, and other Swahili-speaking Afro-Arabs of the Kenya coastal town of Vanga and the neighboring village of Jego irrigate from the Umba river, which floods in January and February. The Digo, Bondei, and other Afro-Arabs of the Pangani region in Tanzania use the Pangani river. The Pokomo of Kenya employ the waters of the Tana river. On the other hand, although they probably know that irrigation will increase their yield, a large number of coastal people grow only dry rice, depending upon the rather uncertain rainfall to germinate the crop. This is true of the Digo of Lungalunga in Kenya, even though they live along the flanks of the Umba river some 12 miles above Vanga and know well that the Vangans grow much more rice per acre than they do. Lungalungans usually sow rice broadcast in low lying swamp land which they have prepared by hoeing, although a few plant it in shallow holes as the Afro-Arabs of Lamu do.

The Lungalungans understand rice raising technology and technically, at least, seem to have the capacity to irrigate. A number of sociocultural factors combine to influence them not to raise rice through irrigation. For one, although they do not state it in so many words, the Lungalungans tend to feel that they and the people of Vanga and Jego should occupy different but complementary "ecological niches" (using ecological niche much as F. Barth employs it to study economic role diversity among the Swat Pathan).[12] The Digo tacitly agree that the Vangans should specialize in rice and get full use of the Umba water, while the Lungalungans should specialize in maize as a staple grain. The Lungalungans have kinsmen, affines, and friends in Jego and Vanga, and often help them to harvest rice in exchange for a share of the product. Such relatives may also attend various Islamic and traditional rituals in Lungalunga and contribute rice as a duty of participation and relationship. Furthermore, Lungalungans can buy Vanga rice through local merchants and traders and at the Vanga market. In turn, Vangans are able to obtain needed Lungalunga products through similar channels.

Unlike the people of Vanga and Jego, the Lungalungans do not have the land tenure system or social, political, or economic organization necessary to implement rice agriculture. The Digo kinship system was once matrilineal. Under an earlier pattern of slavery, which gave a man power over his sons and their offspring born to slave wives, and through more recent Islamic and Western influence, the Digo social structure has developed patrilineal principles to coexist with the matrilineal. In an attempt to obtain maximum advantage, individual Digo employ both principles where it is expedient. They will, for example, seek and often obtain rights and corresponding duties in a father's matrilineage, a mother's patrilineage, or even a father's father's matrilineage. The result is that they have developed what is in fact an ambilineal system[13] in which rights to land use and other rights and duties are not clearly delineated and often conflict. When a man dies his sons and other patrikin tend to conflict with his sister's sons and other matrikin over rights to his property or rights to farm land which he is using. Such conflict is especially marked if he had obtained rights to this land from his matrikin but cleared it using the labor of his sons. They resolve their dispute by various compromise measures. Frequently, all agree to share rights and duties in the land or property and join together to form a mutual aid group in which members exchange gifts and assistance during rituals and generally attempt to show that they are all "brothers" (ndugu). This rather precarious balance is easily upset if any individual appears to profit unduly at the expense of his "brothers," or if he attempts to establish permanent rights in any portion of the disputed land by planting permanent crops in it, having it surveyed by government, or by going to great lengths to improve it.

The Lungalungans are afraid that the balance of rights and duties would certainly be destroyed if they developed an irrigation system. How, indeed, would they allocate rights to increasingly valuable land? They are certain that they would quarrel with kinsmen and neighbors over land, water, and other rights and duties if they irrigated. Furthermore, they have an acephalous political structure, and recognize no clear lines of power, authority, or decision-making. Numerous factions customarily arise to challenge government-sponsored headmen and chiefs if they appear to be too strong or too demanding. The Digo certainly would oppose communal cooperation directed by such leaders, and most Digo headmen prefer to appear permissive and even weak. In short, irrigation seems organizationally impossible and threatens to shatter the unstable community social and political structure. The Digo value at least overtly harmonious social relationships more than they prize increased food production. This is but another example of how progress in food production is often not simply a function of more and better technology. Rather it is a function of a complex of sociocultural, environmental, and technological factors.

Socio-cultural factors also cannot be ignored in programs to provide capital for food production and other economic development. It is frequently asserted that a major barrier to economic development in peasant societies is a lack of capital, and it is often maintained that capital must be injected into such societies from outside agencies. However, the economist Everett E. Hagen, after presenting a useful critique of these views, goes on to show how a complex of sociocultural and psychological factors are the real mainsprings of economic and technical change, and, indeed, of indigenous capital formation and utilization.[14] The anthropologist Raymond Firth agrees that social change is a necessary prerequisite for significant capital development in peasant systems, and points out that the failure of administrators or economists to understand the total system in which capital is developed and utilized may impede their efforts to develop capital or may produce unintended effects.[15] Problems experienced by the Kenya government in its attempts to increase Digo food production by injecting capital illustrate the validity of these arguments.

Kenya administrators assumed that the Digo were poorer than is actually the case. They also seem to have assumed that the Digo would welcome and profit by a program of government loans to provide them with modest capital for small-scale expansion in agriculture and business. Some loans, especially those to traders, did have the desired effects, but others, especially some of those to farmers, failed. To obtain such loans Digo farmers had to prove that they had access to adequate land and would make the best use of it. The agricultural department surveyed the land in question and demanded that farmers follow government advice and employ specific agricultural methods. Many Digo simply refused to accept such loans because they did not want to submit to government control and because, by having the land surveyed and claiming it as theirs to use for a major project, they would anger those who claimed equal rights in the land. In one case two brothers—Kasim and Sulymani—obtained some 600 shillings from the government to help them plant bananas in good river bottom land obtained from their father, Omari, and their father's father, Bukhari. The matrilineal descendents of Bukhari threatened Kasim and Sulymani with violence if they did not admit that only the matrilineage had the right to this land. Indeed, they went so far as to claim that Kasim and Sulymani were descended from female slaves of the matrilineage. Local elders helped to resolve the dispute by effecting a compromise. Kasim and Sulymani secured the right to plant only part of the disputed area in bananas, and agreed not to grow more permanent coconut palms on it. In return, they shared their government loan with some of Bukhari's matrilineage by contributing to a feast in honor of the memory of a long deceased member of this matrilineage. (In so doing they contributed to food distribution but not to food production.) They also used some of the loan to help pay the costs of bridewealth for their own sister's son, arguing that their sister had an equal right in the land they were go-

ing to use, and that her son would in time help them cultivate it.
They never did complete their agricultural project to the satis-
faction of the government. They would have feuded with their kinsmen had they done as the government wished, and after they shared
their loan they had little money left to buy good quality seedlings
or to pay young Duruma to work for them. The government blamed
their failure on their dishonesty and laziness, but it was far more
complicated that that!

     This case also tells us something about Digo attitudes to-
wards work and patterns of cooperation. Kasim and Sulymani, both
middle-aged men, feel that hard physical farm labor is demeaning,
a sign of inferior status. This opinion is fairly common among
elder Digo, probably because such work was assigned to slaves of
the Digo and Arabs until slavery was ended some forty years ago.
Richards suggests a similar set of attitudes among the Bemba.[16]
Many younger Digo, who are less concerned than their elders about
past slavery, indicate a greater willingness to labor with their
hands. The Duruma, who may not have had so pervasive a slave system as the Arab-influenced Digo, also tend in general to have a
higher regard for manual labor and are often hired by the Digo to
work for them. It should be added, however, that as cattle pastoralism increases in importance among the Duruma, Duruma men show
signs of losing interest in agricultural work. On the other hand,
they are motivated to work hard at least in their youth in order
both to earn enough money to pay their high bridewealth costs and
to purchase cattle.

     There are no clear divisions of labor by sex or age among
the Digo, although men tend somewhat to perform heavier and more
dangerous work than women, while women perform routine agricultural
and household work. If anything, Digo women are more touchy than
their men about indications of slave status, and will leave their
husbands if they feel that they are being asked to do more than
their share. Duties to work and to assist husband, father, or
mother's brother are in part a function of the form of marriage.
The traditional (kidigo or kuhala) form of marriage among the Digo
required low bridewealth payments, but gave men few rights in
their wives or their children. They formerly could marry slave
wives (kisuria), from whom they could expect far more subservience
and hard work than from non-slave wives. This kisuria system is
now prohibited, but a rather similar alternative exists. If Digo
are quite wealthy, they can effect a high cost bridewealth marriage called king'ombe or "by cattle," since payment is, theoret-
ically at least, made in cattle. Digo women refuse to be married
king'ombe, since they lose rights in their matrilineal kin group
and owe many seemingly onerous duties to their husbands and his
group, but the Digo can obtain wives in this fashion from the
Duruma, Giriama, and some other Nyika groups, among whom the
king'ombe form is common. A third and increasingly popular type
of marriage among the Digo is the kiislamu (or "Islamic style")

marriage, by which the Digo marry according to Islamic law. This is more expensive than the kidigo form, but cheaper than the king'ombe. It gives men more rights over wives and children than the kidigo form, but less than the king'ombe, and it is more prestigious than either of the other forms.

Sons born to a kidigo marriage legally have no rights to inherit the property of their father, since this should descend to his matrikin. Sons born to a kiislamu marriage, on the other hand, legally have the right to inherit a major portion of those permanent or semipermanent crops which they and their mother helped their father plant. As noted above, they also have a right to claim and will usually obtain a share in the use of land which they helped their father clear. The Digo allege that kiislamu marriages will increase food production because women married by kiislamu will work hard to help their husbands develop their property and land and will encourage their children to do likewise, since all will share in the wealth after their husbands die. On the other hand, it is claimed that women married by kidigo will sabotage the efforts of their husbands, since their children will not inherit a thing.

Though there is much to these arguments, the present situation is not so clear-cut as they would indicate. Irrespective of the type of marriage, both matrilineal and patrilineal kinsmen of a deceased property owner quarrel over inheritance and succession. Women may work harder for a kiislamu husband than for a kidigo one, but they will still maintain a strong association with their brothers, sometimes helping them at the expense of their husbands. Children certainly tend to play father against mother's brother and also mother against father's sister. If father makes them work too hard, they will go to mother's brother, and vice versa. They will try to inherit and obtain gifts from each. By the same token, men will attempt to gain the support of both sons and sister's sons. A Digo cannot, however, clearly depend upon specific individuals to help him by virtue of any abiding principle in the Digo social structure. Since the Digo cannot depend upon anyone, they attempt to get at least potential support from everyone, but this is not an efficient way to organize work teams. The most assured way of getting labor for a project is to pay for it; this is why Kesim and Sulymani wanted the government loan.

The government has attempted to get the Digo to form a system of cooperative work groups similar to the dopkwe system of the West African Dahomey[17] or to the mwethia system of the Kamba neighbors of the Digo in the hope that this will be utilized to increase food production and otherwise develop the country. These attempts have failed, although the Digo once had a system similar to mwethia which they called mweria. The Digo of some locations do, however, cooperate in one activity related to food getting. The young men work together both to drive large and often danger-

ous animals from their growing crops and to hunt larger animals for
food. They fence off fairly extensive areas with nets which each
household is supposed to help keep in repair, and they drive animals into the nets to be speared or shot with arrows. A lucky and
skillful hunter serves as the hunt leader, directing operations
and rather successfully demanding obedience to his orders. He cannot, however, organize and direct other community enterprises, nor
can the hunting organization be directed to new tasks. It is not
regarded as an important organization. Like the Bemba, the Digo
enjoy hunting, but it is hardly a significant occupation and in
itself does not provide the Digo with much food. Cooperation in
hunting is possible because it does not threaten anyone's vital
interests.

A final factor needs to be considered in this brief discussion of food production among the Digo, and it is one which is
crucial not only to production but to distribution and, indeed,
all aspects of economic development. If a typical Digo is successful in agriculture or any other major enterprise, he will be greatly envied by his kinsmen and neighbors, who fear that he may use
his growing wealth to increase his power and to extend his influence and control over local resources at their expense. His wife,
especially if married by kidigo, will probably fear that he will
now be rich enough to afford a mistress or another wife, and that
this will threaten her interests.

The Digo commonly respond to the economic success of a
fellow Digo by calling upon him to finance various kinds of cere-
monials or rituals in which food and other goods are distributed.
Digo wives characteristically become ill--possessed, as it were,
by spirits which demand expensive curing rituals and such gifts
as jewelry and clothes. The Digo who clearly refuse to share
their wealth are frequently accused of being witches who became
prosperous not by hard work but by cheating and stealing from
their neighbors, often using black magic. At the very least they
are denied financial and other aid if they need it.

This sytem facilitates food distribution and tends to prevent Digo society from being divided into opposing groups of well-
fed and prosperous "haves" and hungry "have-nots." On the other
hand, it gives the Digo yet another reason to feel that hard work
and individual effort are not always worth the effort, and it prevents many Digo from saving profits and personally accumulating
cash or produce for reinvestment. Of course some clever Digo find
ways of manipulating even such a system to their advantage, so
that they obtain more aid and support than they give, and are able
to become successful businessmen in the developing market-exchange
economy of the coast. (It is clear that one thing a Digo should
do to protect his assets and his reputation is to appear poor,
hungry, and needy, no matter how successful he is.)

Now let us turn to the Duruma, who live in the more arid hinterland of the Kenya coastal belt, and briefly examine their use of livestock. I have already commented on Duruma attitudes to work, and will only add that the Duruma are also under considerable pressure to share their wealth and to pretend to be poor. Cattle, goats, and sheep provide the chief source of food and income for most of the Duruma. They are the most important form of heritable wealth and investment, and are used to pay bridewealth, blood debt (kore), and to provide food for rituals and ceremony. Men rise to power and influence by giving cattle and goats to kinsmen and friends to herd and milk. In short, cattle and other livestock are crucial to the life of the Duruma, and, indeed, the Digo who take up cattle pastoralism are in time often regarded as Duruma (much as Kachins in E. R. Leach's analysis of Burma become Shans when they take up Shan economic pursuits).[18] On the other hand, the Duruma are essentially converted agriculturalists and do not conform in all respects to the model of cattle pastoralism which Herskovits has labeled "the cattle-complex."[19] The Duruma admit, and unpublished government records in Kwale, Kenya, confirm, that they subsisted primarily on millet until the 1920's, when the Pax Britannica and Western technique and medicine enabled them to develop their large herds of livestock.

The Duruma, like their Giriama neighbors, have been quite pleased to see their animals multiply rapidly, and have willingly used veterinary services to help them prosper. However, they have not been willing to keep the size of their herds to that which the government says their land can carry. While they recognize the value of quality in cattle, they will not sacrifice quantity to get it. A few scrawny animals are still worth more to them than one fine beast. They recognize that the mortality rate of their livestock is relatively high, but argue that for this reason they must have large enough numbers so that some will always remain alive to reproduce and provide them with food, bridewealth, and other necessities. Those who herd and seem to own the animals are often not their real owners and cannot unilaterally agree to reduce their number to meet government standards. Such herdsmen care for cattle in return for the right to their milk. The real owners of the cattle are in turn afraid to tell the herders to reduce their stock because they may then shift allegiance to another man providing more cattle.

The introduction of Western techniques has thus led to serious overgrazing in the Duruma and Giriama cattle belt. Under various political pressures, the government has been opening new areas of grassland to Duruma and Giriama cattle by clearing it of the tsetse fly or inoculating cattle against sleeping sickness. This may lead to an immediate increase in milk production, but in time these areas may also be overgrazed and turned into eroded wasteland and useless thornbush desert. Here again, rather sweeping sociocultural change must accompany technological development

if such development is not to have adverse consequences and lead
in time to reduced rather than expanded food production.

In any event, food production among the Digo and Durama is
not great enough to give the people the food that they need. In
addition to production, preservation and distribution of food are
also vital considerations, and both clearly relate to a complex
of technical, economic, and other factors. Let us first of all
consider food preservation.

FOOD PRESERVATION

The Digo and Duruma preserve their maize, millet, and other
grains by smoking them over the same wood and charcoal fire which
cooks their food and then storing them. Smoking may give these
grains a flavor which Americans and Europeans dislike, but it does
protect them from insects, just as such smoking fumigates the roofs
of Digo and Duruma houses.

The Digo maintain that beans are far more easily attacked
by insects than their other grains, and not even smoking will protect them. They give this as a reason for selling much of their
bean crop to local Indian merchants soon after harvest, when the
market is glutted and the price is low. Later in the year they
must buy beans from the same merchants at a very high price. The
merchants, in turn, complain that even they cannot store the beans
and must sell them to buyers in Mombasa and Tanga at low prices,
rebuying later in the year when they are expensive. Here, it seems,
the Digo do require technological aid to help them preserve their
crops.

The Digo and Afro-Arabs have well-developed methods of
preserving fish, apparently chiefly learned from the Arabs. Such
methods include drying in the sun, smoking, or frying. The introduction of more effective and rapid distribution of fish from
places of origin now enables the Digo to procure fresh fish easily
and limits somewhat the need for preserving this food.

FOOD DISTRIBUTION

Food is distributed partly by patterns of extensive gift
exchange and reciprocal aid, partly by the practice of sharing
in feasts at frequent rituals and curing ceremonies, and partly
by systems of trading and marketing. Trading and marketing, which
I have discussed in detail elsewhere,[20] are increasing in importance, but the other forms of distribution are also significant.
Let us briefly survey some of these forms.

Rituals and Festivals: Rituals and festivals fall into

two major categories, as far as food distribution is concerned:
essentially traditional (kidigo) ritual, which coincides with the
agricultural cycle, either preceding or following it, and essentially Islamic ritual, which coincides with the Islamic lunar cal-
endar. Weddings tend to be held after harvests.

Much kidigo ritual--for example, spirit possession ritual--
follows the harvests of major crops or the sale of copra, peppers,
cotton, and other cash crops. Indeed, the Digo maintain that the
"spirits sleep" during the period following such harvest or sale.
Most Digo rituals attract large numbers of people, partly because
the Digo enjoy such gatherings and partly because they must attend
to reaffirm social ties and meet socioeconomic obligations. All
rituals involve communal feasting. Most of the food is customarily
supplied by a small group of individuals responsible for the ritual, such as the husband, father, mother's brother, and siblings
of a woman requiring the curing ceremony (ngoma). Others attending
the ritual are also expected to contribute food and/or small amounts
of money if they can afford it. Even minor contributions are rather elaborately made in full view of everyone, and symbolize the
giver's identification with the group.

Food consumed during such rituals varies greatly in quantity, quality, and type, depending chiefly upon available resources,
but also upon the demands of particular rituals and the special
desires of the major participants. Almost invariably, however,
both kidigo and kiislamu feasts require the sacrifice of animals,
whose flesh is eaten chiefly by the adult males present, but is
often shared with children and women. Where they can afford it
and where enough persons are on hand to justify it, the Digo will
sacrifice a steer, either buying one from the Duruma or bringing in
an animal owned by a Digo but herded by a Duruma. It is far more
likely that they will sacrifice goats, sheep, or chickens, with
chickens being most popular. Indeed, one reason the Digo give for
raising chickens, but refusing to sell them or their eggs, is that
they must be prepared for inevitable and frequent contributions to
rituals. Even in kidigo rituals, animals are killed by cutting
their throats (kuchinja) while reciting (after a fashion) the
first surah of the Koran. The dead animals are hastily skinned or
plucked but are often not gutted. They are then cut up and the
pieces thrown directly on a low fire to roast for a few moments.
Such meat may be charred on the outside, and spotted with wood
ash, but it is normally more raw than cooked. The Digo like to
flavor such meat with a mixture of red pepper seeds and coarse
salt. Practically all digestible parts of the animal are eaten,
with choice pieces, such as liver and tender fat, being given to
head elders.

Feasts at kidigo rituals, especially spirit possession
rituals chiefly involving women, often also include the serving
of typical Digo maize meal or cassava meal porridge, and/or boiled

bananas, or boiled or roasted cassava. In customary fashion this
is flavored by a sauce of fish, meat, sour milk, or wild greens.
Traditionally, palm wine was served in great abundance at kidigo
rituals, although only adult males and important older women were
allowed to drink it. Partly as a result of Islamic influence, the
Digo no longer drink such wine, although they sell it to the hard-
drinking Duruma. The common drink at ritual is tea, heavily sweet-
ened and frequently flavored with ginger or mixed with a bit of
tinned or fresh milk. I might add that the Digo also often drink
tea during the course of an ordinary day, making it either at home
or buying it at the local tea shops (hoteli).

In the past an important kidigo ritual was rainmaking. Apparently the head elder in any area secured his political position
by being successful as a rainmaker. To be a rainmaker he not only
had to know certain magical techniques, he also had to provide meat,
grain, and palm wine for the feast following the incantation. Furthermore, he had to be strong enough to cause others also to contribute food to this feast. He had to save food during the "time
of hunger," and make sure that others did the same. The Digo "made
rain" when the clouds were gathering and they were clearing and
hoeing their land. In short, they made rain and had the feast accompanying it when they were engaged in their heaviest work and
most needed to have food. For most, this was a time when food was
otherwise in very short supply, a time when their granaries were
empty. Thus, rainmaking, in addition to its social structural and
psychological functions, also seems to have had a food-saving and
food-distributing function.

Nowadays the Digo occasionally make some half-hearted attempts to bring down the rain, but it no longer seems to be important to them. Government-appointed chiefs and headmen perhaps do
not think that their political future depends on rainmaking skills;
indeed, one chief felt that the district government would remove
him if he did this "pagan thing." They are not willing to provide food for the ritual, and they cannot make others do so. Finally, the periodic cycle of famine preceding heavy cultivation
is more or less a thing of the past, at least for most of the Digo.

Kiislamu ritual has not replaced kidigo ritual in most instances. Rather, as Carleton S. Coon has noted for other areas
of the Islamic world,[21] it has added to and complemented these
traditional practices. In many cases kiislamu and kidigo patterns
have blended to form new systems of ritual, but the Digo tend to
distinguish between the Islamic and the more traditional. Food
served at kiislamu events--at least the major ones--is distinctly
different from food served at kidigo rituals. For one thing (although this hardly makes a difference in the actual eating), white
chickens and goats are sacrificed in Islamic ritual, while black
or brown animals are used in the "pagan" kidigo ritual. Rice,
rather than other grains, is desired as a food during Islamic

feasting, and meat is customarily cooked until well-done rather than merely tossed on hot coals. A favorite dish during Islamic ritual is pilau, combining rice, meat or chicken, spices, and cashew nuts.

An important kiislamu ritual event is the celebration of the birthday (maulidi) of the prophet. In a number of Digo and Duruma locations, wealthy merchants, especially Indian Muslim merchants, sponsor a maulidi celebration at which they serve tea, pilau, and a variation of halwa (sweetmeat). Digo and Duruma Muslims of both sexes and all ages are invited to attend such a maulidi, and many pagan Duruma also manage to slip in, at least to feast.

Perhaps the most important kiislamu ritual activity is the observation of fasting and feasting during the lunar month of Ramadan. Unlike the ritual discussed above, Ramadan does not characteristically lead people to share food with others. People eat the food which they have themselves produced or bought, although they may invite a few close friends or kinsmen to have dinner with them. Feasting during Ramadan is more of an individual or small group affair.

In Ramadan, the Digo fast during the day but feast at night. They attempt to avoid all food and drink from sunrise to sunset, and break their fast at sunset with a light meal of such goodies as tea, raised cakes (which some Digo women specialize in baking from rice flour), white bread, fresh fruit, cooked mangoes or papaya, eggs, and roasted cassava. Then, at midnight, they eat a large and elaborate meal painstakingly prepared during the course of the day. Rice flavored with beef, goat, or chicken is a popular and prestigious dish, although few Digo can afford it each night. Cassava meal porridge (prepared from dry cassava) or maize meal porridge flavored with such delicacies as dried shark or other fish or greens is a somewhat more common midnight dinner. Ramadan ends with the Id 'el Fitr celebration, at which time the Digo do their utmost to feast on pilau.

Since Ramadan follows the lunar system, it occurs at slightly different times each year. If it is held during the period following harvests, all well and good. But it does occasionally fall during a period between harvests. It is true, as Sulymani Mwarongo said, that the Digo now have such a varied agricultural inventory that they ordinarily do not experience a crucial "time of hunger" as they did in the past. However, there are times when most do not have enough food to provide such feasting as Ramadan requires, and a good many do not have sufficient cash crops to sell or exchange for food. The Digo claim that if necessary they will go in debt to Indian merchants or mortgage their coconut palms to provide food for Ramadan. If Ramadan occurs during the period when the Digo are engaged in the heaviest agricultural work, it often impedes their efforts. For one thing, they lack food for energy during the day, and, for another, they do not sleep much at night. However, many women do not actually observe the fast if there is work to be done (though they do join in the feasting), and some men may actually try to work harder during Ramadan than other times just to prove that they are strong.

Most of the Duruma remain pagan, and few observe Ramadan or other Islamic rituals. They prepare their food for ritual feasting much as do the Digo in their kidigo system. They are far more lavish in their sacrifice of cattle than the Digo, and all the Duruma, both young and old, male and female, share in the eating of the beef. That which is not eaten on the spot is parcelled out to be taken home to kinsmen who could not come to the ceremony. Rituals thus help contribute to the "subsistence role of cattle."[22] Duruma settlements are rather widely dispersed, and there are only a few Duruma locations where population is dense enough to support a butcher regularly selling beef. Since Duruma do not have refrigerators, they cannot store beef for long. A man who slaughters a steer must be sure of disposing of all of the beef in a day or so or see it go to waste. A cycle of rituals in which cattle are sacrificed by different men at different times and places and which feeds a large population serves a useful function in such a situation.

Beef as well as other meat is sold at the large markets in Duruma and Digo country, such as at Kinango and Kwale. Furthermore, a few bicycling traders are beginning to carry beef from house to house. Perhaps in time the marketing and trading system will reduce the significance of the ritual means of distribution. Let us briefly survey the market and trading system.

Marketing and Trading: Most locations hold small daily markets, often consisting of no more than a gathering of a handful of men and/or women selling a few items of agricultural produce, sour milk, or fish in order to earn a few cents for a special need. A few locations, such as the Duruma administrative center of Kinango or the coastal fishing village of Vanga hold relatively large and increasingly important daily markets at which a combination of ordinary householders, casual hawkers, and professional Digo, Duruma, Afro-Arab, Arab, and other traders buy and sell a multitude of foodstuffs and other wares.

Of probably even more significance than such daily markets are the various "weekly" markets conducted at certain of the larger population or economic centers. Some of the weekly markets are held on the fourth day of the traditional four-day Digo or Duruma week. Others are held on Wednesday or Thursday of the Afro-Arab-Islamic seven-day week, while a growing number follow the European cycle and fall on Saturday and Sunday. A discussion of four typical markets--Kinango, Kwale, Mtoto Hovu, and Madzoreni--will clarify this.

In addition to its daily markets, Kinango supports a large and bustling fourth day market and cattle auction. Both daily and fourth day markets combine to make Kinango an important center for the purchase and sale of livestock, ghee, sour milk, and meat, as well as all manner of agricultural produce and fish, both fresh and preserved. Duruma men are the chief sellers of livestock, while Duruma women dominate the trade in milk, ghee, and annual garden crops. The Digo, especially the younger men, come rather regularly to buy livestock and dairy produce, often for resale. Many also buy and sell bananas, coconuts, oranges, and other tree fruits, as well as fish, palm wine, notions, and trinkets. A few Afro-Arabs from Mombasa and coastal fishing villages come chiefly to sell fish, while Indian women, wives of the Indian merchants in Kinango, attend the market to buy all manner of foods.

Kwale, the administrative center for the Digo or Kwale District of the Kenya coast, has a Sunday market serving government personnel and the surrounding Digo and Duruma populations. It is not as large as the Kinango market by far, and specializes in agricultural products and fish. An Arab butcher is located in Kwale, and, until 1960 at any rate, he sold fresh beef about twice a week, and goats and sheep on the other days.

The large sisal plantation at Mtoto Hovu along the Tanzania coast has an interesting Saturday market in which the Digo and other coastal peoples sell all manner of foodstuffs and other wares. The large labor force of the plantation, many of whom are Africans from other areas who do not have land along the coast, depend upon this market for their major food supply. Indeed, these laborers rather than management are responsible for the development and administration of the market.

All of the above markets are cash markets, in which goods and services are exchanged through the medium of the standard currency of East Africa--the shilling. At least one important barter market remains active in the coastal area. This is the Thursday market held on a sand spit along the Indian Ocean near the south Kenya fishing and agricultural village of Madzoreni. The primary function of this market is to enable the Afro-Arab fishermen living on the tiny and barren offshore islands to exchange their fish for agricultural produce brought chiefly by Digo and Afro-Arab women gardeners. It is felt that this exchange, so vital to the fisherfolk, can be implemented best by bartering fish, usually preserved, directly for the garden produce. Money can be used only to buy a few trinkets, clothing, or ginger tea sold by itinerant traders at the market. The market begins at the crack of dawn and lasts but an hour at the most. No one can barter until the market master, an elder of Madzoreni, calls out "haya, guzeni"-- "yes, yes, begin selling." This assures that all have an equal

opportunity to obtain what they need and then return home before
the tide changes and before the hot sun has time to spoil the fish.

Most of those who visit markets still do so on foot, although a growing number make use of expanding bus services, especially if they wish to carry a large amount of produce or produce
which readily spoils. Bus service is also quite a boon to traders
in foodstuffs, although it is the Digo, Duruma, or Afro-Arab trader
on bicycle who is most important in developing the coastal trading
system and in distributing foods. Such traders deal in fresh and
sour milk, meat, fresh and dry fish, all manner of vegetables, and
fruit, as well as trinkets, notions, and dry goods. Increasingly,
such traders are coming into competition with the Indian and Arab
merchants who own or operate the general stores or "dukas" found
in every coastal village or hamlet.

These merchants, especially the Indians, play an important
role in the Digo and Duruma food economy. They sell Africans a
wide variety of grains and tinned foods, create demand for new
though not always desirable foods, help Africans market produce,
give them credit, and serve as models of entrepreneurship. On the
other hand, they charge very high overt or concealed interest, and
often tie Africans to them economically and socially in a patron-
client relationship which helps them monopolize the African economy
and block the African entrepreneurs.

A typical Indian or Arab merchant will tie Africans to him
economically by loaning them money or selling them food or other
wares on credit with the understanding that they will henceforth
do business almost exclusively with him. They will be expected to
buy other goods from him even though his prices are somewhat higher
than those of a competing merchant, and to sell their cash crops,
fish, milk, or other wares to him even though he pays them less
than a competitor. In keeping with the Islamic prohibition against
usury (riba), the merchant will charge no explicit interest for
his credit or loan, but he will obtain it through this tie system.
It is unfortunate that a joint Kenya government-UNICEF project to
improve milk production and distribution did not take into account
either this tie system or the developing Digo and Duruma bicycle
trade in milk and other produce.

This joint project, known as the Mariakani Milk Scheme,
organized and financed the development of a government milk processing and marketing system along the Kenya coast. Indian bus
and truck owners were encouraged to purchase milk from coastal Africans, including the Duruma and Giriama, and sell it to the government scheme for processing and resale in Mombasa through Indian
merchants. When this program was initiated before World War II,
Indian merchants were probably the only persons able to buy, transport, and sell milk in this fashion. In 1960 UNICEF contributed
funds to help subsidize the Scheme so that it could rebuild its

plant and expand. Although the Scheme has been lauded by local and international authorities and by representatives of the International Bank for Reconstruction and Development,[23] it seems dysfunctional in many respects. In anticipation of regular milk sales to Indian merchants, Duruma now go into debt to these merchants and in time must often sell more milk than they can part with if their subsistence is to be maintained. Cattle owners, often urged on by local politicos, have come to demand and get far more for their milk than it is really worth on the Kenya market, and still they believe that both the government and Indian merchants are cheating them of just profits. Most of the Scheme milk is sold in Mombasa, although up-country milk producers need the Mombasa market to dispose of their surplus. Finally, high milk costs together with Indian control over the milk trade through the tied credit system have damaged the milk trade of the bicycling entrepreneurs and may also have a bad effect on trade in other products. It appears that the government should do everything possible to encourage the development of the bicycling trade, since this trade will best market milk in rural areas where it is most needed, and will also stimulate or increase demand for both new and traditional foods and products.

ACCEPTANCE AND CONSUMPTION OF FOOD

Finally, it must be emphasized that, even if technological, economic, and other changes cause more food of different types to be made available to the coastal Africans than ever before, this does not necessarily mean that these foods will be used and diet improved. Habits of food preparation and consumption are hard to change,[24] and the coastal Africans, like many other peoples throughout the world, may well reject new and better foods in favor of more traditional foods, or they may continue to cook their food in such a way that much of its nutritional value is lost. For example, many coastal Africans, perhaps influenced by Cushitic fish taboos,[25] still regard fresh fish as bad for their health and will eat only dried fish, such as shark from South Arabia. Digo, Duruma, and other coastal fish traders peddling fresh fish on bicycle are doing their best to change this attitude so that they may sell their product, and since about 1959 they have stimulated many women to demand that their husbands purchase fresh fish at least three times a week.[26]

Another innovation--the distribution of free powdered milk in this area--has in many cases backfired because of local habits of food preparation and use. Nyika women have been slow to believe that this substance was really milk which could supplement or replace milk from their breasts for their children. Also, they have frequently mixed the powdered milk with unboiled, contaminated water and have fed it to their infants, causing illness and perhaps death.

The Digo and Duruma, like many other Africans, believe that the only proper food, especially for infants and ill adults, is a starchy, protein-deficient porridge or gruel made from corn, millet, cassava meal, or rice.[27] Only this can properly be termed "food" (chakuria in Digo, chakula in Swahili); only this is emotionally satisfying; only this "fills the belly" and makes one feel as if he has really eaten well. Meat, fish, eggs, animal milk, and the like are all regarded not as "food" but as "sauce" or "dressing" (chitoweo). The Digo and Duruma are convinced that while healthy adults can eat such chitoweo with relative impunity, children under about three or four years of age must be protected and should be restricted to a diet of mother's milk and chakuria. Those who are sick, no matter how old, should also be limited to a diet of chakuria.

We found it possible to encourage some women of one Digo location to mix their maize (corn) meal with chicken eggs, milk, and sugar (all available locally at low price) and to feed the resulting chakuria-like pudding to their infants. Presumably it would be possible to cause this innovation to spread throughout the coastal area, and it might be truly beneficial if enough of this mixture were eaten. Presently, however, most infants do not obtain protein other than that in the customary chakuria and in mother's milk, and few mothers are able to provide adequate milk for the required period.

MALNUTRITION

Protein malnutrition or kwashiorkor is not uncommon among infants and some adults in the coastal area, but when local Africans see a person suffering from what Western observers diagnose as inadequate nutrition, the Africans feel instead that this person is suffering because he or his parents broke important sexual taboos. The term chirwa, which is the passive form of the verb kuchira, meaning in effect "to do something forbidden," is used to identify those suffering from these violated prohibitions. The major taboos, violation of which leads to chirwa, are sexual intercourse between husband and wife during the period before a child born to them is old enough to be weaned (three to four years of age), and adultery by either parent during this period or during the period of gestation of the child. If a new child is conceived before its sibling has reached the desired age for weaning, it is said that the new child will "steal the strength" of the former. While few Digo are willing to abstain from sexual intercourse for the required period, they do make every attempt to prevent conception. If conception does occur or if there is other evidence that the taboos have been violated, the close relatives of an endangered child may well accuse the guilty parent or parents of trying to kill the child.

NUTRITION IN ITS SOCIOCULTURAL MATRIX

Western observers have most incorrectly translated this term chirwa as "rickets" or "protein malnutrition"; it most certainly does not mean any such thing to the Africans. When Western medical authorities ask to see those suffering from chirwa, they are usually shown no one, since the Digo hate to admit publicly that they have broken the sexual taboos, and that they have a child with chirwa. When the Western officials argue that the Digo should feed their children more "food" (chakuria) to counter chirwa, they are regarded by the Africans as quite foolish if not presumptuous. First of all, the Digo feel that they give their children more than enough chakuria; second, they know quite well that one does not remedy broken taboos by eating more chakuria. They believe that only traditional Digo methods administered by specialists can be employed to deal with chirwa.

Not even the best intentioned technical expert, nutritionist, aid administrator, or Peace Corps volunteer can effectively counter protein malnutrition in this area of Africa unless he understands the concept of chirwa as the local African understands it, and unless he can also change some fundamental attitudes and food habits so that available protein foods can be eaten by children and those who are ill. But even here it must be noted that seemingly desirable change may perhaps have some undesirable consequences. Abandonment of the concept of chirwa as a retribution for "out of season" intercourse, combined with improved health and diet, may well lead to such an increase in births and in longevity of life that malnutrition will result from too little food for too many people rather than from inadequate use of available food.

SUMMARY

We have seen that the coastal ecosystem can be divided into agricultural, cattle husbandry, and fishing regions or "niches" producing a diverse array of foods. To these should be added urban and plantation wage-labor regions. The products, services, and wages of these various regions are distributed throughout this ecosystem by an integrated marketing and trading system and various ritual forms of sharing. Methods of food production, distribution, and preservation, though defective in some respects, seem to provide the basis for adequate nutrition (although a proper evaluation would require biochemical and medical analysis), but because of food consumption habits and associated magico-religious beliefs and practices, the Digo and other coastal peoples do not make adequate use of the foods which these systems combine to provide.

In short, the nutritional status of a people is seen to be dependent upon their patterns of food production, preservation, distribution, and utilization. These, in turn, are dependent upon a complex web of intertwining social, economic, political, magico-religious, technological, attitudinal, and environmental factors.

Those who wish to improve food economy and diet must therefore study food-getting and using in its sociocultural matrix, and design development programs accordingly. As has often been said, authorities who do not do this may cause harm to the people they wish to help.

NOTES

[1]Margaret Mead, "The Contribution of Cultural Anthropology to Nutrition." [Background paper for Conference on Malnutrition and Food Habits, Cuernavaca, Mexico, 1960.]

[2]Land, Labour and Diet in Northern Rhodesia (London: 1939).

[3]L. P. Gerlach, "Economy and Protein Malnutrition among the Digo," Proceedings of the Minnesota Academy of Science, 29 (1961), pp. 1-13; "Traders on Bicycle: A Study of Entrepreneurship and Culture Change among the Digo and Duruma of Kenya," Sociologus, XIII (1963), 1, pp. 32-49; "Sociocultural Factors Influencing the Diet of the Northeast Coastal Bantu," Journal of the American Dietetic Association (1964); "Nyika," in Encyclopaedia Britannica (1965).

[4]Africa: Its Peoples and Their Culture History (New York: McGraw Hill, 1959).

[5]A. H. J. Prins, The Coastal Tribes of the North-Eastern Bantu (London: 1952) and The Swahili-Speaking Peoples of Zanzibar and the East African Coast (London: 1961).

[6]J. L. Krapf, Reisen in Ost-Africa (2 vols., Stuttgart: 1858); O. Baumann, Usambara and Seine Nachbargebiete (Berlin: 1891); Sankt Paul Hilaire, Ueber die Rechtsgewohnheiten der im Bezirk Tanga ausaessigen Faerbigen: Mitteilungen aus den Deutschen Schutzgebieten, 8 (1895); W. E. H. Barrett, "Notes on the Customs of the Wa-Giriama," Journal of the Royal Anthropological Institute, XLI (1911), pp. 20-40; Alice Werner, "The Bantu Coast Tribes of the East African Protectorate," Journal of the Royal Anthropological Institute, XLV (1915), pp. 326-54; J. B. Griffiths, "Glimpses of a Nyika Tribe: Waduruma," Journal of the Royal Anthropological Institute (1935), pp. 267-96; H. M. T. Kayamba, "Notes on the Wadigo," Tanganyika Notes and Records, XXIII (1947), pp. 80ff.; E. C. Baker, "Notes on the History of the Wasegeyu," Tanganyika Notes and Records, XXVII (1949), pp. 16-41.

[7]Richards, op. cit., pp. 288-95 (see note 2).

[8]G. H. T. Kimble, Tropical Africa (2 vols., New York: Anchor, 1962), I, pp. 53-57 [Abridged edition]; George Peter Murdock,

op. cit., p. 6 (see note 4); L. D. Stamp, Africa: A Study in Tropical Development (London: 1953), p. 71.

[9] Richards, op. cit., p. 308 (see note 2).

[10] Op. cit., esp. pp. 92-106 (see note 8).

[11] Op. cit. (see note 2).

[12] "Ecologic Relationships of Ethnic Groups in Swat, North Pakistan," American Anthropologist, LVIII (1956), p. 1079.

[13] Raymond Firth, Bilateral Descent Groups: An Operational Viewpoint. Occasional Paper #16, Royal Anthropological Institute (1963).

[14] On the Theory of Social Change (Homewood, Ill.: Dorsey, 1962), esp. pp. 36-52.

[15] Raymond Firth and B. S. Yamey, eds., Capital, Saving and Credit in Peasant Societies (Chicago: Aldine, 1964), pp. 33, 20-21.

[16] Op. cit. (see note 2).

[17] Melville J. Herskovits, Economic Anthropology (New York: Alfred A. Knopf, 1952), p. 101.

[18] Political Systems of Highland Burma (Cambridge: Harvard University Press, 1954).

[19] Melville J. Herskovits, "The Cattle Complex in East Africa," American Anthropologist, XXVIII (1926), pp. 230-72, 361-80, 494-528, 633-64.

[20] Op. cit. - 1963 (see note 3).

[21] Caravan: The Study of the Middle East (New York: Holt, 1958), p. 92.

[22] See H. Schneider, "The Subsistence Role of Cattle among the Pakot and in East Africa," American Anthropologist, LIX (1957), pp. 278-300.

[23] The Economic Development of Tanganyika (Baltimore, 1961).

[24] Margaret Mead, The Problem of Changing Food Habits. National Academy of Science, National Research Council Bulletin #108 (1943).

[25] See Murdock, op. cit. (see note 4).

[26] Gerlach, op. cit. - 1961, 1963 (see note 3).

[27] Richards, op. cit. (see note 2).